Statistical methods for decision making

IRWIN SERIES IN QUANTITATIVE ANALYSIS FOR BUSINESS

CONSULTING EDITOR   ROBERT B. FETTER   *Yale University*

Statistical methods for decision making

WILLIAM A. CHANCE
Associate Professor of Quantitative
Methods and Economics
University of Missouri at Kansas City

1969

RICHARD D. IRWIN, INC., Homewood, Illinois
IRWIN-DORSEY LIMITED, Nobleton, Ontario

First Printing, January, 1969

Library of Congress Catalog Card No. 69-17164
Printed in the United States of America

To Barbara
and our sons
Richard, Craig, *and* Greg

Preface

This book is intended to serve as an introduction to the wide range of statistical methods which are available to the modern decision maker. This range includes the traditional statistical methods which have served so well for many years, as well as techniques of Bayesian analysis which have regained major impetus in the last decade. Attention is also given to the category of statistical inference commonly designated as "nonparametric statistics."

In addition to the methods mentioned above, today's decision maker should have a knowledge of other aspects of statistical analysis. Primary among these are simulation procedures and the use of computers in easing and advancing the scope of analysis. One chapter of the text is devoted to the fundamentals of Monte Carlo simulation. Also, a series of appendixes containing computer programs appear in conjunction with various chapters of the book. These programs are designed to perform the major procedures of analysis which are presented in the chapters. In most cases there will be a program written in FORTRAN and one written in BASIC, a language developed at Dartmouth College.

A separate appendix, Statistical Analysis and the Computer, constitutes an introduction to FORTRAN programming. The programs appearing in appendixes throughout the book are used as a vehicle for developing programming concepts and techniques within this separate appendix.

The insertion of material on computer programs has been accomplished in such a manner that it does not interfere with the main theme of statistical method. At the same time, the material is easily accessible so that the programs can be used with a minimum of explanation to support the work of the class. Finally, the instructor may elect to use the appendix, Statistical Analysis and the Computer, to develop in his students a better understanding of, and facility in, computer programming. All of this would be accomplished within the context of the main theme, statistical analysis.

The book is planned for the student who will find application of the methods valuable in his chosen field. Consequently, the major emphasis is on *application*, rather than the theoretical or mathematical aspects of the methods. The student is made aware of the assumptions underlying each method, however, and is shown how these assumptions relate to the applicability of the method. Throughout the book every effort is made, by way of example and problem sets, to relate the concepts developed to the concrete business of making decisions.

A book such as this owes many things to many people. I am indebted to the Literary Executor of the late Sir Ronald A. Fisher, F.R.S., and to Oliver and Boyd Ltd., Edinburgh, for their permission to reprint Table IV from their book *Statistical Methods for Research Workers*. I also wish gratefully to acknowledge my debt to the following authors and publishers, for permission to use the material cited:

Appendix E of Frederick E. Croxton and Dudley J. Cowden, *Practical Business Statistics*, 2d ed., 1948, Prentice-Hall, Inc.;

Table 3.1 of D. B. Owen, *Handbook of Statistical Tables*, 1962, Addison-Wesley Publishing Company, Inc.;

Table 41 of E. S. Pearson and H. O. Hartley (eds.), *Biometrika Tables for Statisticians*, Volume 1, 1954, Biometrika Trustees;

Appendix B of William A. Spurr and Charles P. Bonini, *Statistical Analysis for Business Decisions*, 1967, Richard D. Irwin, Inc.; and

Table CC of Acheson J. Duncan, *Quality Control and Industrial Statistics*, 3d ed., 1965, Richard D. Irwin, Inc.

The normal random variate generator developed in the appendix, Statistical Analysis and the Computer, depends on the result presented in G. E. P. Box and Mervin E. Muller, "A Note on the Generation of Normal Deviates," *Annals of Mathematical Statistics*, Vol. 29, 1958, which is used with the kind permission of the authors and editors. Finally, I am grateful to the School of Administration, University of Missouri, Kansas City, for support in providing facilities to ease the task of manuscript preparation. The following persons contributed valuable services in various phases of manuscript preparation: Mrs. Mary Ingman, Judith Stafford, Judy Rockwell, and Charlene Schoen.

December, 1968   WILLIAM A. CHANCE

Table of contents

associated with each state of the process. Determination of the conditional costs resulting from the testing procedure. Procedure for minimizing expected cost. Calculating expected cost, $\alpha = 0.01$. Choosing the best value for α. The effect of factors other than α on the "best" decision. Bayes' theorem. Bayesian analysis and the ball-socket problem. The role of sample information in the decision. Revision of probabilities for a given sample result. Determining the best decision, given the revised probabilities. Determination of the critical values of the sample mean. Determining the value of the testing procedure. Appendix A.

chapter 1

Probability
and
uncertainty

Introduction

The function of the executive is to make decisions. Sometimes the decision is a small one, sometimes a large one. Often the decision is routine, but sometimes it is complex and "one of a kind." Generally, the status of the executive in his organization will correspond closely to the type of decision he must make: the larger and more complex the decision he is called upon to make, the higher his status. Now, decision making on the higher levels is still an art, which means that it involves the exercise of a high degree of personal judgment by the decision maker. On the lower levels of decision making, the element of personal judgment plays a less critical role, until in the case of routine decisions the executive is able to rely almost completely on a standard formula or set of rules.

For all decisions, whether complex or routine, there are certain common elements. For one thing, there must be more than one course of action open. Otherwise there is nothing to decide. Another element that will be found in all decision problems is uncertainty. The decision maker will not know with certainty the outcomes of all the alternative courses of action open to him. If he did, the decision problem would be a trivial one. This element of uncertainty can be said to arise from lack of complete information.

1

Consider, for example, the question of whether a firm ought to introduce a new product on the market. If the executive who ultimately must make the decision were certain that the product would capture 40 percent of the market within the first year, thereby assuring the company added profits of $100,000 per year, he would have no problem. The real situation is by no means that simple, however. The executive does not know how all potential customers will respond to the new product. He does not know with certainty the expenditures that will be required to achieve varying levels of market saturation. Neither is he fully informed as to how much revenue will be generated at each marketing level.

Of course, we would expect our executive friend to make a market survey before he decides what level of market acceptance to expect. He also may have ordered a pilot run for the new product in one of the firm's plants, in order to get an estimate of costs which can be anticipated with full production levels prevailing. But in both cases he will have achieved only an approximation to the actual values he would like to have. The results are necessarily estimates, because he is forced to make his evaluations on the basis of partial information.

This is the critical factor in a problem situation that makes statistical methods useful to the decision maker. In fact, we might say that a statistical problem exists whenever a decision is required on the basis of less than complete information. Certain steps in the procedure of solving such a decision problem are peculiarly statistical in nature: (1) collecting and organizing data relevant to the problem, (2) distilling from these data certain key values (such as the mean value, for example), and (3) deciding on the basis of the small amount of information that we have in our collected data what we would find to be true if we could collect all of the relevant data. The third step is called *statistical inference*, since we are forced to infer what is true of the full set of data, which is unavailable to us, on the basis of what we find to be true of the set of data we actually have been able to collect.

In the following chapters, we shall consider methods of collecting and organizing data. We shall also be concerned with procedures for finding the important key values in the collected data. By far the largest task of this book, however, will be to present the techniques of statistical inference which can prove so valuable to the decision maker in the performance of his function.

We have already noted that the decision maker is forced to make inferences concerning the real situation affecting his decision because of inescapable elements of uncertainty which surround that situation. The major aim of our course of study will be to develop an understanding of how statistical methods allow the decision maker systematically to determine the best course of action to take in a decision problem involving uncertainty. Our first step in this task is to consider the notion of uncertainty—what it is, and how one might express meaningful statements relating to uncertainty.

Uncertainty and risk

When the outcome (or effect) of some action (or condition) is not known in advance, we say that the outcome (effect) is uncertain. The term "uncertainty" refers to this lack of advance knowledge concerning the outcome of an action or the effect of a condition. A bit of reflection makes it clear, however, that there are at least two types of situations in which we may lack advance knowledge of the outcome of an action. One type of situation can be illustrated by the tossing of a coin. When we toss a coin, we lack advance knowledge of the outcome of the toss. We do believe, however, that if the coin is a fair one the outcome is as likely to be "heads" as it is to be "tails." Because of the definiteness which we can attach to the relative likelihoods of the two possible outcomes, we can think of the action of tossing a coin as belonging to one category of situations involving uncertainty which is quite distinct from a second category.

Consider, now, a situation in which you are handed a many-sided solid, on one side of which is inscribed the letter H and on the remaining sides of which is inscribed the letter T. Suppose that we agree that the outcome of a toss of this solid is "heads" if the solid comes to rest upon the H-side. If the solid comes to rest on one of the T-sides, the outcome is "tails." In this situation we may be reluctant to say anything very definite about the relative likelihoods of the outcomes "heads" and "tails." Our reluctance would reflect doubts we might feel concerning whether the material of which the solid is made is uniformly consistent, whether the many sides of the solid are of the same size and shape, and so forth. The lack of definiteness qualifies the present situation as one that falls in a second category of situations involving uncertainty.

When a distinction is made between these two types of situation, the first situation (one involving definiteness concerning relative likelihood) is usually referred to as a *risk* situation. The second type of situation is referred to as a situation involving *uncertainty*. Throughout our discussion of statistical methods, we shall find ourselves considering both types of situation. We shall not, however, concern ourselves actively with the distinction just explained between these two types. Consequently, we shall use the term "uncertainty" to apply to both of them. Having agreed on this understanding of the notion of uncertainty, let us direct our attention to the question of how one might make a statement expressing the degree of uncertainty he feels concerning an outcome.

Probability and uncertainty

Consider the following two statements. The probability is 1 that the sun will rise in the east tomorrow. The probability is zero that an iceberg will be discovered in the basement of the public library tomorrow morning. What meaning can be attached to these statements? In the first case, we were stating a degree of belief that we have that the sun will rise in the east tomorrow. There may be some others who would rather say that the probability is *almost* 1 that the sun will rise in the east tomorrow. It would be perfectly legitimate for them to do so. They would be saying, in effect, that they are almost certain, but not quite, that the sun will rise in the east. Let us consider the second statement. When we say the probability is zero that an iceberg will be discovered in the public library, we are stating our belief that it is a virtual certainty that this event will *not* occur. From the point of view of the decision maker, perhaps this is the best way to look on probability—as an index of his degree of belief that one of a set of possible events will occur.[1]

We should like such an index to have extreme values of zero (indicating that we fully believe an event assigned such a probability will not occur) and 1 (which would indicate our firm belief that an event so indexed is certain to occur). Intermediate values such as ½ and ¼ would then correspond to varying degrees of uncertainty as to whether the event will occur or not. Along with such an index, it would be most helpful to the decision maker if we could provide him with a set of rules to help him reach a rational decision in those cases where he is able to assess the probabilities attached to the set of events he considers to be possible outcomes of a decision.

In the area of mathematics known as probability theory, such a set of rules has been developed. We can make use of the ideas contained in probability theory to help us devise a set of rules for the decision maker to follow in reaching rational decisions. The mathematician's definition of probability is abstract; that is, it has been divorced from the context of any particular application. We shall see, however, that the rules and procedures that follow as logical consequences of probability theory have direct relevance to the problem of decision making under uncertainty. Let us look at mathematical probabilities to see what their characteristics are and to learn the rules for using them.

Basic properties of probabilities

The mathematician requires that probabilities have three characteristics. First, the probability assigned to any event must be a number be-

---

[1] The student should be made aware, however, that this view is subject to much controversy. Some mathematicians would say that it is outdated.

tween zero and 1, inclusive: $0 \leq P(E) \leq 1$. Second, if one considers the set of all events that could possibly occur in the circumstances considered, the probability is 1 that one of these events will occur: $P(S) = 1$, where S indicates the set of all possible events.[2] Third, if one considers two *mutually exclusive* events (if two events are so related that the occurrence of one guarantees us that the other cannot occur, they are said to be *mutually exclusive*), the probability that either one or the other will occur is equal to the sum of their individual probabilities: $P(A$ or $B) = P(A) + P(B)$.

These three requirements of probabilities are not subject to proof,[3] but must be accepted as true if we wish to make use of the rules for manipulating probabilities. Let us examine them, one by one, and see if they seem consistent with our needs.

$$P\text{-}1 \colon 0 \leq P(E) \leq 1 \,.$$

The probability that an event will occur cannot exceed 1, nor be less than zero. We noted above that our index of belief should have extremes of zero and 1 corresponding to the firm belief that the event *will not* occur, in the first instance, that it *will* occur in the latter. Any fractional value represents some degree of uncertainty as to the occurrence of the event.

$$P\text{-}2 \colon P(S) = 1 \,.$$

Here, S is shorthand for "one or the other of all the events possible will occur." Consider the prospective birth of a child, for example. The born child will be either a boy or a girl. These two events comprise the list of possible events. We can say, then, P (child is either a boy or a girl) $= 1$. Of course, for the decision maker a decision problem may offer more than two possible events as the outcome of his actions. In most cases, too, it may not be so easy to recognize the possibilities. But we can agree that, in principle, the decision maker should be able to list all events that might possibly result from his decision and that the probability would then be 1 that one or the other of these events would occur.

$$P\text{-}3 \colon \text{For } A \text{ and } B, \text{ two mutually exclusive events,}$$
$$P(A \text{ or } B) = P(A) + P(B) \,.$$

To see what this means, suppose a company executive has in mind a decision that may affect company sales, but he is not certain exactly what the outcome will be. Two of the outcomes that he considers to be possible are: A—sales will double; B—sales will remain the same. Suppose he believes that sales are as likely to double as not. In probability notation this becomes $P(A) = \frac{1}{2}$. If he also believes that sales are half as likely to remain the same as they are to double, we record $P(B) = \frac{1}{4}$. It is easy

---

[2] We shall limit our discussion only to cases where there are a finite number of possible outcomes.

[3] The mathematicians call such statements axioms, or postulates.

to see that the events A and B are mutually exclusive: if sales double (A), they cannot also remain the same (B). Requirement P–3 specifies that the probability that sales will either double or remain the same as a result of the decision is $\frac{3}{4}$: $P(A$ or $B) = P(A) + P(B) = \frac{1}{2} + \frac{1}{4} = \frac{3}{4}$. Notice that if the executive is consistent in his thinking, there must be some other changes in sales that he considers possible. This is so because $P(A$ or $B) = \frac{3}{4}$, which is less than 1, but requirement P–2 states that the probability that one of the set of all possible events will occur is 1. In the example of the birth of a child, by contrast, the events "boy" and "girl" *exhaust* the possibilities—there are no others. Consequently, the sum of the probabilities for these two mutually exclusive and exhaustive events is 1.

After an examination of the requirements of probabilities, we can agree that these requirements are consistent with the conditions we could expect of a decision maker's assessments of degrees of uncertainty. Agreement on this point will allow us to use the rules of probability that follow as logical extensions of the three requirements. It will be worth our while, therefore, to consider in some detail the more fundamental of these rules, which can be useful in decision-making problems. It will be helpful to us in our further discussion of probability if we introduce at this point the notions of experiment, sample space, and event. Our purposes will be facilitated if, as a first step, we develop notation which will allow us to state more succinctly the propositions we wish to develop concerning probability.[4]

Experiment, sample space, events

The concept of an experiment is that of a series of one or more operations, either naturally induced or man-made, which will result in one of a number of outcomes. Which one of the several possible outcomes will result from a single trial of the experiment is a matter governed by the "laws of chance." That is, the experiment is considered to be a random process for which we are not able to predict on any one trial what the outcome will be. We assume, however, that there is some pattern to these outcomes. Although we may not be able to predict which particular outcome will occur, we can usually say that it will be one of a given set of possible outcomes. Thus, using the example of the birth of a child,

---

[4] As a matter of historical interest, we might note that probability theory received much of its early impetus from questions put to mathematicians by wealthy men of Europe. These men of wealth wished to know how to wager wisely in various gambling games they favored. It is also true that many contemporary introductions to probability are couched in the terms of examples taken from the area of games. Some of this may be due to historical parallel, but it is also true that such game situations provide a satisfactory first approch to probability concepts. The following discussion will honor tradition.

we cannot predict whether the child will be a boy or a girl, but we can predict that it will be one or the other.

As an example of an *experiment*, consider the operation of tossing a pair of dice. We describe the outcome of any one trial of the experiment as a pair of numbers (x_1, x_2), the number of dots appearing on the first and second die, respectively (we might have one red die and one green one, so that we could distinguish easily which was the "first" die and which the "second"). It is easy to list the possible outcomes of the experiment. They are the pairs: $(1, 1)$, $(1, 2)$, . . . , $(6, 6)$. We can also represent these pairs as points on the Cartesian plane. This has been done in Figure 1–1, where distance along the horizontal axis represents the value

Figure 1–1

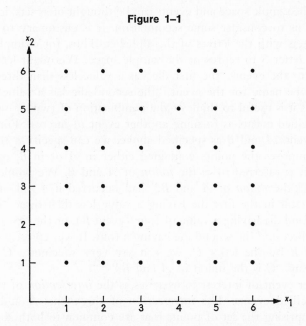

of x_1 and distance along the vertical axis represents values of x_2. There are 36 such points, which results from the fact that each die has six faces that might come up on any one trial.

The 36 pairs of numbers which describe the possible outcomes of the experiment comprise what is called the *sample space* for this experiment. Generally, a sample space is the set of all possible outcomes to an experiment. Usually, we are able to give a numerical description of the outcomes of the experiment we are considering. In such cases, we can represent the sample space in tabular form or in a graphic presentation, as in Figure 1–1.

While the sample space is the set of all possible outcomes, it is often the case that we wish to consider an *event* which may correspond to a set of outcomes smaller than the full sample space. Consistent with our definition of sample space, an *event* can be looked upon as a subset[5] of points in the sample space. As an example, suppose we were for some reason interested in the event, "the value on the first die is less than three." This event corresponds to the 12 points of Figure 1–1 which have the values of one or two for x_1. We would say that the event had occurred if any one of these 12 outcomes were the result of the roll of the dice. Another event that we might consider is "the value on the second die is four." Usually there are several events that we could specify relative to a given sample space.

Since the sample space and events can be thought of as sets, it is worthwhile for us to consider some set notation. It is customary to represent different sets with the letters of the alphabet. Thus, for example, we can allow the letter S to represent the sample space. We might let the letter A represent the event, "the first die has a value less than three"; and B could be the name for the event, "the second die has a value of four." Sometimes it is useful to think of the combination of two or more previously specified events as forming another event of interest. For example, for the events A and B as specified above, we can specify a third event which comprises the points contained either in A or in B, or in both. This event is referred to as the *union* of A and B. We would say that the event, "the *union* of A and B," had occurred if a roll of the dice were to result in the first die having a value less than three (event A), or the second die having a value of four (event B), or the first die having less than three *and* the second die having a four. If we represent the union of A and B by the letter C, we can say very succinctly $C = A + B$, which means "C is the union of A and B."

Another event of interest to us arises as the *intersection* of two previously specified events. The *intersection* of the events A and B is the event comprising the set of points that are common to both A and B. In our example, we would say that the event, "the *intersection* of A and B," had occurred if the roll of the dice resulted in *both* of the following: the value of the first die was less than three *and* the value of the second die was four. Letting D represent the intersection of A and B, we say $D = A \cdot B$.

Finally, let us consider the *complement* of an event. Looking on the event A as the set of outcomes where the first die has a value less than three, the *complement* of A is the set of outcomes in which the first die does *not* have a value less than three. Generally, the *complement* of an event comprises the set of points in the sample space that is not in the

---

[5] One of the "subsets" is the sample space, itself.

event. We denote the complement of an event, say, A, by placing a bar over the letter naming the event: $\bar{A}$. Notice that for any experiment and for any specification of A, all outcomes of the experiment must be either in A or in $\bar{A}$. An equivalent statement is that the union of A and $\bar{A}$ is the sample space: $A + \bar{A} = S$. For the specification of A given above ("the first die has a value less than three"), $\bar{A}$ is the event, "the value of the first die is three or greater."

In our earlier discussion, we mentioned the notion of mutually exclu-

Figure 1–1(a)

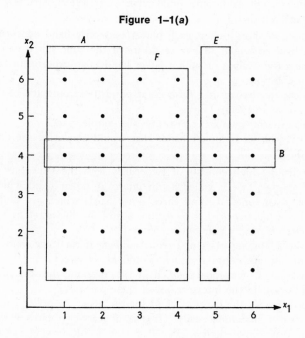

sive events. Let us see what this means in terms of set notation. Let us specify the event E as "the first die has a value of five." Looking at Figure 1–1, we note that the event E is the set of six points arrayed above the value $x_1 = 5$. Examination of Figure 1–1(a) makes it clear that the events E and A have no points in common. We say that the events E and A are mutually exclusive. Consider, now, the event B in its relation to A. We see from Figure 1–1(a) that there are two points that A and B have in common. Because of this, A and B are not mutually exclusive events. With these considerations in mind, we can say that two events are mutually exclusive if their intersection contains no points. For A and E as specified above, we note that they are mutually exclusive, and we can write $A \cdot E = O$, where O denotes the "empty set" or the "null set."

Problem Set 1–1

1. Concerning the relationship between the outcome of an experiment and an event:
   a) Is it possible for an event to be the same thing as an outcome?
   b) Give an example from the experiment discussed in the preceding section to support your answer to (*a*).
   c) Do the concepts "outcome" and "event" differ? If so, what is the relationship between them?

2. In the game of draw poker, each player bets on a hand consisting of five cards. A hand in which all five cards are of the same suit is called a *flush*. Considering the dealing of such a poker hand as an experiment, answer the following questions.
   a) Does the occurence of a flush correspond to an outcome of the experiment, or to an event? Why?
   b) In this experiment, what constitutes the sample space?
   c) Describe the set of poker hands that would constitute the complement of a flush.

3. A poker hand which consists of two cards with the same face and three cards of another face is called a *full house*. A poker hand which consists of two cards of one face and three other cards which are unmatched in the hand is called a *pair*. Let us denote a flush by the letter F, a full house by the letter H, and a pair by the letter P.
   a) For the following pairs of events, indicate if they are mutually exclusive or not, and why: F and P, F and H, H and P.
   b) For the pairs of events specified in (*a*), describe the sort of hand that would occur in the intersections of these pairs.
   c) Suppose we let the letter P stand for the event, "a poker hand contains at least two matching cards" (that is, at least two cards with the same face). With this redefinition of P, review your answers to (*a*) and (*b*) and indicate the changes that are required in these answers.
   d) For the events F and H as specified above, describe the events $\bar{F}$ and $\bar{H}$.
   e) Substitute $\bar{F}$ for F and $\bar{H}$ for H in (*a*) (let P be a *pair*), and answer (*a*) and (*b*) with these specifications.

4. Dogs come in many sizes and appearances. We can categorize them as long haired and short haired, or as big and small, to mention two possible sets of categories. Let us denote that a dog is long haired by the letter L and that a dog is big by the letter B. Suppose, now, that we were to select a dog at random from the population of all dogs.
   a) If a dog so selected corresponded to the event $\bar{L}$, what sort of dog would it be?
   b) If a dog so selected corresponded to the event $\bar{B}$, what sort of dog would it be?
   c) Is it possible that a dog so selected would correspond to the intersection of $\bar{B}$ and $\bar{L}$? If not, why? If so, give an example of such a dog.
   d) Copy the following table and put "X" in each place in the table which

indicates the listed events to which each of the dogs named to the left would correspond.

	L	$\bar{L}$	B	$\bar{B}$	L and B	L and $\bar{B}$	$\bar{L}$ and B	$\bar{L}$ and $\bar{B}$
Great Dane								
Chihuahua								
Saint Bernard								
Pomeranian								
Chow								
Boxer								
Poodle								

e) Did any of the dogs listed above cause you difficulty in completing the table? If so, why? If not, why not?

f) Suppose that our "selection" procedure happened to "net" a Siamese cat. To what event would this outcome correspond?

g) Are there any general comments that you can make concerning the concepts of experiment and events, on the basis of your answers to (e) and (f)?

h) Consider the Boxer and the Chow to be large dogs and the Poodle to be a small, short-haired dog. For the following unions of events, list the dogs from the above table that would correspond to each union:

$$B + L, \ B + \bar{L}, \ \bar{B} + L, \ \bar{B} + \bar{L}.$$

5. Duplicate the graph of Figure 1–1, and on this graph encircle the following events, where A, F, B, and E are as indicated in Figure 1–1(a):

a) $A \cdot B$, b. $A \cdot F$, c. $A + F$, d. $F + \bar{A}$, e. $E + \bar{A}$, f. $B + E$, g. $B \cdot E$.

6. Interpret the three requirements of probabilities, P–1: $0 \leq P(E) \leq 1$, P–2: $P(S) = 1$, P–3: $P(A + B) = P(A) + P(B)$, if A and B are mutually exclusive, in the various contexts of the experiments listed below.

a) Tossing one die.

b) Accepting a contract to make delivery on a machine within two months.

c) Buying an insurance policy which pays \$10,000 if the insured is disabled but does not die, \$20,000 if the insured dies, and nothing if the insured neither dies nor is disabled during the period of the policy.

7. Suppose that a card is drawn from a standard deck of playing cards. Letting C designate that the card drawn is a club and K designate that the card drawn is a king, describe what each of the following events is:

a) $K + C$.　　　　　　　　e) $K \cdot \bar{C}$.
b) $K \cdot C$.　　　　　　　　f) $\bar{K} \cdot C$.
c) $\bar{K}$.　　　　　　　　　g) $\overline{K + C}$.
d) $\bar{C}$.

8. Consider an experiment consisting of the tossing of three coins—a dime, a nickel, and a penny. Following each toss, the number of heads and tails appearing is noted. Let the following events be as denoted.

        A: two or more heads; *B:* one or more heads;
        C: exactly one head; *D:* one or more tails;
        E: exactly one tail; and *F:* no head.

a) How many possible outcomes are there to this experiment?

b) List the sample space, maintaining the order of dime-nickel-penny.

c) List the outcomes in the following events: $A + B$, $A \cdot B$, $B + D$, $B \cdot D$, $A + E$, and $A \cdot E$.

Rules for calculating probabilities

With this much of an introduction to set notation, let us turn our attention once again to probability statements. We begin by listing the three requirements of probabilities already discussed:

P–1: $0 \leq P(E) \leq 1$.
P–2: $P(S) = 1$.
P–3: $P(A + B) = P(A) + P(B)$, if A and B are mutually exclusive.

For the experiment of tossing two dice, we were able to list a sample space consisting of 36 points which correspond to the values the two dice might take. Now, if we assume that these outcomes are randomly determined, then we have no basis in logic for assuming that any one of these outcomes is more likely than any other. We would consider the 36 outcomes to be equiprobable. Since we also know from Rule P–2 that the sum of the probabilities assigned to these 36 points must equal 1, we are led to assign a probability of 1/36 to each outcome.

Consider, now, the event A specified above as the set of outcomes where the value of the first die is less than three. There are 12 points in the sample space that correspond to this event. We can look at each of these 12 outcomes as an event in its own right; and this will allow us to say that the probability of the event A is equal to the sum of the probabilities of these 12 (mutually exclusive) outcomes, by application of Rule P–3. Thus, the probability of the event A is $P(A) = 12/36$.

A generalization of what we have just done for the event A leads to the following rule: If a sample space consists of n equiprobable points and if the event A corresponds to x of these points, then:

$$P\text{–4: } P(A) = x/n.$$

This rule is useful in many applications. We shall return to it later.

We have noted above that the events A and E are mutually exclusive. We are able to apply Rule P–3 to find that $P(A + E) = P(A) + P(E) = 12/36 + 6/36 = 18/36$. Now consider the events A and B. If we were to try an application of Rule P–3 for this pair, we should get an answer of 18/36 in this case also. Application of Rule P–4, however, would lead us to count the number of points in the union of A and B and express this number as a ratio to 36. We count 16 points in the union and thus write: $P(A + B) = x/n = 16/36$. The result of our second calculation does not agree with our first answer. The reason for the disagreement lies in the fact that A and B are not mutually exclusive events. When we used Rule P–3, we added the sum of the probabilities of the outcomes in A to the sum of the probabilities of the outcomes in B. In so doing, we double-counted the two points contained in the intersection of A and B. When we applied Rule P–4 we were not guilty of this error, and we found only 16 points in the union of A and B. Rule P–3 must be modified, therefore, in the case of a pair of events that are not mutually exclusive. We note that our answer for the probability of the union of A and B would have been correct if we had subtracted from the sum of the probabilities of A and B, the probability of the intersection of A and B: $12/36 + 6/36 - 2/36 = 16/36$. A generalization of this result leads to:

P–5: $P(A + B) = P(A) + P(B) - P(A \cdot B)$ if A and B are not mutually exclusive.[6]

Conditional probability

We also need a rule for determining the probability of the intersection of two events. Preliminary to this, however, we must develop the concept of conditional probability. Conditional probability is closely related to the idea that the more information we have as a basis for making a prediction, the better the prediction is likely to be. To illustrate this point, consider once again the event A. The probability of 12/36 assigned to A can be called the *unconditional* probability of the event A. It is based solely on the information that the experiment consists of the tossing of two dice and that the 36 possible outcomes are considered equally probable. Suppose, however, that the toss has already been made and we are informed by an observer that the value of the first die is less than five (let F be the event, "the value on the first die is less than five"). The effect of this additional information is that we now know the outcome is one of the 24 outcomes involving a value of one, two, three, or four on the first die. Since 12 of these points are in the event A, and because we still are not aware of the exact value on the first die, we say that the probability that A has occurred, given that F has occurred, is 12/24. In probability notation: $P(A|F) = 12/24$.

We might pause for a moment to consider a philosophical question at this point. In the paragraph above we used the statement, "the probability that A *has occurred*." In an interpretation of probability as involving predictions concerning *future events only*, this statement would be without meaning. If we choose to allow probability statements to represent levels of uncertainty, however, the statement makes good sense.

---

[6] This rule can be extended to cases involving the union of more than two events. We shall not require such a rule, however, so that a generalization of the rule is omitted here.

Even though the event A either has occurred or has not, we are still uncertain of the outcome at the time the statement is made. This distinction occurs from time to time in future discussions.

Continuing with the development of the concept of conditional probability, let us look at the reasoning we followed to get the statement, $P(A|F) = 12/24$. The added information that the event F had occurred led us to consider only 24 points in the sample space, rather than all 36. We can say that the additional information *reduced* the sample space. We then applied Rule P–4 where $x = 12$, as before, but $n = 24$ because of the reduction in the sample space.

Let us note, now, that the same result can be achieved in a second manner which can be generalized to give us another useful rule for the calculation of probabilities. We define, for any two events A and B, where $P(B) > 0$, the conditional probability of A, given B:

$$P\text{–}6: \quad P(A|B) = \frac{P(A \cdot B)^7}{P(B)}.$$

To see how this rule works, let us use it to find $P(A|F)$. We find that $P(AF) = 12/36$, since for these two events $A \cdot F = A$ (this is a happenstance that is not necessary for the result, as we shall see in later illustrations). The probability of F is, of course, $24/36$. Application of Rule P–6 yields

$$P(A|F) = \frac{P(A \cdot F)}{P(F)} = \frac{12/36}{24/36} = \frac{12}{24},$$

which checks with the answer obtained earlier.

Notice that, while $P(A) = 12/36$, we have just found that $P(A|F) = 12/24$. The probability of A, conditional on F, is different from the unconditional probability of A (in this particular case, it is larger). In such cases, where the probability of one event, conditional on some second event, is different from its unconditional probability, we say that the first event *depends* on the second event. Thus, the event A *depends* on the event F.

If we consider the pair of events A and B, we shall find a different result:

$$P(A|B) = \frac{P(A \cdot B)}{P(B)} = \frac{2/36}{6/36} = \frac{2}{6}.$$

We find that the conditional probability of A, given B, is $\frac{1}{3}$, which is the same as the unconditional probability of A. In such cases, we say that

---

[7] A useful way to explain this formula is to note that since we know that B has occurred, we now have the revised probability, $P'(B) = 1$. Consistent with this revision, all probabilities for events included in B, in particular $A \cdot B$, are "scaled up" through division by $P(B)$. This assures that the probabilities attached to the revised sample space ($S' = B$) sum to 1.

the two events are *independent*. Thus, the events A and B as specified on the sample space are *independent*. In commonsense terms this means that knowing the toss of two dice resulted in a value of four for the second die does not allow us to modify the probability that the first die had a value less than three. We would expect this to be the case. The value of the first die should be independent of the value of the second.

Let us consider one final example. The conditional probability of the event A, given E, is zero:

$$P(A|E) = \frac{P(A \cdot E)}{P(E)} = \frac{0}{6/36} = 0 .$$

We get this result because the intersection of A and E is the empty set. The result agrees with common sense. If the roll of two dice results in E (the first die has a value of five), then it cannot result in A (the first die has a value less than three). In this case, again, A *depends* on E.

We are now ready to set down the rules for finding the probability of the intersection of two events. If we multiply through the equation given as Rule P–6 by $P(B)$, we find that for any two events A and B:

$$P\text{–}7: P(A \cdot B) = P(B)P(A|B) ,[8]$$

and by symmetry,

$$P(A \cdot B) = P(B \cdot A) = P(A)P(B|A) .$$

If it happens that the events A and B are independent, then $P(A|B) = P(A)$, so that:

$$P\text{–}8: P(A \cdot B) = P(A)P(B), \text{ for } A \text{ and } B \text{ independent} .$$

A very useful probability rule arises from the relationship between an event and its complement. We defined the complement of an event in such a way that the union of any event and its complement is the sample space: $(A + \bar{A}) = S$. We know by Rule P–2 that $P(S) = 1$. We can therefore write $P(S) = P(A + \bar{A}) = 1$. But A and $\bar{A}$ are by definition mutually exclusive events. Using Rule P–3 we get $P(A + \bar{A}) = P(A) + P(\bar{A}) = 1$. From this last expression we derive our rule:

$$P\text{–}9: P(A) = 1 - P(\bar{A}) ,$$
$$P(\bar{A}) = 1 - P(A) .$$

As an illustration of these ideas, the specification of A as we used it above is "first die has a value of less than three." Then $\bar{A}$ is "the value of the first die is *not* less than three." This can be stated as well by "the

---

[8] Rules P–7 and P–8 have rather obvious generalizations to the case of the intersection of more than two events. Where we need them, we shall use them without additional comment.

first die has a value of three or greater." We have already determined that

$$P(A) = \frac{12}{36}.$$

Thus, by Rule P–9,

$$P(\bar{A}) = 1 - \frac{12}{36} = \frac{24}{36},$$

which the student can verify by examination of Figure 1–1*a*.

A final rule for the calculation of probabilities requires an understanding of the notion of a *partition*. Consider the sample space of Figure 1–1 and suppose we define the events: $A = "x_1 = 1$ or 2"; $B = "x_1 = 3$ or 4"; and $C = "x_1 = 5$ or 6." These three events are *mutually exclusive*, and they *exhaust* the sample space. In other words, each outcome in the sample space will be in one, and only one, of the three events; and all outcomes will be included in some one of the three events. In such a case, A, B, and C are said to *partition* the sample space. It is possible, of course, to specify a number of different sets of events which partition a given sample space. The exact partition which is useful will depend on the particular problem.

Now consider the event $D = "x_2 = 3$ or 4." Quick examination of the sample space indicates that the unconditional probability of this event is $P(D) = \frac{12}{36} = \frac{1}{3}$. We can arrive at the same answer through use of the partition accomplished by A, B, and C. For each of these three events, we can specify its intersection with D. Thus we have the three intersections $A \cdot B$, $B \cdot D$, and $C \cdot D$, which are mutually exclusive. For the union of these three intersections, we have

$$P(A \cdot D + B \cdot D + C \cdot D) = P(A \cdot D) + P(B \cdot D) + P(C \cdot D).$$

But note that the union "$A \cdot D + B \cdot D + C \cdot D$" is just the event, D. Thus,

$$P(D) = P(A \cdot D + B \cdot D + C \cdot D) = P(A \cdot D) + P(B \cdot D) + P(C \cdot D).$$

Finally, for each intersection, such as $A \cdot D$, we can use Rule P–7 to get,

$$P(A \cdot D) = P(A)P(D|A).$$

Substituting for corresponding intersections, we arrive at rule

$$P\text{–}10: P(D) = P(A)P(D|A) + P(B)P(D|B) + P(C)P(D|C)$$

if the events A, B, C partition the sample space.

To illustrate this rule for the particular situation described above, we note that: $P(A) = \frac{1}{3}$, $P(B) = \frac{1}{3}$, $P(C) = \frac{1}{3}$, $P(D|A) = \frac{1}{3}$, $P(D|B) = \frac{1}{3}$,

$P(D|C) = \frac{1}{3}$ (the fact that all these probabilities are ⅓ is not, of course,

significant). Substituting these values in *P*–10, we have

$$P(D) = \left[\frac{1}{3} \cdot \frac{1}{3}\right] + \left[\frac{1}{3} \cdot \frac{1}{3}\right] + \left[\frac{1}{3} \cdot \frac{1}{3}\right]$$

$$= \frac{1}{9} + \frac{1}{9} + \frac{1}{9} = \frac{1}{3}$$

which checks with our original calculation.

The importance of this rule springs from the fact that we can often identify a number of different conditions under which some particular event may occur. These conditions can be looked upon as partitioning the sample space in which the event of interest is included. If we can determine the probabilities attaching to these conditions, and the conditional probabilities of the event, given these conditions, Rule *P*–10 will allow us to calculate the unconditional probability of the event (the probability the event will occur under any and all conditions). An illustration in terms of a machine process will clarify these comments, later in the chapter.

This completes our inventory of rules which we shall find useful in the calculation of probabilities. We turn our attention now to some illustrations of how these rules can be used to find the probabilities of more-or-less complex events. As a first approach, let us consider uses of Rule *P*–4: $P(A) = x/n$. This rule is useful wherever we can list easily the outcomes in a sample space consisting of equiprobable points or where we can apply some systematic method of counting equiprobable outcomes without listing them. Suppose, for example, we wish to find the probability of drawing a royal flush (the five cards *A, K, Q, J*, 10, all of one suit) in a draw poker hand. (In draw poker, five cards are dealt to each player initially. He may subsequently discard some of these cards if he chooses, and draw as many new cards as he discarded. We will consider only the five cards dealt initially.) To use Rule *P*–4 we need the values of *x* and *n*. It is easy to see that *x* = 4, since there are four suits in a deck of cards. Determination of the value of *n* is a different matter, however. We could, in principle, set down a list of all the possible draw poker hands that could be drawn and count them. This procedure would give us the value of *n*, if we had not omitted any hands and if we could count that far without error. Both of these "ifs" are rather large. Moreover, the procedure would be exceedingly lengthy and tedious. It will pay us to give some preliminary attention to methods of counting.

Problem Set 1–2

1. Consider, once again, the experiment described in problem 8 of of Problem Set 1–1, and, defining the events, *A, B, C, D, E,* and *F* as indicated there, answer the following:
   a) Determine the probabilities of the events listed in (*c*), first by Rule P–4 and then by the appropriate one of the rules: P–3, P–5, P–7, or P–8.
   b) The event *E* is the intersection of two other events specified in the introduction. Which two?
   c) Find the following: *P* (all coins match $|A$), *P* (all coins match $|F$), *P* (all coins match $|E$).
   d) Specify a set of three events, among *A, B, C, D, E,* and *F,* that partition the sample space. For this set, use Rule P–10 to find the probability that all three coins will match.
   e) Suppose the three coins have been tossed, but we are not yet aware of the outcome. A disinterested observer tells us that the dime and nickel both show head. What is the probability that all three coins match? Are the events "dime and nickel are head" and "all three coins match" independent? Why, or why not?
   f) In (*e*) above, suppose that the observer told us that he had examined the three coins and that at least two were heads. Under these circumstances, what is the probability that the three coins match? Are these two events independent? Why, or why not?

2. A prominent French mathematician once was asked the probability that the toss of two coins would result in a match. He reasoned that the outcomes were "two heads," "a head and a tail," and "two tails." Since there were three possible outcomes and two of these resulted in a match, he reasoned that the sought probability was ⅔. Where was his error?

3. We often are interested in a number, called a random variable, associated with the outcome of an experiment. In the toss of two dice, for example, the sum of x_1 and x_2 might be of interest.
   a) List in a column the different values for $x_1 + x_2$ associated with the points of the sample space. In a second column, list the probability of each value, as determined through use of rule P–4.
   b) Reproduce Figure 1–1 of the text and draw lines around the following events: "$x_1 + x_2 = 8$," "$x_1 = 2$," and "a 2 appears on at least one die."
   c) Find: $P(x_1 + x_2 = 8)$, $P(x_1 + x_2 = 8|x_1 = 2)$, $P(x_1 + x_2 = 8|$ "a 2 appears on at least one die").

4. The credit department of a large retailing firm has found that one tenth of their new accounts become delinquent in the first month. Of the accounts delinquent in the first month, one fourth are finally written off as a bad debt. Of the new accounts that do not become delinquent in the first month, only one tenth must be written off as a bad debt. What is the probability that a new customer will become a "bad debt"?

5. The clientele of a shop for which you work as a clerk has the following composition: 0.1 are men over forty years of age; 0.1 are men under forty;

In some weeks, Mr. Salem makes a sale to Mr. Smith both days he visits him. In other weeks, he makes a sale on the first call or the second call only. Some weeks, he sells nothing to Mr. Smith. For any one week, the probability that he will make a sale the first call is 0.2. The probability that he will sell Mr. Smith something on the second call is 0.3. If he sells Mr. Smith something on the first call, the probability that he will also sell him something on the second call is 0.4. The probability of a sale on the first call of the week is not conditional on what happened the week before.

Let A denote the event, "Mr. Salem sells something to Mr. Smith on the first visit of the week" and B denote the event, "Mr. Salem sells something to Mr. Smith on the second visit of the week." Write a description of each of the events listed below:

a) $A + B$.

b) $A \cdot B$.

c) $A \cdot \bar{B}$.

d) $\overline{(A + B)}$.

19. For the situation described in the preceding problem, evaluate the probabilities for the following events:

   a) "Mr. Salem makes two sales to Mr. Smith in a given week."

   b) "Mr. Salem makes at least one sale to Mr. Smith in a given week."

   c) "Mr. Salem makes no sale to Mr. Smith in a given week."

   d) "Mr. Salem makes a sale to Mr. Smith on the first day only in a given week."

Rules for counting

It often happens that some operation to be performed can be broken down into a number of individual steps. In many cases, some of these steps can be performed in more than one way. When this is true, the entire operation can be performed in as many ways as the product of the numbers of ways the individual steps can be performed. For example, suppose that we are ordering a new car and that we have certain options that we can specify. We can have (1) a V–8 or a six; (2) a straight stick, four-on-the-floor, or an automatic transmission; (3) a choice of 12 colors; and (4) a choice of convertible or hard-top sedan. The operation of ordering the car involves the four steps of specifying engine, transmission, color, and body style. The number of ways each step can be accomplished are, respectively: 2, 3, 12, and 2. The operation of ordering a car can therefore be performed in $(2 \times 3 \times 12 \times 2) = 144$ ways. The appropriate generalization of this result is our first rule for counting:

> C–1: If an operation consists of r separate steps, which can be accomplished in $n_1, n_2, \cdots, n_r$ ways, respectively, then the operation can be performed in $(n_1 \cdot n_2 \cdots n_r)$ ways.

Next, we consider a situation in which we have a collection of n objects. We are to draw r objects from the collection, and our problem is to count the number of ways this can be done. As a specific example, suppose the collection contains five objects labeled *A*, *B*, *C*, *D*, and *E*. We can systematically list the possible ways we could draw, say, two items from this collection:

A,B	A,C	A,D	A,E
B,A	B,C	B,D	B,E
C,A	C,B	C,D	C,E
D,A	D,B	D,C	D,E
E,A	E,B	E,C	E,D

With the list before us, we can count to find that there are 20 ways to draw two objects from a collection of five. Once again, however, this method of listing and counting the items becomes very lengthy for a large collection.

We can shorten the work involved by treating the drawing of the two objects from the five as an operation consisting of two steps. The first step is to draw the first object; this can be done in five ways. The second step is to draw the second object. Since we have reduced the collection of objects from five to four by the previous draw, we can accomplish the second step in four ways. Using Rule *C*–1, we find the number of ways to perform the operation is $(5 \times 4) = 20$, which agrees with our first answer. We shall call these 20 ways of drawing two objects from a collection of five the *permutations* of five objects taken two at a time. We introduce the term *permutation* to denote that two sets of objects are considered different if they differ from each other by as much as the order of their appearance in the set. For example, the results (A,B) and (B,A) which appear in the list above are two different *permutations*. Although they consist of the same objects, they appear in different orders.

In general, if we are to draw *r* objects from a collection of *n*, we will find that this operation can result in $n \cdot (n-1) \cdots (n-r+1)$ permutations. This last expression can be written as the ratio of $n!$ to $(n-r)!$[9], so that we have the second rule for counting: the number of permutations of *n* objects taken *r* at a time is

$$C\text{–}2: P_{n,r} = \frac{n!}{(n-r)!}.$$

The list set out above of the 20 ways to draw two objects from a collection of five is really a list of the *permutations* of five objects taken two at a time. Another list could have been set down, if we had agreed that two different "ways" must differ with regard to the objects drawn. In this second sense, the results (A,B) and (B,A) would be considered the same, since they both consist of the objects *A* and *B*. When we count

---

[9] The term $n!$ is read "factorial *n*" and denotes the product $n(n-1)(n-2) \ldots 1$. For example, $5! = 5 \times 4 \times 3 \times 2 \times 1 = 120$. By definition, $0! = 1$.

ways of drawing r objects from n in this second sense, we count the *combinations* of objects. Two *combinations* of objects must differ in that there is at least one object not common to both.

We wish to develop a rule for counting combinations. We do this by a consideration of the list of permutations. Notice that for every combination of two objects given, there are two permutations. For example, the two permutations (A,B) and (B,A) comprise one combination of A and B. In the case of drawing two objects from five, then, the number of combinations must be equal to $20/2 = 10$. The factor of two enters in here because of the fact that there are, for any combination of two objects, $2! = 2 \times 1 = 2$ permutations of these two objects. In general, if we are to draw r objects from a collection of n objects, there will be a number of permutations equal to $n!/(n-r)!$; and there will be $r!$ times as many permutations as there will be combinations. Letting $C_{n,r}$ denote the number of combinations of n objects taken r at a time, we derive a third rule for counting from this fact:

$$\text{C--3: } C_{n,r} = \frac{P_{n,r}}{r!} = \frac{n!}{(n-r)!r!}$$

Problem Set 1–3

1. A student returns to his college campus with a wardrobe consisting of three sports jackets, two vests, and five pairs of slacks. How many basic outfits can be assembled from his wardrobe if an "outfit" consists of jacket, a vest, and a pair of slacks?

2. In a telephone system, the number assigned to each telephone subscriber is composed of two letters followed by five digits. Assuming that any of the 26 letters of the alphabet and any of the 10 digits can be used in constructing a telephone number, how many such numbers are available to the telephone system?

3. Find the value of $C_{n,r}$ for the following values of n and r:

    a) $n = 10$, $r = 2$.   *b*) $n = 10$, $r = 8$.

    c) $n = 5$, $r = 3$.   *d*) $n = 5$, $r = 2$.

   (If the student has evaluated these properly, he will find that $C_{10,2} = C_{10,8}$ and that $C_{5,3} = C_{5,2}$. This can be justified in the commonsense observation that to draw 2 objects from a collection of 10, for example, is the same thing as to choose 8 objects of the 10 to remain in the collection. The general relationship is $C_{n,r} = C_{n,n-r}$.)

4. Find the values of $P_{n,r}$ for the values of n and r set out in problem 3.

5. Mr. Jones is one of 10 members in his lodge. The annual selecting of officers is scheduled for next week. In this lodge, a "slate" consisting of president, vice president, and treasurer is selected by lottery. The first name drawn from a hat containing the names of the 10 members is designated president, the second vice president, the third treasurer. How many possible "slates" of officers are there?

6. The lodge described in (5) must select a committee of three members to meet with the mayor. How many possible committees can be selected?

7. How many three-letter words can be formed from the first five letters of the alphabet:
   a) If the letter used in any draw is replaced before the next letter is drawn?
   b) If the letters used are not replaced and we define the term "word" so that two words are different if they vary by so much as the order of the letters?
   c) If the letters are not replaced and two words must differ by the letters letters they contain?
   d) Is the probability of selecting the word "ABC" independent of the methods of selection suggested in (a), (b) and (c) above?

8. The three word-pairs listed below all represent pairs of ——— of the 26 letters of the alphabet:

   > sore, rose.
   > latent, talent.
   > shrub, brush.

9. In a certain state the automobile license plates are stamped with a prefix consisting of three letters. How many different prefixes can be formed?

10. In the state mentioned in problem 9, there are expected to be 2 million registered automobiles next year. If the three-letter prefix is to be followed by a series of numeric digits, how many digits must be allowed for on a plate to assure that each automobile will have a unique license plate?

11. Mr. Salem, a traveling salesman, visits four different cities daily—*A, B, C, D*—from his home town, *E*. To relieve the monotony, he often will change the order in which he visits the four cities, since this has little effect on the time required to make his "rounds." How many different routes are available to Mr. Salem?

12. On one particular day Mr. Salem got a late start, and he found that he had time to visit only two of the four cities. How many choices does Mr. Salem have of the two cities he will visit that day?

Some illustrative problems: hypergeometric and binomial probabilities

With these rules for counting at our disposal, we return to the question, What is the probability of drawing a royal flush in a draw poker hand? We wish to use Rule *P-4*, and we have already noted that the value of *x* would be four, since there are four different suits in which we might have a royal flush. We shall determine the value of *n* by Rule *C-3*. Any poker hand can be looked upon as a combination of 5 cards drawn from a collection of 52 cards. We treat a draw poker hand as a combination, rather than a permutation, because the value of the hand is determined only by the cards drawn and not by their order. The number of possible draw poker hands is, therefore, $C_{52,5} = 2,598,960.$[10] Thus we have

$$P \text{ (drawing a royal flush)} = \frac{x}{n} = \frac{4}{2,598,960} \simeq 0.00000154 .$$

No wonder one does not see a royal flush very frequently in an honest poker game!

To get some more practice, let us consider a little more complex question. This time, suppose that you are playing bridge and that the hand you have just been dealt contains no aces. What is the probability that your partner's hand will contain exactly two aces? The basic problem here is the same as in the last sample: we must count hands. In this example, however, we are concerned with a conditional probability, since you know that you have 13 cards in your hand, none of which is an ace. That leaves 39 cards allotted to the other three players, 35 of which are nonace and four of which are aces.

The reduced sample space consists of the number of bridge hands that can be (could have been) dealt from the 39 "other" cards; there are $C_{39,13}$ of these. A deal of two aces to your partner is an operation (in the sense used above) consisting of two steps: (1) he is dealt 2 of the 4 aces in the 39 "other" cards, and (2) he is dealt 11 of the 35 nonaces to complete a hand of 13 cards. The number of ways each step can be accomplished is $C_{4,2}$ and $C_{35,11}$, respectively. The operation can be performed, then, in $(C_{4,2})(C_{35,11})$ ways. The probability of your partner holding two aces in his bridge hand, given that you have no aces, is

$$\frac{x}{n} = \frac{(C_{4,2})(C_{35,11})}{C_{39,13}} \simeq 0.308 .$$

For completeness, we could let X denote the number of aces your partner might have, given that you have none, and calculate $P(X)$ for $X = 0, 1, 2, 3, 4$. These represent the complete list of possible outcomes for your partner's hand. Table 1–1 shows the possibilities. The last line of the table has been added to show that Rule P–2 applies in the case of a reduced sample space. Given that your hand contains no ace, your partner's hand must contain no ace, one, two, three, or four aces: $P(S') = 1$, where S' denotes the reduced sample space.[11]

---

[10] $C_{52,5} = \dfrac{52!}{(52 - 5)!5!} = \dfrac{52!}{47!5!} = \dfrac{(52)(51)(50)(49)(48)}{(5)(4)(3)(2)(1)} = 2,598,960 .$

[11] The term "reduced" refers to the fact that we directed our attention to the $C_{39,13}$ "other" hands, not to a reduction in the possible number of values for X. In the present example, your partner may have any number of aces from zero to four, since your hand contains no ace. If your hand had contained one ace, however, your partner's could have had no more than three.

Table 1–1 describes a *probability distribution*. It indicates the exact manner in which the total probability of 1.000 associated with the sample space is *distributed* among the possible events into which we have partitioned that sample space. There are many different types of probability distribution. We shall become acquainted with several of them throughout this book. The type depicted in Table 1–1 is called the *hypergeometric distribution*. It has several important applications, with some of which we shall familiarize ourselves later.

Table 1–1

X	P(X)
0	$\dfrac{(C_{4,0})(C_{35,13})}{C_{39,13}} \simeq 0.182$
1	$\dfrac{(C_{4,1})(C_{35,12})}{C_{39,13}} \simeq 0.411$
2	$\dfrac{(C_{4,2})(C_{35,11})}{C_{39,13}} \simeq 0.308$
3	$\dfrac{(C_{4,3})(C_{35,10})}{C_{39,13}} \simeq 0.090$
4	$\dfrac{(C_{4,4})(C_{35,9})}{C_{39,13}} \simeq 0.009$

$P(X = 0 \text{ or } 1 \text{ or } 2 \text{ or } 3 \text{ or } 4) = 1.000$

A final illustration for this section will be an example (admittedly simplified) to illustrate how the rules of probability we have developed might be used in a practical application. Assume that you supervise a process in which, say, a roller bearing is produced by a machine. Suppose further that a bearing produced by this machine may be unsatisfactory because of the following circumstances: it may be out-of-round, it may be too long, or it may be both out-of-round and too long. We assume that we have the following information:[12]

P ("part is out-of-round") $= P(R) = 0.1$.
P ("part is too long") $= P(L) = 0.2$.
P ("part is out-of-round, given it is too long") $= P(R|L) = 0.25$.

The economics of the process are such that if a part is out-of-round only, or too long only, it is profitable to remill it to correct the condition. If a part is both out-of-round and too long, however, the part is scrapped.

We start by asking, What is the probability that a part will have to be scrapped? We scrap a part if it is both too long and out-of-round, that is, if the event which occurs is the intersection of L and R: $L \cdot R$. The required answer, then, is, by Rule P–7:

$$P(L \cdot R) = P(L)P(R|L) = (0.2)(0.25) = 0.05 .$$

---

[12] This information might have come to us as the result of engineering specifications of the performance of the machine, for example, or we might have past records from which we have calculated the portions of parts in past production that were out-of-round, too long, etc. If we felt justified in the belief that future proportions would remain the same as in the past, and that the occurrences of these defects were randomly caused, then we could treat the proportions as probabilities.

We can now find the probability that a part will be too long, given that it is out-of-round. By Rule P–6:

$$P(L|R) = \frac{P(L \cdot R)}{P(R)} = \frac{0.05}{0.1} = 0.5 \ .$$

What about the probability that a part will be defective? In saying a part is defective, we mean that it has one or the other or both of the defects. A part will be defective if the outcome of its production is in the union of the two events, "too long" and "out-of-round." We have, therefore, by Rule P–5:

$$P(\text{"part is defective"}) = P(L + R) = P(L) + P(R) - P(L \cdot R)$$
$$= 0.2 + 0.1 - 0.05 = 0.25 \ .$$

If the probability that a part is defective is 0.25, we have by Rule P–9:

$$P(\text{"part is \textit{not} defective"}) = 1.0 - P(\text{"part is defective"})$$
$$= 1.0 - 0.25 = 0.75 \ .$$

Before continuing with the present illustration, let us digress to introduce a simple device that is very helpful in analyzing probability problems: the Venn diagram. In a Venn diagram, the sample space for the experiment under consideration is represented by a rectangle. Any events of special interest are represented by circles inscribed within the rectangle. Thus, for the events L ("a part is too long") and R ("a part is out-of-round"), the Venn diagram would appear as in Figure 1–2, with the numbers in parentheses indicating the respective probabilities. We can indicate the union of L and R as in Figure 1–2(a) and the intersection of these two events as in Figure 1–2(b). Notice that if the two events had been mutually exclusive, we would have drawn their circles so that they would not be joined. We knew that they were not mutually exclusive from the original information because $P(R|L) = 0.25$, which is not zero. Diagrammatically, $P(R|L)$ is the ratio of the area of the intersection to the area of the circle L. A similar interpretation is possible for $P(L|R)$.

To continue the illustration, suppose that as a regular part of your program of supervising this process, you occasionally select a random sample[13] of five parts produced by the machine. You very carefully check each of the five parts comprising the sample to see if it is out-of-round, too long, or both. If any of these conditions apply, you label the part "defective." In these circumstances let us ask, What is the probability that such a sample will contain three defective parts? We find an answer in stages.

To facilitate the analysis, let us make use of a little mental imagery.

[13] A random sample is selected in such a way as to assure that each object has an equal chance to be in the sample. We shall say more later about methods of achieving this.

Figure 1–2

S (1.0)

L (0.2)

R (0.1)

Figure 1–2(a)

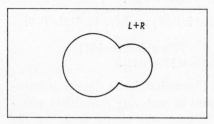

L+R

Figure 1–2(b)

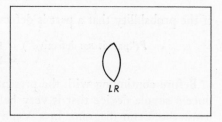

LR

We shall suppose that we have a basket containing five compartments; and that we put each of the five parts selected for the sample in one of the compartments, moving from left to right across the basket. Then, if we have a sample of five parts with three defectives, it might appear as follows, where *D* indicates a defective part and G indicates a good part: *DDDGG*. The probability that this would be the particular outcome is easily calculated. We noted above that the probability that any part will be defective is 0.25 and the probability that a part will be a good one is 0.75. The particular arrangement of the basket shown above can be regarded as the intersection of five events: ("the first part is defective" *and* "the second part is defective" *and* "the third part is defective" *and* "the fourth part is good" *and* "the fifth part is good"). Thus, we need the probability of an intersection; and we should use either Rule *P–7* or Rule *P–8*. Since the parts have been selected randomly, we are justified in treating the occurrence or nonoccurrence of a defective part at any point in the selection of the sample as an event independent of what has happened in any of the other selections. This means that we may use Rule *P–8* to find the probability of the intersection of independent events. We find, then:

$$P(DDDGG) = P(D)P(D)P(D)P(G)P(G)$$
$$= [P(D)]^3[P(G)]^2$$
$$= (0.25)^3(0.75)^2 \simeq 0.00879 \ .$$

We have found that $P(DDDGG) \simeq 0.00879$. Of course, the arrangement in the basket, for a sample of five with three defectives, might have been $DDGGD$. By the same reasoning as in the previous paragraph, we would find that $P(DDGGD) = P(D)P(D)P(G)P(G)P(D) = (0.25)^3$ $(0.75)^2 \simeq 0.00879$. There are 10 possible arrangements that might appear in the basket: $DDDGG$, $DDGGD$, $DGGDD$, $GGDDD$, $GDGDD$, $GDDGD$, $GDDDG$, $DGDDG$, $DDGDG$, and $DGDGD$. Each arrangement has the same probability of occurring. The event, "a sample of five has three defectives," is just the union of these 10 *mutually exclusive* arrangements. An obvious extension of Rule P–3 indicates that we must sum the probabilities attached to the 10 arrangements in order to get the probability of three defectives in the sample of five. Since each arrangement has the same probability, 0.00879, it is easier to show the required probability as $10(0.00879) = 0.0879$.

We could have saved ourselves a good deal of effort in the paragraph above if we had counted the number of arrangements of the three defectives in the sample of five in a different way. By assumption, we have a sample of five objects, three of which are defective. We wish to know in how many ways these objects can be assigned to the five compartments in our fictitious basket. We could suppose that we assign the three defectives first (if we assigned the two good objects first, the result would be the same). Then the number of assignments can be made in $C_{5,3}$ ways, since there are that many ways to select three of the five compartments to contain the defective objects. Note that $C_{5,3} = 10$, which agrees with the result we got by listing all the possible arrangements.

The reasoning above has led us to the following formulation:

$$P(\text{"a sample of five will contain three defectives"})$$
$$= C_{5,3}(0.25)^3(0.75)^2$$

$$= \frac{5!}{2!3!} (0.25)^3(0.75)^2 .$$

We have been concerned with the specific example of a sample of five parts taken from the output of a machine for which the probability of a defective is 0.25. To generalize the result, we could consider a sample of any specified size, n, with the probability of a defective any number, p, such that $0 \leq p \leq 1$. We could then express the probability that the sample of n would contain r defective parts $(0 \leq r \leq n)$ as

$$P(r) = \frac{n!}{(n - r)!r!} p^r(1 - p)^{n - r} .$$

Substituting values of $n = 5$, $p = 0.25$, and $r = 3$, one can easily verify that this formulation leads to the same result as we developed above for a sample of size five with three defectives.

For completeness, we can set down Table 1–2, indicating all the possible values for the number of defectives we might find in our sample of five, with the associated probabilities. Table 1–2 depicts a second type of probability distribution. Its name is the *binomial distribution*, and it has many important applications to which we shall return later.

It was pointed out earlier that the rule for adding probabilities across a partition of the sample space, Rule P–10, is very useful in practical ap-

Table 1–2

r	$P(r) = \dfrac{n!}{(n-r)!r!} p^r(1-p)^{n-r} (n=5, p=.25)$
0	$\dfrac{5!}{5!0!}(0.25)^0(0.75)^5 \simeq 0.2373$
1	$\dfrac{5!}{4!1!}(0.25)^1(0.75)^4 \simeq 0.3955$
2	$\dfrac{5!}{3!2!}(0.25)^2(0.75)^3 \simeq 0.2637$
3	$\dfrac{5!}{2!3!}(0.25)^3(0.75)^2 \simeq 0.0879$
4	$\dfrac{5!}{1!4!}(0.25)^4(0.75)^1 \simeq 0.0146$
5	$\dfrac{5!}{0!5!}(0.25)^5(0.75)^0 \simeq 0.0010$

$P(r = 0 \text{ or } 1 \text{ or } 2 \text{ or } 3 \text{ or } 4 \text{ or } 5) \quad = 1.0000$

plications. With a slight modification of the present machine-part example, some indication can be given of its usefulness. Suppose that the part we discussed above is actually produced by two machines (we could consider more than two machines, but this would only extend the arithmetic and add nothing to our understanding). One machine produces the part with a defective rate of 0.25, as developed above. We shall designate this machine with the roman numeral, I. The second machine, II, produces the part with a defective rate of 0.20, we shall suppose. Let us suppose, further, that machine II produces the part at three times the rate of machine I, so that three fourths of all the parts produced come from machine II and only one fourth are produced by machine I. The output of both machines move in two separate streams to one common conveyor belt, where they intermingle in a presumably random manner. At a point further along the common conveyor belt, the parts are inspected prior to packing for shipment. Our problem is, What is the probability that a part selected at random for inspection will be defective?

The first step in arriving at a solution is to note that the relevant sample space in this situation is partitioned by the fact that some of the possible outcomes relate to machine I and the remainder relate to machine II. Letting *I* denote the event "the part is produced by machine I" and *II* denote the event "the part is produced by machine II," the events *I* and *II* partition the sample space. The probability that a part is defective is conditional on the events *I* and *II*, as described in the preceding paragraph. Specifically, we have P ("defective part" | *I*) = 0.25 and P("defective part" | *II*) = 0.20. We also know, from our knowledge of the relative rates of production of the two machines, that the probability that a randomly selected part will have been produced by machine I is $\frac{1}{4}$: $P(I) = 0.25$. It is also true that $P(II) = 0.75$. With this information, we can calculate the unconditional probability of a defective part by Rule P–10:

$$P(\text{"defective part"}) = P(I)P(\text{"defective part"} | I) + P(II)P(\text{"defective part"} | II)$$
$$= (0.25)(0.25) + (0.75)(0.20)$$
$$= 0.2125 .$$

With this illustration in mind, it is easy to give a commonsense interpretation to Rule P–10. It states that the unconditional probability of an event may be found as the weighted sum of the conditional probabilities of the event. The sum must extend over a set of conditions (conditioning events) which partition the sample space, and the weights required are just the probabilities that the different conditions will obtain.

Comparison of the binomial distribution and the hypergeometric distribution

Two probability distributions were introduced in the preceding section: the binomial distribution and the hypergeometric distribution. In the case of both distributions, an experiment is performed and one notes whether or not some specified event occurs. In the machine-part problem used to illustrate the binomial distribution, for example, a part would be either defective or not. In the problem involving the hypergeometric distribution, the appropriate thing to note was, for each card your partner might draw in his bridge hand, whether the card was an ace or not.

The basic distinction between the two situations lies in the fact that in the machine-part problem we could assume that the result on any one trial was independent of the outcome on any other trial, whereas this could not be done in the bridge hand problem. That is, knowing that a particular part selected was defective did not lead us to assume that the probability of the next part being defective would differ accordingly. In contrast, in the bridge hand problem, if we knew that the partner had drawn an ace as the first card in his hand, this would change the probability that he would get an ace as the second card. On the second draw, only three of the 38 remaining cards would be aces. Thus, the probability of drawing an ace on the second card, given that the first card was an ace, is 3/38. However, if the first card had not been an ace, then the probability of drawing an ace on the second card would have been 4/38. We see, then, that the probability of drawing an ace in any one draw is dependent on what the outcomes were on previous draws.

A convenient way to illustrate the difference is to consider a bag containing 10 marbles. Suppose that four of these marbles are red and six are green. Let us determine the probability of having two red marbles and two green marbles in four marbles selected at random from this bag, under two different assumptions concerning the procedure for drawing the marbles.

As the first case, suppose that one marble is drawn at a time, its color is noted, and it is then replaced in the bag before another marble is drawn. In this procedure of drawing with replacement, on each successive draw the probabilities associated with the two possible colors will not be affected by the results on previous draws. That is, the probabilities on any one draw will be independent of the other draws. In this case, we can find the probability of getting two red and two green marbles in the first four draws by using the binomial formula. There are 10 marbles in the bag. Since four of these are red, the probability of drawing a red marble on any one draw is $p = 0.4$. The probability of drawing a green marble is, of course, $1 - p = 0.6$. We are to draw four marbles, so the number of trials is $n = 4$. We wish to evaluate the probability of drawing $r = 2$ red marbles in these four trials. Using the binomial formula, we find the answer:

$$P(r = 2) = \frac{4!}{(2!)\,(2!)} \, (.4)^2 (.6)^2 = 0.3456 \, .$$

As the second case, suppose that when a marble is drawn from the bag it is not replaced before the next marble is drawn. In this circumstance, obviously, the probability of drawing a red marble on the second draw will be different from the probability on the first draw. On the first draw the probability of a red marble is 0.4. On the second draw, however, the probability of a red marble will be either 3/9 or 4/9, depending on whether the first marble drawn was red or green, respectively. The probabilities associated with the third draw also depend on the results of the first two draws, and the probabilities of the fourth draw will be affected by the results of all three preceding draws. Lack of independence in this circumstance makes this a different problem which seems vastly more complex, at first blush. The solution can be found as a hypergeometric probability, and a relatively simple device reduces the complexity considerably.

Let us view the bag containing the 10 marbles as if it were divided into two compartments. One of these compartments contains the four red marbles and the other contains the six green marbles. We ask, first, in how many different ways could four marbles be drawn from the 10 marbles in the bag? The answer can be expressed as $C_{10,4} = 210$. We ask, next, in how many ways could four marbles be drawn, with two of these red and two of them green. The procedure can be looked upon as an operation of two steps: (1) to choose two marbles from the compartment containing four red marbles, and (2) to choose two marbles from the compartment containing six green marbles. The first step can be performed in $C_{4,2} = 6$ ways; the second step can be performed in $C_{6,2} = 15$ ways; and the operation can be performed, therefore, in $6 \times 15 = 90$ ways. We can now use Rule P-4, letting $n = 210$ and $x = 90$ to find:

$$P(\text{two red marbles}) = 90/210 \simeq .429 .$$

We can generalize the procedure for calculating a hypergeometric probability and thereby arrive at a formula for this probability. Suppose that in a collection of N items there are a number, D, of these items with the characteristic of interest to us (they might be red, as in the example above). The remaining $N - D$ items, of course, do not have this characteristic. We are to draw n items from this collection, without replacement. Then the probability that r of the n items drawn will have the characteristic of interest is

$$P(r) = \frac{C_{D,r} \cdot C_{N-D,\, n-r}}{C_{N,n}} .$$

Problem Set 1–4

1. In the machine-part example of the text, calculate the probability that the part selected for the common conveyor belt will be nondefective. Do this by application of Rule P-10 and then by application of Rule P-9, using the information developed in the text.

2. Evaluating the probabilities of various poker hands is a good exercise in the use of counting rules and Rule P-4. It was shown in the text that the total number of poker hands is 2,598,960. To evaluate the probability for any given hand, then, it is only necessary to determine x, the number of outcomes corresponding to that event and to use Rule P-4. We work through one such problem here, before asking you to work those assigned

below. If a poker hand contains two matching cards (same face) and three nonmatching cards, it is called a *pair*. We find the probability of dealing a *pair*. Consider the dealing of the hand as an *operation* in the sense of the text. We can look on this operation as consisting of six steps: (1) choose one from 13 faces for the two matching cards; (2) choose two of the four cards in this face to be placed in the hand; (3) choose 3 more faces from the 12 remaining faces, for the three nonmatching cards; (4), (5), and (6) choose one card from the four in each of these three faces to be played in the hand. If we use the number of combinations corresponding to each step, we have for the number of ways each step can be performed, respectively: (1) $C_{13,1}$; (2) $C_{4,2}$; (3) $C_{12,3}$; (4), (5), and (6) $C_{4,1}$ at each step. We find x, the number of ways the operation of dealing a *pair* can be performed, by Rule C–1:

$$x = \text{number of } pairs = C_{13.1} \cdot C_{4.2} \cdot C_{12.3} \cdot C_{4.1} \cdot C_{4.1} \cdot C_{4.1}$$
$$= 13 \cdot 6 \cdot 220 \cdot 4 \cdot 4 \cdot 4 = 1{,}098{,}240 \,.$$

Now, by application of Rule P–4, $P(\text{pair}) = 1{,}098{,}240/2{,}598{,}960 \simeq 0.423$.

Using similar procedures calculate the probabilities of the following events:

a) Dealing a full house (three cards of one face, two cards of another face).

b) Dealing four of a kind (four cards of one face).

c) Dealing a spade flush (all five cards are spades).

d) Dealing a hand with at least two different suits.

3. Suppose that a bag contains five identical chips. One chip has the number 1 printed on it, another has the number 2, and so on, through the number 5. A person is asked to draw two chips from the bag. The person is blindfolded, and the bag is well shaken before each draw. Assume that the person holds the first chip in his hand while he draws the second chip. Upon completion of the two draws, we note the numbers of the two chips and calculate their sum. Letting s denote the sum appearing on the two chips, calculate the probability that for any one pair of chips drawn from the bag, s will equal 0, 1, 2, . . . , 10.

4. Repeat problem 3, only this time assume that the first chip is replaced in the bag, after the number on it is noted, before the second chip is drawn.

5. Suppose that it is decided by the flip of a coin whether the two chips are to be drawn with or without replacement (see problems 3 and 4). On any one trial of this experiment, what is the probability that s will equal 2, 5, 10?

6. A small boy is employed by a golf driving range to cull out defective golf balls from baskets containing 100 golf balls each. If the basket placed before him contains 20 defective golf balls, what is the probability that 2 defective balls will be among the first 10 that he inspects?

7. A manufacturer of a breakfast cereal places a small plastic toy in each box of the cereal. There are four different toys from which one is selected to be inserted in each box. The manufacturer endeavors to select a toy to be

placed in each box in a random fashion. Jimmy Jones very much wishes to have a complete set of these toys. Consequently, he asks his mother to buy a box of the cereal each week, when she does the weekly grocery shopping. Referring to the four toys as *A*, *B*, *C*, and *D*, answer the following questions.

a) What is the probability that in the first four weeks, Jimmy will receive four of the toy *A* and none of the others?

b) Explain the difference between the question of (*a*) and the following question: What is the probability that in the first four weeks, Jimmy will receive four of one type of toy and none of the other three types?

c) Calculate the probability asked for in (*b*).

d) What is the probability that Jimmy will receive all four different toys in the first four boxes of cereal his mother brings home?

8. A stockbroker has carefully charted the movements of the closing price of a particular stock for several months. He has found that if the stock has increased in price a given day, 20 percent of the time it has arisen on the following day, 30 percent of the time it has remained unchanged on the following day, and 50 percent of the time it has fallen in price the following day. On the days when the price has not changed, 50 percent of the time it has risen on the following day, 10 percent of the time it has not changed the following day, and 40 percent of the time it has fallen the next day. On those days when the price has fallen, 40 percent of the time it has risen on the following day, 20 percent of the time is has remained unchanged the next day, and 40 percent of the time it has fallen the next day.

Let us suppose that the stockbroker is willing to treat the relative frequencies indicated above as probabilities. We let R_1 represent the event, "the price rises one day," and R_2 represent the event, "the price will rise the following day." In similar fashion we have:

U_1—"price unchanged one day."
U_2—"price unchanged following day."
F_1—"price falls one day."
F_2—"price will fall following day."

a) Rewrite the nine facts concerning relative frequencies which are given in the first paragraph above as probability statements, using the symbols for various events as specified in the second paragraph.

b) Suppose that, as of today, the stockbroker assesses the following probabilities for the performance of the stock: $P(R_1) = 0.50$, $P(U_1) = 0.10$, $P(F_1) = 0.40$. On the basis of these assessments and the statements of (*a*) above, calculate the probabilities of the following events:

    i) "price rises both today and tomorrow."
    ii) "price rises today and falls tomorrow."
    iii) "price rises today and does not rise tomorrow."
    iv) "price rises tomorrow."
    v) "price rises either today or tomorrow or both days."

c) Suppose that the stock fell in price yesterday. To be consistent with the assumptions above, what probabilities should the stockbroker assign to the three possible outcomes for today's price?

9. Suppose a bag contains 10 marbles, 5 of which are red and 5 green. If four marbles are drawn without replacement, what is the probability that two of the marbles will be red?

10. Set down the probability distribution for *x*, where *x* is the number of red marbles that might appear among the four drawn from the bag described in problem 9. What is the name of this distribution?

11. If, in problem 9, the draws had been made with replacement, what is the probability that two marbles would be red?

12. Repeat problem 10, this time for the case where the draws are made with replacement. What type of distribution have you constructed?

13. A mother gives her two young sons eight pieces of toffee to divide equally between them. In these eight pieces, there are only two pieces of chocolate toffee. If the division of the toffee is to be made by random draws from a hat, what is the probability that the older boy will get both pieces of chocolate toffee?

14. In the preceding problem, what is the probability that one of the boys will get both pieces of chocolate toffee?

15. Assume that a machine produces a certain part with the probability that any one part will be defective equal to 0.1. Suppose we were to draw a random sample of four parts from the output of the machine. What is the probability that exactly half of the parts in the sample will be defective?

16. Construct a probability distribution for *r*, the number of defective parts in the sample described in problem 15.

17. Explain exactly why the assumption of independence is critical to the use of the binomial distribution.

18. If, in pursuing the line of problem 14, we were to define *x* as the number of pieces of chocolate toffee that one of the boys would get, it seems that the possible values of *x* could be listed as 0, 1, or 2. Such a listing would involve double counting, however. Why?

Probability and experience

The discussion of this chapter has centered on rules which will allow us to calculate the probability of events on the basis of probabilities of other events. In order to use these rules, we must have knowledge of the probabilities attaching to *some* set of events. Otherwise we have nothing to "plug in" to the formulas we have set down. We have already hinted in footnote 12 that, as a matter of practical application, we need some way to determine for the events relevant to a given problem what the probabilities of occurrence of these events are. How this is to be done depends somewhat on circumstance. If, for example, we are considering the toss of a coin, we may wish to know the probability of the coin falling with head facing up. We may decide to rely on the logic of the situation. If a careful examination of the coin does not lead us to suspect that the coin is biased, we are likely to decide that the probability of a head coming up is the same as that of a tail. Since the probability that one or the other of these two outcomes will occur is 1,[14] it follows that the probability is ½ for either.

Suppose, however, that the coin is tossed 100 times and that the result of these trials is that a head appeared on 60 tosses and a tail on only 40 tosses. On the basis of this result, we might begin to doubt our original assumption. If in further trials a tendency for heads to appear more frequently than tails were to continue, we might finally decide to revise our estimate in favor of the evidence of our experience. In most practical applications, as a matter of fact, the probabilities we assign to events are related to observations based on our own experience or on the experience of others.

It will often be the case, when confronted with a new problem, that there will not be ample past experience to which an appeal can be made. In the problem of determining the probabilities of differing numbers of defective parts in a sample of the production of a machine, for example, we may be forced to wait for the evidence to accumulate as we use the machine in production of the part. Another possibility is to note the behavior of other processes similar to the one of interest to us. Thus, if we have already used a machine similar to the one with which we are presently concerned, we may initially assume that the probabilities to be assigned to the new machine are the same as those assigned to the older machine. In other words, data relating to our experience with the phenomenon in question, or with similar phenomena, will usually serve as a basis for estimating the probabilities that we require. As more data accumulate with our continuing experience, we may adjust the original estimates if this seems necessary.

This procedure is a reasonably safe one when the estimates are based upon fairly extensive experience. It becomes safer as our experience grows, assuming that the process of interest is a stable one. The reason for this can be illustrated with an example of tossing a coin. Suppose that the coin in question is a fair coin, that is, the probability of a head appearing on any given toss is ½. As we toss the coin, we keep track of the number of tosses and the number of heads that appear. After each toss, we calculate the ratio of the number of heads to the number of tosses. This ratio will be either 0 or 1 following the first toss. Following the second toss, the ratio might remain the same as it was following the first toss. It might also be 1/2. As we continue to toss the coin, it is possible that the ratio will remain at either 0 or 1. The probability that a long sequence of

---

[14] We neglect the highly unlikely, but not impossible, outcome "edge up."

tosses of a fair coin would yield a ratio of 0 or of 1 is very small, however, and as the number of tosses that we consider increases, the probability of such a result rapidly becomes smaller. As a matter of fact, the usual outcome of such an experiment is for the ratio of heads to number of tosses to tend to approach a ratio of 1/2, as one would expect. In 100 tosses, the probability is small that the ratio would be more than a few hundredths away from the expected value of 0.50.[15] Looked at the other way around, if we were to toss the coin 100 times and use the ratio of heads to tosses as an estimate of the probability of a head appearing on any one toss, the probability is small that we should be in error by more than a few hundredths. Since it is frequently the case that we must rely on past observations as a basis for estimating probabilities, this tendency for large errors (or errors of any size) to become less likely with additional observations is most gratifying, indeed.

We have gone to some trouble to develop the fundamental rules of probability. In order to illustrate their interpretation, some simplified examples have been given. These problem situations have little relevance to real problems, except to the extent that the reader may be an ardent card player. Their purpose, it is worth repeating, was to illustrate in a reasonably unencumbered fashion the interpretation of the rules. But usually the student becomes happier with new knowledge when he has found a way in which that knowledge can be practical and useful. Our concern in the next chapter, consequently, will be to illustrate some relatively powerful (and useful) techniques in statistical inference. To apply these techniques requires no more knowledge than we have developed in this chapter.

Problem Set 1–5

1. It was noted in the text that one may assign probabilities to different events on the basis of the logic of the situation, or he may assign the probabilities on the basis of the relative frequencies with which the events have occurred in the past. Discuss which of these bases would be appropriate for the following probability statements:

   a) The probability that a coin will land heads up is ½.

   b) The probability that a man whose current age is 40 will live to be 70 is ²⁄₁₀.

   c) If half of the citizens in a state are over 25 years in age and half are 25 or younger, then the probability that a citizen selected at random will be over 25 years in age is ½.

   d) The probability is ⁹⁄₁₀ that a beginning law student will pass his bar examinations three years hence.

---

[15] As a matter of fact, the probability is only about 0.035 that the ratio would differ from 0.50 by more than 0.10.

e) The probability that the sum on two dice will be seven is greater than the probability that the sum will be four.

f) The probability that a rocket launched toward the moon will orbit the moon and return to earth is $\frac{4}{10}$.

2. Select a coin from your pocket and toss the coin 20 times. Keep track of the number of heads that have appeared in the series of tosses and record the ratio of heads to total number of tosses, doing this after each toss. Graph the ratio of heads to total number of tosses for the first toss, the second, and so forth through all 20 tosses. Is there some pattern of behavior apparent in this graph? Does this pattern tend to confirm any preexisting notion you had concerning the probability of a coin landing heads up?

3. In class, pool the results of the individual students' results in problem 2 and consider the questions raised there.

4. Discuss the question of what bases can be used by insurance companies to construct actuarial tables of mortality rates.

5. Discuss the question of what bases can be used to determine the probability of success in orbiting a satellite.

6. Discuss the question of what bases can be used to determine the probability of success in launching a moon probe.

7. Discuss the question of what bases can be used to determine the probability of success in introducing a new consumer product in a market.

chapter 2

Tests of hypotheses, part one

Statistical quality control, a first example

In the introduction to this study of statistical methods, it was pointed out that many, if not all, decisions are made under conditions of uncertainty. It is a lucky circumstance, indeed, when the executive is able to make a decision with advance knowledge of the exact outcomes of the alternative actions open to him. The methods of statistical analysis are not able completely to dispel this pall of uncertainty. They do enable the decision maker to make a rational decision, to get the most mileage out of the information available to him.

One particularly important technique is referred to as "the test of a hypothesis." This rather opaque phrase means that the statistician decides, on the basis of observed facts that he has collected, whether or not an assumption (assumed by himself or by others) seems to be valid. One area in which tests of hypotheses are made on a routine basis is the area of statistical quality control. In quality control work these tests have been reduced to standardized procedures that allow management to discover variations in the quality of their firm's production or variations in the quality of goods supplied them by another firm. We shall defer considerations of control of a production process and concentrate at this point on acceptance sampling, a procedure whereby a purchasing firm decides whether or not a *lot* of items supplied by a vending firm is of acceptable quality.

It is common practice for firms that have an extended requirement

41

for some particular item to enter a contract with one or more other firms to supply that item through a series of future shipments. It often is the case that the purchasing firm will insist on the right to inspect incoming shipments, or some part of them, and to decide on the basis of the results of the inspection whether or not to accept the shipment (the *lot*). Such arrangements require an agreement as to what constitutes an acceptable quality level for all incoming lots. The purchaser and vendor might agree, for example, that a lot is acceptable if no more than 10 percent of the items in the lot are defective.

With such a contractual arrangement in force, the next question becomes, How shall they decide whether a lot should be accepted or rejected? In earlier times, largely before World War II, a common procedure was for the purchaser to perform a 100 percent inspection. In that situation, if the purchaser were to find that 10 percent or fewer of the items were defective, the lot would be acceptable. If more than 10 percent were defective, the vendor would be required to make restitution in some way. But this put nearly the entire load of controlling quality on the purchaser. Moreover, to perform 100 percent inspection of every incoming lot meant that the purchasing firm was required to maintain a large group of inspectors. During the war a new procedure gained impetus, particularly in those situations where a government agency was the purchaser. The contract between the vendor and the purchaser came to allow the purchaser to reject the *entire lot* if the results of an inspection of a relatively *small sample* of the items in the lot indicated that the lot was not at an acceptable quality level. Since that time much effort has been expended in developing a variety of acceptance sampling procedures adequate to the needs arising in different situations. We shall not discuss these, but we can use the basic framework of acceptance sampling as a concrete introduction to the technique of testing a hypothesis.

Suppose that the vendor and purchaser we have been discussing have a contract specifying that the vendor will deliver to the purchaser once a month a lot containing 50 items. The purchaser is to select a random sample of 10 items from each lot of 50 that he receives. If the number of defective items in the sample of 10 is greater than one, the purchaser will reject the entire lot. Otherwise, the lot is to be accepted. This sampling plan can be described briefly by the specification of three numbers: the lot size, $N = 50$; the sample size, $n = 10$; and the maximum number of defectives the sample may contain for the lot to be accepted, $a = 1$.

A question of concern to both the purchaser and the vendor is, How well does the sampling plan ($N = 50$, $n = 10$, $a = 1$) work? The vendor can conceive of the possibility that a lot with 10 percent defective would be rejected by the purchaser. Such a lot would contain 5 defective items, and it certainly is possible that more than 1 of these 5 items would find their way into the sample of 10 items. On the other hand, the purchaser can conceive of the possibility that a lot might contain more than 10 percent of the items defective and yet he would accept it on the basis of the sample result. The vendor and the purchaser can be helped in their dilemma by approaching the problem in the following way. Assume that the lot to be sampled does in fact have a 10 percent defective rate. On the basis of that *hypothesis*, what is the probability that the result of the random sample of 10 items selected will lead to rejection of the lot? What is the probability that the lot will be accepted?

If the hypothesis is true, there will be exactly 5 defective items in the lot of 50. For the lot to be accepted, the sample of 10 must contain none, or at most, 1 of these 5 defective items. Thus, the event "the lot is accepted," is the union of the mutually exclusive events "the sample has no defective items" and "the sample has one defective item." If we let r represent the number of defective items found in the sample, we have, by Rule P–3:

$$P(\text{"lot is accepted"}) = P(r = 0 \text{ or } r = 1) = P(r = 0) + P(r = 1) .$$

The two probabilities, $P(r = 0)$ and $P(r = 1)$, are probabilities from the hypergeometric distribution. To have $r = 1$ for the sample requires that 9 of the items in the sample must have been selected from the 45 good items in the lot, while 1 of the 10 came from the 5 defective items. Since the sample was selected by random choice of items, each possible sample of 10 items that could be selected from the lot of 50 had equal probability of selection. There are $C_{50,10}$ such samples.[1] We need to know how many samples would have exactly one defective and nine good items. The selection of such a sample can be regarded as an operation performed in two steps: the first step involves the selection of 9 good items from among the 45 good items in the lot; the second step requires the selection of 1 from the 5 defective items. The first step can be performed in $C_{45,9}$ ways, and the second step can be performed in $C_{5,1}$ ways. A sample of 10 with exactly 1 defective can therefore be selected in $(C_{45,9})(C_{5,1})$ ways. It follows that

$$P(r = 1) = \frac{(C_{45,9})(C_{5,1})}{C_{50,10}} \simeq 0.4313 .$$

In exactly the same way, it can be shown that

$$P(r = 0) = \frac{(C_{45,10})(C_{5,0})}{C_{50,10}} \simeq 0.3105 .$$

---

[1] Notice that we are concerned only with how many defective and good items there are in the sample, not with their order of appearance. Thus, we want the number of combinations, rather than the number of permutations.

Finally, we have

$$P(\text{"lot is accepted"}) = P(r = 0) + P(r = 1) \simeq 0.3105 + 0.4313 = 0.7418 \, .$$

The practical interpretation of the result above is that if the vendor were consistently to suply the purchaser with lots that were 10 percent defective, he could expect that approximately three fourths of these lots would be accepted and one fourth of them would be rejected. He might consider these proportions rather heavily weighted against a lot that really was acceptable. In that case, he might suggest that the sampling plan be modified to $(N = 50, n = 10, a = 2)$. With this modification the student can verify that for a lot 10 percent defective,

$$\begin{aligned} P(\text{"lot is accepted"}) &= P(r = 0) + P(r = 1) + P(r = 2) \\ &= 0.3105 + 0.4313 + 0.2098 = 0.9516 \, . \end{aligned}$$

In other words, approximately 95 times in 100, the vendor could expect a lot with 10 percent defective to be accepted. Five times in 100, such a lot would be rejected by this plan.

Notice, in the above illustration, that if the sample result is close to what one would expect on the basis of the hypothesis, the purchaser should be more willing to accept the hypothesis than if the sample result varied widely from expectations. The purchaser might be willing to accept the lot under consideration if there were no more than 2 defective items in a sample of 10. But what about three defectives, or four, or five? Evidently, the purchaser would become increasingly reluctant to accept a lot, as the number of defectives in the sample rose. The reason for this is clear. If a random sample of 10 items taken from a lot of 50 were to have 3 or more defective items, this fact would cast strong doubt on a hypothesis that the lot contained only 10 percent defectives in the first place. The strength of this doubt is indicated in the fact that the probability is somewhat less than 0.05 that such a sample would be selected:

$P(\text{"the sample contains three or more defectives"})$
$\quad = 1 - P(\text{"the sample contains 0, 1, or 2 defectives"}) = 1 - 0.9516 = 0.0484 \, .$

The considerations noted in the last paragraph are typical of tests of hypotheses. In these situations, someone is interested in testing a hypothesis about a set of data. A randomly selected sample is obtained from the data, and the result found in the sample is compared with what one could expect if the hypothesis were true. The larger the disparity between the sample result and this expectation, the greater the doubt placed on the original hypothesis. The person testing the hypothesis must decide some level of doubt at which he will reject the hypothesis. This level of doubt is expressed as a probability, in the form: If the sample result is one which I could expect to happen with probability of α or less, assuming the hypothesis to be true, I shall reject the truth of the hypothesis. If the purchaser in the above example were to agree to the sampling plan ($N = 50$, $n = 10$, $a = 2$), the value of α implied in his agreement would be approximately 0.05, since the probability is 0.05 or less that a sample would contain three or more defectives, given that the lot contained 10 percent defectives.

Problem Set 2–1

1. Suppose that the purchaser and vendor agree that a defective rate of 10 percent in a lot is satisfactory. For the sampling plan ($N = 20$, $n = 5$, $a = 1$), determine the probability that a lot with this percent defective will be accepted.

2. Work problem 1, this time on the assumption that the sampling plan to be used is ($N = 100$, $n = 5$, $a = 1$). Comparing your answer to this problem with the answer to problem 1, which of the two sampling plans seems to be better, and why?

3. Set down the probability of accepting a lot that is 10 percent defective under the two sampling plans ($N = 20$, $n = 5$, $a = 0$) and ($N = 100$, $n = 5$, $a = 0$). Which plan seems to be better, and why?

   In order to get a good comparison of different sampling plans, the characteristics of these plans are usually portrayed in a table which relates the probability of accepting a lot, under a given sampling plan, to various possible values of the percent defective rate that might occur in the lot. The problems below are meant to lead the student to some insight into these characteristics.

4. There appear below four tables relating the probability of accepting a lot, P(Accept), to various values of proportion defective, p. Each table corresponds to the sampling plan described at the head of the table. Some entries of these tables have been omitted. You are to fill them in.

($N = 20$, $n = 5$, $a = 0$)		($N = 100$, $n = 5$, $a = 0$)		($N = 20$, $n = 5$, $a = 1$)		($N = 100$, $n = 5$, $a = 1$)	
p	P(Accept)	p	P(Accept)	p	P(Accept)	p	P(Accept)
0.05	0.750	0.05	0.770	0.05		0.05	0.981
.10	.553	.10		.10		.10	.923
.15	.399	.15	.436	.15	0.860	.15	.839
.20		.20	.319	.20	.752	.20	.739
.30	.129	.30	.161	.30	.516	.30	
.50	.016	.50		.50	.152	.50	.181

5. Plot the points from the completed tables for the two sampling plans ($N = 20$, $n = 5$, $a = 0$) and ($N = 100$, $n = 5$, $a = 0$). Plot values of p on the horizontal axis and values of P(Accept) on the vertical axis. Join the

points of each sampling plan with a smooth curve. Such a curve is called the *operating characteristic curve* of a sampling plan.

6. Examine the curves which you plotted in the preceding problem and indicate which of the two sampling plans is better, and why,

    a) From the point of view of the vendor.

    b) From the point of view of the purchaser.

7. Plot the points from the completed tables for the two sampling plans ($N = 20$, $n = 5$, $a = 1$) and ($N = 100$, $n = 5$, $a = 1$). Plot values of p on the horizontal axis and values of $P(\text{Accept})$ on the vertical axis. Join the points of each sampling plan with a smooth curve, thereby forming each plan's *operating characteristic curve.*

8. Examine the curves which you plotted in the preceding problem and indicate which of the two sampling plans is better, and why,

    a) From the point of view of the vendor.

    b) From the point of view of the purchaser.

9. If you have graphed the operating characteristic curves of all four sampling plans, indicate which seems to you to be superior, and why.

10. Which of the following two statements is true concerning the point ($p = 0.05$, $P(\text{Accept}) = 0.750$) on the operating characteristic curve for ($N = 20$, $n = 5$, $a = 0$)? Explain.

    a) If the sampling plan ($N = 20$, $n = 5$, $a = 0$) is instituted, then we can expect that about 75 percent of all lots submitted by the vendor will have a defective rate of 5 percent.

    b) If the sampling plan ($N = 20$, $n = 5$, $a = 0$) is instituted, then we can expect to accept about 75 percent of all lots submitted by the vendor that have a defective rate of 5 percent.

11. Discuss the advantages and disadvantages that are apparent to you of a sampling plan of the type considered in this section, as compared to a system of 100 percent inspection by the purchaser of all incoming lots,

    a) From the point of view of the purchaser.

    b) From the point of view of the vendor.

12. In the text it was shown that for the sampling plan ($N = 50$, $n = 10$, $a = 1$), the probability of acceptance is 0.7418 if the lot is 10 percent defective. If the lot had been 6 percent defective, then the probability of acceptance would have been:

$$P(\text{Acc}) = P(r = 0) + P(r = 1) = \frac{C_{47,10}C_{3,0}}{C_{50,10}} + \frac{C_{47,9}C_{3,1}}{C_{50,10}} \simeq 0.9021 .$$

    a) Find the probability of acceptance if the lot were 4 percent defective.

    b) On a graph with p, the percent defective, on the horizontal axis and $P(\text{Accept})$ on the vertical axis, plot the three points for $p = 0.1$, 0.06, and 0.04. Plot, also, the points ($p = 0.14$, $P(\text{Accept}) = 0.5707$), ($p = 0.18$, $P(\text{Accept}) = 0.4120$), and ($p = 0.22$, $P(\text{Accept}) = 0.2888$). Join these points with a smooth line. This line is the *operating characteristic curve* for the sampling plan ($N = 50$, $n = 10$, $a = 1$).

    c) For a sampling plan ($N = 50$, $n = 5$, $a = 0$), find the probability of acceptance if the percent defective in the lot is 4, 6, and 10, respectively. Plot these points on the graph of (*b*). Plot, also, the points ($p = 0.14$, $P(\text{Accept}) = 0.4532$), ($p = 0.18$, $P(\text{Accept}) = 0.3504$), ($p = 0.22$, $P(\text{Accept}) = 0.2717$). Join these points with a smooth line.

d) Assume that the vendor and purchaser agree that a lot with 10 percent or less defective is to be satisfactory. Discuss the relative effectiveness of the two sampling plans from the point of view of the vendor and the purchaser, respectively. What types of error can be made in the use of a sampling plan such as these? (In answering this question, bear in mind that lots with more than 10 percent defective are unsatisfactory from the purchaser's point of view.)

e) Neither of the sampling plans you graphed in (*b*) and (*c*) is a good sampling plan. Better plans often require the possibility of taking more than one sample if the results of the first sample seem inconclusive. Plans embodying these improvements can yield an operating characteristic curve shaped much like the one depicted below. Explain why such an operating characteristic curve is desirable.

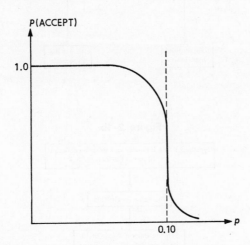

Flow diagram for tests of hypotheses

There will be more examples in our later discussions of situations in which a test of a hypothesis is required. This being the case, it will be helpful for the student if we devise a common procedure to be followed in testing a hypothesis. In later applications, this same procedure will be relevant. The procedure is set forth in Figure 2–1a in the form of a flow diagram, a device that has found wide application in computer programming. Figure 2–1a is duplicated in 2–1b with the appropriate entries for the purchaser in the previous example, on the assumption that he has agreed to sampling plan ($N = 50$, $n = 10$, $a = 2$).

Figure 2–1a

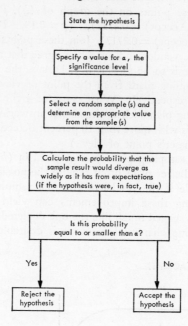

State the hypothesis

Specify a value for α, the significance level

Select a random sample (s) and determine an appropriate value from the sample (s)

Calculate the probability that the sample result would diverge as widely as it has from expectations (if the hypothesis were, in fact, true)

Is this probability equal to or smaller than α?

Yes   No

Reject the hypothesis   Accept the hypothesis

Figure 2–1b

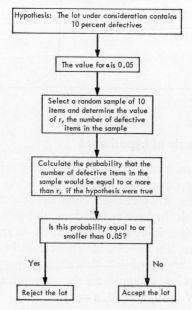

Hypothesis: The lot under consideration contains 10 percent defectives

The value for α is 0.05

Select a random sample of 10 items and determine the value of r, the number of defective items in the sample

Calculate the probability that the number of defective items in the sample would be equal to or more than r, if the hypothesis were true

Is this probability equal to or smaller than 0.05?

Yes   No

Reject the lot   Accept the lot

To accept the hypothesis or not, that is the question

Although most of the points to be discussed in this section will receive further elaboration in later sections, it may be helpful to give a preliminary outline of the logical problem involved in the test of a hypothesis. Hopefully, this outline will take on added meaning as the student progresses through the chapter.

Suppose that, in the process of testing some hypothesis, a sample is randomly selected for which the probability (given the stated hypothesis) is less than the value of α specified in advance of the test. What possible conclusions might be drawn on the basis of this result? It appears that there are three:

1. The sample is biased, and therefore the probability calculated for this result actually understates its likelihood.
2. Both the sample result and the hypothesis are correct, and the wide disparity between them is due to the occurrence of a rather rare result.
3. Either the sample result is incorrect, or the hypothesis is incorrect.

If the person responsible for the test has proceeded with the test in a correct manner, he would choose the third alternative. The first conclusion would be eliminated from consideration, because the sample would have been chosen randomly. A random choice of items to include in the sample will eliminate any tendency toward sampling bias. The second alternative also should be eliminated from consideration. This is so because, in specifying the value for α, the person responsible for the test stated, in effect, that a result less likely than this is too rare to be considered.

That leaves the investigator with the third alternative: Either the sample result is incorrect, or the hypothesis is incorrect. But the sample result is presumably correct. It is the outcome of careful collection of data which is subject to verification, in most cases. In other words, the investigator has the result of the sample, and probably the sample itself, in hand. It is not subject to doubt. Acceptance of the third conclusion therefore leads to rejection of the hypothesis.

Now, suppose that the probability attached to the sample result is greater than α. The conclusion in this case is simple. The disparity between the sample result and the hypothesis is not wide enough to lead the investigator to entertain any of the three conclusions specified above. In particular, no doubt is associated with the hypothesis. This is the chain of reasoning that leads to an answer of the question, "to accept the hypothesis or not?"

Problem Set 2–2

1. Suppose that you were to toss a coin 10 times and note the number of heads in the 10 tosses. Would you doubt the fairness of the coin:

   a) If heads appeared five times?
   b) If heads appeared seven times?
   c) If heads appeared nine times?

   If your attitude concerning the coin changed as you considered successively larger numbers of heads, explain why. If not, explain.

2. The scene is a saloon in the Old West. In the corner, half-a-dozen men are seated around a table, cards and multicolored chips before them on the table. Suddenly one man jumps to his feet, points a menacing finger at the man wearing the green eyeshade, and cries, "You've won every one of the last fifteen hands. Nobody is that lucky!" What did he mean? Be specific in terms of the concepts in preceding sections of the chapter.

3. A current debate that rages through the advertising media of the nation centers on the effectiveness of toothpaste in fighting tooth decay. It is claimed by one brand that tests show no other brand is significantly better in fighting tooth decay. Translate this assertion into the language of the preceding sections.

4. The gentleman has owned the car for four years. In that time, he has worn out two sets of tires and is ready to buy a third set. The brand of tires that he bought as the second set seemed to him to perform better than the first set, so he decided to buy that brand once again. Put his reasoning in the context of the current chapter.

5. One of the good effects of integrated schooling is expected to be an improvement in the results of education for many of the children. Explain how one might go about subjecting that assertion to an objective test.

6. A manufacturer of ammunition for the U.S. Army has developed a new gunpowder which it asserts is superior in the muzzle velocity that it imparts to rounds propelled with it. How might one test this assertion?

7. Mr. Smith and Mr. Jones are technicians employed by a testing laboratory. They have been assigned the task of testing the claim of the ammunition maker of problem 6. Prior to actually performing a testing procedure, they consider the question of the value to set for α, the significance level of the test. Smith would like to make it $\alpha = 0.10$, but Jones insists on a value of $\alpha = 0.05$. If you were a representative of the ammunition manufacturer, which of the two men would you support, and why?

8. Suppose that two toothpaste manufacturers submit their toothpastes to an independent testing agency and that one test is performed using the two toothpastes. The results of these tests are mailed to the two companies without evaluation by the independent agency. Is it possible that one of the companies, using the general procedures and concepts outlined in the preceding section, could truthfully assert that the results support the assertion that their toothpaste is superior to the other company's, while the second company could assert just as truthfully that the results do not support that assertion? Why?

9. Evaluate the following statement: "The value of α to be assigned to a test of a hypothesis should usually be 0.05 or less, and in no case should it be larger than 0.10."

10. A manufacturer of electronic devices has a new contract to supply a large quantity of a certain type of vacuum tube to a large buyer. The buyer specified in the contract that the minimum life of the tubes supplied should be about 300 hours. A random sample of 100 tubes is selected from the current production and subjected to a life test. It is found that one half of these burn out before 300 hours. As statistician for the firm, it is your job to inform the manager of the production department that it appears the production is not up to the required standard. When you fill him in on all the details he replies, "Well, it is possible, isn't it, that nearly all the tubes produced in our department meet the standard, but your random sample just happened to contain a disproportionate number of poor tubes?" Formulate an argument to this question in terms of the concepts of the preceding section.

Fisher-Irwin test

The first illustration of testing a hypothesis involved a hypothesis concerning some single value for the data in question. Another sort of hypothesis commonly tested is that there is no difference among two or more sets of data. Such tests are employed to determine whether one can reasonably asume, for example, that two supposedly different treatments are, in fact, different in terms of the results they produce. One such test is the Fisher-Irwin test, which we illustrate next.

Suppose that a firm has a continuing need for production workers to perform certain operations that require a relatively high degree of skill and knowledge. Reflecting this continuing need, the firm has developed a set of procedures for selecting and training workers to perform these operations. At the completion of their training, these workers are given an examination that has been designed to determine how well they have assimilated the required knowledge and skill. The management has been dissatisfied with the results of this program. It has felt that the preponderance of shortcomings lay in the training phase of the program. Consequently, it has directed the design of a new training procedure. This new training procedure is now ready, and management wishes to test its performance against that of the older training procedure.

The test is performed as follows. A number of newly selected workers, say, 12, are chosen for an experiment. These workers have undergone the standard selection procedure used in the program and are therefore considered to be of approximately equal ability prior to the experiment. The group of 12 is divided into two groups of 6 each, one group for each training procedure. The assignments of individual workers to the two groups are made randomly. Each group of six workers is put through its complete training program. At the completion of their training, all workers are given the same examination, and it is noted whether they fail or pass.

Suppose the results of the examination break down as shown in Table 2–1, where A indicates the new training, B the old. Evidently, the results of the experiment indicate that the new training is superior to the old. But does it? Is it not possible that the new training is not superior to the old, and yet more workers in group A would pass the

Table 2–1

	Fail	Pass	Total
A............	1	5	6
B............	3	3	6
	4	8	12

examination than workers in group B? The answer is, of course, yes, it is possible. Well then, if a result such as the one in Table 2–1 could occur even though the two training methods were equally good, how can a decision be made? The answer to this last question is: The decision must be made by appealing to the probability that the particular result would occur if the two training procedures were, in fact, equally good.

The hypothesis is that the two methods are equally good. This hypothesis must be related to the results of the 12 examinations. Under the hypothesis, the four workers who failed and the eight who passed would have performed in the same way, no matter which training they had. Under the hypothesis, the uneven distribution of failures and successes between the two groups is due merely to chance factors operating through the random selection of the two groups. Now the question becomes: Under the hypothesis, what is the probability that a distribution of four failures and eight successes between two groups would be as uneven as the one shown in Table 2–1, or more so? The answer can be stated as the probability that group A would do as well or better, or as the probability that group B would do as poorly or worse. Let us consider the former.

Group A was made up of 6 individuals randomly selected from a group of 12. The group of 12 contained 4 workers who, by the hypothesis, would have failed whether they were in group A or group B, and 8 workers whose successes were unaffected by the assignments to different training methods. The ways in which group A could have done as well or better than in Table 2–1 are (1,5) and (0,6), where the first number in each pair indicates the number of failures and the second the number of successes. Then,

$$P(\text{"A do as well or better"}) = P(1, 5) + P(0, 6) .$$

Using Rule P–4, $P(1,5) = x/n$, where x is the number of ways to select one of the four failing workers for group A and five of the eight passing workers, and where n is the number of ways to select 6 workers from the 12 workers. $P(0,6) = x/n$, also, with parallel interpretations of x and n. Each of these probabilities is, of course, a hypergeometric probability. The number of ways to select 6 workers from the 12 is $n = C_{12,6} = 924$. The number of ways to select one from the four failures and five from the eight successes is $x = (C_{4,1})(C_{8,5}) = 224$. Thus, $P(1,5) = 224/924 \simeq 0.24$. In the same way, for $(0,6)$: $n = 924$, $x = (C_{4,0})(C_{8,6}) = 28$, and $P(0,6) = 28/924 \simeq 0.03$. Finally,

$$P(\text{``A do as well or better''}) \simeq 0.24 + 0.03 = 0.27 \,.$$

Calculations indicate that for 8 successes and 4 failures among 12 workers, group A would have done as well or better than they did 27 times out of 100 solely by chance. Should the result of the experiment therefore be considered "significant"? The answer is up to management. If it decides that this result is unlikely enough, it can reject the hypothesis. It would be saying that the evidence is strong enough to allow the presumption that the new training method is superior. Or management might be inclined to view the evidence as not indicating superiority for the new method; it will continue the old training method. Finally, it might reserve judgment. In that case, more experimentation would be performed with the two methods, to compile a larger set of data as the basis for a final decision.[2]

Significance of a test

It was noted above that whether or not the result in Table 2–1 is "significant" is a matter to be decided by the person(s) making the test. Of course, some results are more "significant" than others. For example, if the results had been $(0,6)$ for group A—no failures and six successes —the probability would have been only about 0.3 under the hypothesis $[P(0,6)$ was shown to be about 0.03 earlier]. Because of this fact, the statistician puts a special interpretation on the word "significant." Specifically, he associates the term "significant" with a specific probability, often denoted by α, decided upon prior to testing the hypothesis. Thus, he might state that the hypothesis will be rejected only if the sample result is *significant at a level of 0.05*. To be *significant at a level of 0.05*,

---

[2] As a practical matter, this last decision probably would be the outcome in the present example. A probability of 0.27 associated with a sample of only 12 observations is rather inconclusive. For reasons of expository convenience, the example was developed in terms of a small number of observations. Throughout the following discussion, the assumption will be that one of two decisions must be made—either reject the hypothesis being tested, or accept it. It should be borne in mind that "reserve judgment" is a third alternative.

the sample result must diverge far enough from expectations entertained under the hypothesis that such a result would occur with probability of 0.05 or less if the hypothesis were true. The result in Table 2–1 is not significant at a level of 0.05, since the probability of this result is 0.27 under the hypothesis—much above the *significance level* of 0.05. If the result of the experiment had been (0,6) for group A, this would have been significant at the level of 0.05—the probability of this result is only 0.03 under the hypothesis.

Notice that the statement of a significance level should be made prior to testing the hypothesis. This is necessary to avoid the possibility of vacillation on the part of the decision maker. If the probability of the sample result should turn out to be 0.06, for example, the decision maker might decide "this is *almost* 0.05, so I will reject the hypothesis." Or, if he were unconsciously biased in favor of the old training method, a result with a probability of only 0.04 might lead him to decide in favor of the older method. The point is not that 0.05 is a sacred number. The significance level is at the discretion of the person testing the hypothesis. The point is, this decision should be made prior to testing and respected following the test!

It is important to guard against bias, conscious or unconscious, creeping into the result. This is the reason underlying the fact that the division of the 12 workers into two groups of 6 must be accomplished randomly. Although all 12 workers had been subjected to the same selection procedure in order to be eligible for the program, it is certain to be the case that all 12 did not have exactly the same abilities prior to their training. The possibility for bias exists in that there might be a tendency to assign naturally superior workers to one group or the other. Random selection avoids such a tendency. It is upon this element of randomness, ultimately, that our faith in the probabilities we assign to the various outcomes must rest.

The Fisher-Irwin test which has been illustrated is applicable for those situations where the observed result for each item in the sample can be classified into one of two mutually exclusive categories. In the example given, the workers' performances on the examination were classified as pass or fail. For certain characteristics, this is the most information that can be gleaned from the data. A lens to be used in a telescope may be classed as satisfactory or unsatisfactory, for example, but there may be no method for saying to what degree it is satisfactory or unsatisfactory. In other situations, more information may be available. The training example is a case in point. There could be a score attached to each examination. If that is the case, we will have discarded useful information by limiting our attention only to whether a worker passed or failed and ignoring how well he scored! The test that we consider next is designed to take this additional information into account.

Problem Set 2–3

1. What are the characteristics of the situation in which the Fisher-Irwin test is applied that make the hypergeometric probabilities the proper probabilities to use in conducting the test?

2. In the text, the Fisher-Irwin test was used to test the hypothesis that training method A was superior to method B, on the basis of sample results in Table 2–1. Now, test the hypothesis that method B is inferior to method A. Are results of the two test procedures equivalent? Why, or why not?

3. A housing contractor plans to build a large number of brick homes in the coming year. Two brickmaking firms have given him nearly identical low bids for the delivery of the bricks he expects to require. In order to choose between the two firms, he decides to subject a sample of bricks from each firm to a "breaking test." If the test indicates that the bricks of the firm with the higher bid, firm A, seem to be significantly stronger than those of firm B, he will choose the higher priced bricks. He decides on a level of significance of $\alpha = 0.05$ for the test. The nature of the test is to subject each brick to a force of 1,000 pounds. The test is performed on eight bricks randomly chosen from a day's production of firm A and on the same number of bricks randomly chosen from a day's production of firm B. The results of the test were: of the eight bricks from firm A, two were broken; of the eight bricks from firm B, five were broken.

   On the basis of these test results, determine whether the contractor should choose the bricks of firm A, or use those of firm B.

4. In discussing the need for randomness in the assignment of workers to the two different training methods, the statement is made that, "It is upon this element of randomness, ultimately, that our faith in the probabilities we assign to the various outcomes must rest." Explain why "faith in the probabilities we assign" is crucial in the procedure for testing a hypothesis.

5. Suppose that the testing agency charged with testing the two brands of toothpastes, as described in problem 8 of Problem Set 2–2, performed the test as described here. Fourteen children of generally the same background were chosen and assigned randomly to two groups, with each group containing seven children. These children were instructed in how to brush their teeth and given identical schedules to follow in brushing their teeth. One group of children was provided with Brand X toothpaste throughout the year, which they used according to the schedule. The second group used Brand Y throughout the year. At the end of the year, the number of new cavities was counted for each child. If a child had two or fewer cavities the result was described as "good." If a child had more than two new cavities, the result was described as "poor." On the basis of the test results given in the table below, test at a significance level of $\alpha = 0.05$ the hypothesis that Brand X and Brand Y are equally effective.

	Good	Poor
Brand X	7	0
Brand Y	3	4

6. Suppose that the testing agency of problem 5 had chosen only six children, which were divided into two groups of three. The results of the test were as favorable to Brand X as it would be possible for them to be under the method of describing the results as given in problem 5. Set up the table as it would look in these circumstances. Calculate the probability that the result could be this favorable for Brand X. If you were to make the test of superiority for Brand X on the basis of these results, at a significance level of 0.05, would you conclude that Brand X is superior to Brand Y? Does the result in this test lead you to any conclusions concerning the amount of information available from the test and the effectiveness of the test?

7. One of the liabilities in the marketing of cigars is the fact that many women find the odor of cigar smoke offensive. A prominent cigar manufacturer is convinced that he can increase his sales if he can develop a process by which the odor of cigar smoke can be improved. Months of research has led to the identification of a liquid which, when applied to the tobacco leaf used in the cigars, seems to impart a less pungent odor to cigar smoke.

   In order to test the liquid, 40 women are assigned randomly to two different groups of 20. The women of group A are asked to enter a room in which a man is smoking a cigar that is treated with the liquid. The second group of 20 women enter a room in which an untreated cigar is being smoked. After one minute in each room, the women are asked to check one square on a card to indicate whether the cigar smoke is offensive to them or inoffensive. On the basis of the results set forth below, test the hypothesis that smoke from the two cigars is equally offensive, versus the hypothesis that the untreated cigar smoke is more offensive (use $\alpha = 0.10$).

	Number of Women Who Found Smoke Offensive	Number of Women Who Found Smoke Inoffensive	
Treated cigar................13		7	20
Untreated cigar...............18		2	20
Total:..................31		9	40

8. Suppose that a manufacturer of small-arms ammunition for the U.S. Army has developed a new shell for use in the standard army rifle. He claims that the new shell is an improvement over the old because it generates a greater muzzle velocity. As a test of this claim, seven rounds of the new and eight rounds of the old are fired. The shells used were randomly selected from recently manufactured stock.

   The observation made with each shell was whether or not it achieved a muzzle velocity of at least 3,000 feet per second. Of the new shells, only one did not achieve this velocity. Three of the old type shells failed to reach the velocity of 3,000 feet per second. On the basis of these results, test the manufacturer's claim at a significance level of 0.10 in two ways:

   a) By finding the probability that the new shells would have performed as well or better.

   b) By finding the probability that the old shells would have done as badly or worse.

9. In the test of a hypothesis, if the significance level is set at a low value, the result of the experiment must depart widely from the result which one would expect on the assumption that the hypothesis is true. In the context of problem 8, explain why the U.S. Army might be inclined to choose a low value for α, rather than a high value.

10. The owner of a fleet of taxicabs has been impressed with the claims made for a certain brand of gasoline, Brand A. The claim is made that use of Brand A will reduce the need for tune-ups, thereby reducing costs of operation of the automobiles. In his fleet of 25 taxicabs, he instructs 12 of the drivers, selected at random, to use Brand A in their cabs. The other 13 drivers continue to use Brand B. At the end of six months, he examines the service records on the cabs and notes how many have required tune-ups in that period. (They all were given initial tune-ups at the beginning of the experiment.) The results are shown in the table below. Test, at a significance level of $\alpha = 0.10$, the claim of the manufacturer of Brand A.

	Number Needing Tune-ups	Number Not Needing Tune-ups
Brand A.................2		10
Brand B.................4		9

11. In the problem of the taxicabs, the result did not support the hypothesis that Brand A is superior to Brand B. Despite this showing, do you think that the owner of the taxicabs might be well advised to switch all of his cabs to Brand A? Why, or why not?

12. Compare your answers to problems 9 and 11. Can you give reasons for any difference in your position on the two answers?

13. A manufacturer of a widely marketed nasal spray believes that a modification of the ingredients of the spray will lead to more lasting relief of nasal congestion. In order to test this belief, he asks 10 workers in his plant who are currently suffering from hay fever to use the "improved" formula for one week. Another 10 workers with hay fever are asked to use the regular formula. All 20 subjects of the experiment are asked to observe whether the formula they use provides relief for a period of at least one hour. Six of the 10 workers using the regular formula reported relief of at least one hour each time they used the spray. Of the 10 workers using the "improved" formula, 8 persons reported relief lasting one hour or longer in each application.

If the changeover to the new formula would entail a cost of $10,000, would you be inclined to initiate the change? Explain your reasoning.

The Wilcoxon test for unpaired[3] observations

Suppose that the results of the experiment with the twelve workers were as follows:

---

[3] There is another Wilcoxon test for cases of paired samples. In such experiments, the subjects are naturally paired. Examples would be experiments involving differential treatment of the two hands of individuals, or perhaps experiments with identical twins.

Scores for group A: 70, 74, 80, 83, 88, 91
Scores for group B: 55, 63, 65, 68, 71, 77

If a passing score is 70 or above, these results would be described in terms of the last section as (0,6) for group A and (4,2) for group B. It was determined that the probability of the results, expressed in this fashion, is about 0.03, under the hypothesis that there is no difference in the training methods. This conclusion is based on less than the full information available, however. The Wilcoxon test will take into account the ranking of the scores on the examinations.

The first step in the procedure is to set down the scores of both groups, in ascending order of magnitude. For the data above, the array is:

55*, 63*, 65*, 68*, 70, 71*, 74, 77*, 80, 83, 88, 91
 1   2   3   4   5   6   7   8   9   10 11 12

The asterisks beside six of the numbers identify these as scores made by workers in group B. Those without asterisks are the scores of group A. The numbers appearing below the scores identify their rank.[4] Thus, 55 is the lowest score, 74 the seventh, and 91 the twelfth. The Wilcoxon test is based on a comparison of the sums of the ranks for the two groups. The sum of the ranks for group B is $1 + 2 + 3 + 4 + 6 + 8 = 24$. The sum of the ranks for group A is $5 + 7 + 9 + 10 + 11 + 12 = 54$. Obviously, these two sums must add up to the total for all twelve ranks, which is 78.

The hypothesis to be tested is that the two training methods are equally effective. If this were the case, we would expect to find the ranks on either group to be relatively uniformly distributed among the possible values from 1 to 12. We would, of course, not be dismayed to find some unevenness in this distribution. Even if the training methods were equally effective, the individuals making up the two groups would show some variability in their performances. This fact would make an exactly uniform distribution of ranks between the two groups rather unusual in itself. However, the more uneven the distribution of ranks between the two groups, the more doubtful we should have to consider the hypothesis of equal effectiveness. Thus, the test of the hypothesis lies in noting the distribution of the ranks between the two groups and determining how unlikely such a distribution would be if the hypothesis were true.

The most convenient way to gauge the uniformity of the distribution of the ranks is to look at the sums of the ranks for the two groups. We are assuming that training method A is superior to training method B,

---

[4] If two or more values are equal, the procedure is to assign each a rank equal to the mean of the rank numbers allotted to them. Thus, suppose the first four values had been 55, 63, 63, and 68 instead of 55, 63, 65, and 68 as above. In this case, the two values of 63 would be assigned a rank of $(2 + 3)/2 = 2.5$. The mean of 2 and 3 is used since the two values of 63 fall in the second and third places in the array.

and if this is so, we should expect group A to have a sum of ranks larger than the sum of ranks for group B. As a matter of fact, this is the case for the results illustrated: the sum for group A is 54; for group B it is 24. The question is: Is this difference in sums large enough to lead us to reject the possibility that the training methods are equally good? If we reject this possibility, then we shall automatically take the view that training method A is superior. In order to make this decision, we determine how likely it would be that the sums of ranks for the two groups would be as extreme as they appear here (or more so) under the hypothesis of equal effectiveness.

Evidently, the most extreme possibility that could arise in the situation illustrated is that group B would turn in six scores, all of which were lower than the lowest in group A. In that case, the six lowest rank numbers would be assigned to group B and the six highest ranks would be assigned to group A. The sums for the two groups would be $1 + 2 + 3 + 4 + 5 + 6 = 21$; and $7 + 8 + 9 + 10 + 11 + 12 = 57$. Notice that since the total of the two sums must equal 78 in each case, we can confine our attention to the smaller of the two sums in listing the extreme cases. There are a number of possible distributions of the ranks which would give us a sum for group B which is less than or equal to 24, the sum actually recorded for that group. The list follows:

$$1 + 2 + 3 + 4 + 5 + 6 = 21,$$
$$1 + 2 + 3 + 4 + 5 + 7 = 22,$$
$$1 + 2 + 3 + 4 + 5 + 8 = 23,$$
$$1 + 2 + 3 + 4 + 6 + 7 = 23,$$
$$1 + 2 + 3 + 5 + 6 + 7 = 24,$$
$$1 + 2 + 3 + 4 + 6 + 8 = 24,$$
$$1 + 2 + 3 + 4 + 5 + 9 = 24.$$

These seven cases exhaust the set of possibilities in which group A could have performed as well as they actually did in the experiment, or better. We need the probability of such a result, under the hypothesis that method A is equal to method B.

If the two methods were equally effective, the distribution of ranks which would result on any given experiment would be due solely to the random division of the 12 workers between the two groups. Any particular distribution of ranks would be as likely as any other. Thus, group B would be as likely to have the ranks 1, 2, 3, 4, 5, 6 as the ranks 1, 2, 3, 4, 5, 9.[5] Evidently, then, we can specify a sample space for this experiment where the outcomes are equiprobable. The sample space consists of the set of different possible distributions of ranks, as indicated by the ranks of group B. This being the case, we can calculate the probability

---

[5] Indeed, under the hypothesis of equal effectiveness, group B is as likely to have the ranks 7, 8, 9, 10, 11, 12 as either of the possibilities listed above. Such a result would tend to indicate superiority for method B, rather than method A. In that event the proper test would be of equal effectiveness, with rejection of that hypothesis leading to acceptance of the alternative that method B is superior to method A.

we seek if we can determine how many possible outcomes comprise the sample space. The number of these outcomes is $C_{12,6} = 924$. This is easily seen by noting that the assignment of 6 rank numbers to group B is the same problem as selecting 6 items from a group of 12. Finally, using Rule P–4:

$$P(\text{``sum of ranks for group } B \leq 24\text{''}) = x/n = 7/924 \simeq 0.008 .$$

The probability that the result of the experiment would be as favorable for training method A is significant at the 0.05 level, and is even significant at the 0.01 level. If we had tested the hypothesis of equal effectiveness at either of these levels we would have rejected it. That is, we would have decided that the results do indeed show method A superior to method B.

The Wilcoxon test: A generalized procedure

The procedure of the last section was lengthy, involving as it did a listing of the extreme rank distributions. In the illustration given, there were only seven of these. The scores used in the example were so arranged as to lead to a relatively small number of possibilities. In other cases, the list of extreme possibilities might be much lengthier. If the results of the examination had been

Scores for group A: 65, 72, 89, 94, 98, 99
Scores for group B: 50, 60, 68, 71, 77, 88

the sum of ranks for group B would be 27 and for group A, 51. The list of outcomes in which the sum for group B would be 27 or less contains 30 possibilities. The probability of such a result is $30/924 \simeq 0.032$. Listing the possibilities becomes very tedious, however, so it is useful to have a table available in which the correct probabilities can be found. Such a table appears as Table A in the section of tables in this book.

Table A is arranged to give the relevant probabilities easily, if the test is performed in a standard manner. To use the table, one determines the sum of ranks in the two samples, as before. One may use either the smaller of the two sums, or the larger, to perform the test. To facilitate the discussion, let W_s be the smaller of the two sums and W_l the larger. Also, let s be the number of items in the sample with the smaller sum[6] and let l be the number of items in the sample with the larger sum. It is slightly more convenient to perform the test with W_s, so we begin the illustration with this quantity.

For the scores given above for group A and group B, the sums of ranks are 51 and 27 respectively. The value of W_s is 27, the sum for group B. Since group B has six scores, the value of s is 6, which happens

---

[6] Notice that the sample with the smaller sum need not be the sample with the fewer items. If two samples contained four and two items, respectively, the four-item sample could have the ranks 1, 2, 3, 4, which total 10; while the two-item sample had the ranks 5, 6, which total 11.

in this case to be the same as the value for l. We find the difference between W_s and the minimum value it might have taken, given the value of s. The minimum value that W_s could have taken, given that $s = 6$, is the sum of the ranks 1 through 6. It is found to be 21 by looking in the third column of Table A, in the section for $s = 6$. Thus ($W_s -$ Min. W_s) $= 27 - 21 = 6$. To determine the probability that a result as extreme as this, or more so, would occur,[7] we find the cell of the table which is in the column headed by the number 6 and in the row for $s = 6$ and $l = 6$ (the specified values of l are given in the second column of the table). The entry in this cell is 0.032, which agrees with the probability given earlier.

The same result will be found by using the value of W_l. The only difference is that the value of (Max.$W_l - W_l$) is needed. For $s = 6$ and $l = 6$, the table shows that Max.$W_l = 57$. Since for this example, $W_l = 51$, we have (Max.$W_l - W_l$) $= 57 - 51 = 6$. Once again, the probability is in the row for $s = 6$ and $l = 6$, and in the column headed by the number 6. With either procedure, we arrive at a probability of 0.032. One more comment concerning Table A is appropriate. The probability entries in any row are discontinued following the column in which the probability first becomes equal to, or greater than, 0.100, since the significance level in the test of a hypothesis is rarely placed at values higher than 0.100.

The Wilcoxon test we have been considering can be summarized by a flow diagram.

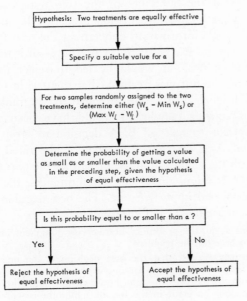

---

[7] Extreme values of W_s correspond to small values of ($W_s -$ Min. W_s). In the most extreme case, $W_s =$ Min. W_s and ($W_s -$ Min. W_s) $= 0$.

The role of information in tests of hypotheses

In the last few sections, two different procedures have been discussed for testing the hypothesis that two samples have received the same treatment: the Fisher-Irwin test and the Wilcoxon (unpaired) test. It has been noted that the difference in the two procedures is basically one of the amount of information utilized. At this point, it will be informative to compare the results of the two test procedures. The comparison will point up graphically the value of additional information.

In the last illustration of the Wilcoxon test, the scores were assumed to be: for group A—65, 72, 89, 94, 98, 99; for group B—50, 60, 68, 71, 77, 88. Under the Wilcoxon procedure, the probability of this result was determined to be 0.032, given the hypothesis of equality. In the Wilcoxon test, therefore, the hypothesis would have been rejected if the value specified for α had been set at 0.05.

Suppose, now, that a failing score for the examination had been specified as any value below 70. Then, in terms of failures and passes, the results for the two groups would be: for group A—one failure and five passes; for group B—three failures and three passes. These are exactly the distributions of failures and passes which were used to illustrate the Fisher-Irwin test, as can be verified by examining Table 2–1, page 52. It will be recalled that under the Fisher-Irwin procedure the probability of a result this extreme or more so was determined to be 0.27. In the Fisher-Irwin test, the hypothesis of equal treatment would have been accepted for an α of 0.05.

A comparison of the outcomes of the two tests underlines the importance of using all valid information available. If management were content to ignore the information concerning the two training methods that is contained in the scores for the two groups—if it tested the method by the Fisher-Irwin test—it would be led to reject the new training method, assuming the test was performed at the 0.05 level. In taking into account the additional information provided by the ranks of the scores, however, management's conclusion would have been that method A was indeed superior to method B. A decision to scrap method B and institute method A is, in the circumstances illustrated, the better decision.[8] Although the claim cannot be made that the two tests will always lead to different decisions under any circumstances, the major point illustrated is a valid and important one. The best decision is the one that takes into account the most valid information.[9]

---

[8] Ignoring, once again, the possibility of reserving judgment until more information is brought to bear on the problem.

[9] The student may protest that the best decision is the one that would have brought the best results in the light of ensuing events following the decision. Decisions are always made on the basis of foresight, however, not hindsight. In a later chapter, the problem of making an error in the test of a hypothesis will be discussed more fully.

Problem Set 2–4

1. Suppose that the "breaking test" described in problem 3, Problem Set 2–3, is modified so that each brick is subjected to an increasing force until it breaks. The force applied at the time the brick breaks (we will call this force the "breaking point") is recorded, with the results indicated below:

Breaking Points, in Ascending Order

A: 980; 995; 1,050; 1,075; 1,090; 1,110; 1,125; 1,130
B: 890; 910; 925; 985; 990; 1,000; 1,005; 1,015

On the basis of these test results, determine whether the contractor should choose bricks of firm A or firm B.

2. Comment on the difference in the two tests of problem 1 above and problem 3 of Problem Set 2–3, in respect to:
   a) The difference in the two situations that called for a difference in test procedure.
   b) How one accounts for the difference in probabilities associated with each test.
   c) The value of additional information, as it is reflected in a comparison of the two tests.

3. Discuss the possible errors the contractor might make in basing his decision on the two tests of problem 1 above and problem 3 of Problem Set 2–3. Is one test better than the other in this respect? If so, why? If not, why?

4. Suppose the testing agency responsible for testing the effectiveness of the two brands of toothpaste (problem 5, Problem Set 2–3) employs a panel of experts in dental hygiene to evaluate the results of the brushing program during the year. These experts examine the 14 children who took part in the program and rank them according to dental hygiene, with lower ranks assigned to the children with less tooth decay. The results of this ranking procedure are given below. On the basis of this information, test the hypothesis that the two brands are equally good, at $\alpha = 0.05$.

Ranks

Brand X: 1 2 3   7 8 9 10
Brand Y: 4 5 6   11 12 13 14

5. Compare the results of problem 4 above and problem 5, Problem Set 2–3, in the following ways:
   a) Is the information provided in problem 4 consistent with the information provided in problem 5 of Problem Set 2–3? Explain.
   b) Do the two tests applied to the information relevant in each test yield the same result (that is, either rejection or acceptance of the hypothesis of equality in both cases)?
   c) Noting your answers to (a) and (b), how do you reconcile them?

6. Concerning the test for offensiveness of cigar smoke, what reasons can you think of which would make it inappropriate to apply a Wilcoxon test to the impressions of the women involved in the test?

7. In the case of the new ammunition which is claimed to impart a greater muzzle velocity to the shell (see problem 8, Problem Set 2–3), suppose an accurate gauging of the muzzle velocities of the shells tested yielded the results of the table below. Test the hypothesis of equality using these data and letting ascending ranks indicate greater velocities. (Use the same value for the level of significance, $\alpha = 0.10$.)

Muzzle Velocity, Feet per Second	
New Shells	Old Shells
3,040	3,025
3,033	3,018
3,029	3,012
3,024	3,008
3,020	3,002
3,017	2,995
2,997	2,990
	2,982

8. Perform the instructions of problem 5 above, only in this case make the comparisons between problem 7 above and problem 8 of Problem Set 2–3.

9. In problem 7 above, will it change the result of the test if the ranks are assigned to the muzzle velocities of the shells in inverse order, that is, with the highest velocity given the lowest rank? Try it and see.

10. Suppose the muzzle velocities of the shells had been such, in problem 7, as to produce the rankings given below:

	Ranks	
New shells:	4 5 6 7 8 9 10	
Old shells: 1 2 3		11 12 13 14 15

Would application of the Wilcoxon test lead to acceptance or rejection of the hypothesis of equality, at $\alpha = 0.10$?

11. Noting the contrast which exists between the result of the tests in problems 7 and 10 above, and considering also your answers to problem 5 or problem 8 above, discuss the relationship between the Fisher-Irwin test and the Wilcoxon test. Explain why the Wilcoxon test is more effective than the Fisher-Irwin test, where it is appropriate.

12. What is the difference in the quality of data which would make the Wilcoxon test appropriate in one case, whereas the Fisher-Irwin test would be appropriate in the other?

13. In problem 10 of Problem Set 2–3, the Fisher-Irwin test was used to test a claim of superiority for a certain brand of gasoline over another. In what manner might it be possible to make a test of the two brands in which the Wilcoxon test could be used?

14. What do you see as the basic difference between the situation of the taxicabs (problem 10, Problem Set 2–3) and the situation of the hay fever sufferers (problem 13 of that set) which would preclude the possibility of using a Wilcoxon test in the latter case?

The null hypothesis and its alternative

The thoughtful student may have felt some confusion with regard to the hypotheses which were actually tested in the procedures discussed throughout this chapter. In each case, the hypothesis tested was of a type called a *null* hypothesis. This term requires explanation. Once the meaning of null hypothesis is understood, an explanation of why it is used becomes clearer. In each of the illustrations, the hypothesis tested was one of equality, in some sense. In the example of acceptance sampling, the hypothesis was that the fraction defective in an incoming lot was equal to 10 percent. In the Fisher-Irwin and the Wilcoxon tests, the hypothesis was one of equal effectiveness. The test in each case consisted in determining if the sample result was significantly different from expectations based on the hypothesis. The hypothesis could just as well have been stated in each case as: The sample result does *not* differ significantly from expectations. This latter statement is the *null* hypothesis, with the term *null* corresponding to the term *not* in the statement.

In the tests relating to the two training methods, the null hypothesis in each case was that the performances of the two groups did not differ significantly. Remember, however, that we were endeavoring to determine if method A was superior to method B, not if they were the same. Why, then, did we test the null hypothesis, rather than a hypothesis that method A was superior? The answer is that on the assumption that the null hypothesis is true, one can determine the probabilities to assign to the different possible sample results; but this cannot be done with the second hypothesis. Under the null hypothesis, we would expect the ranks to be more or less uniformly distributed between the two groups of workers. We were able to test the hypothesis by noting how extremely the results differed from one another. But what can be said about our expectations on the assumption that method A is superior to method B? Obviously, we would expect the results for the two samples to differ. By how much should they differ? We could answer that if we knew the probabilities to assign to various sample results; but we would have no way of assigning such probabilities unless we had some idea of *how much* superior method A is supposed to be! In other words, the hypothesis, "method A is superior to method B," is not specific enough to allow us to test it directly. We therefore test it indirectly, as an alternative to the null hypothesis.

This completes a first introduction to the methods of statistical inference. The discussion was introduced at this point to give the student immediate applications of the probability concepts developed in the preceding chapter. In the process, much of the reasoning underlying tests of hypotheses has been outlined. In a later chapter, we shall return to the subject; but in the intervening chapters, additional concepts must be introduced, to prepare the student for these later discussions.

Problem Set 2-5

1. For the problems listed below from preceding problem sets, write out in detail the following characteristics of the test made in each problem: (1) the null hypothesis (or hypotheses), (2) the alternative hypothesis, and (3) the basis for accepting or rejecting the null hypothesis, in exact terms and making use of the value of α prescribed for the test in each case.

   a) Problem 3, Problem Set 2-3.
   b) Problem 4, Problem Set 2-4.
   c) Problem 7, Problem Set 2-3.
   d) Problem 7, Problem Set 2-4.
   e) Problem 10, Problem Set 2-3.
   f) Problem 1, Problem Set 2-4.

Appendix A: Logarithms

We shall limit our attention to the so-called "common" logarithms (to the base, 10). The logarithm of a number is the power to which we must raise 10 to get that number. More precisely, letting $\log(a)$ denote "the logarithm of a,"

$$\log(a) = x \text{ if } 10^x = a.$$

For example, if $a = 100$, then the logarithm of a is 2 since $10^2 = 100$. Some other values are shown in the table below:

a	$\log(a)$
10,000	4
1,000	3
100	2
10	1
1	0
0.1	-1
0.01	-2
0.001	-3

The logarithm of a value intermediate to two values of a in this table will be intermediate to the logarithms associated with those two values. For example, the number 50 lies between 10 and 100. Its logarithm is 1.6990. As another example, the number 500 has a logarithm of 2.6990, intermediate to the logarithms of 100 and 1,000.

The student will note that the portion of the logarithms to the right of the decimal point is the same in $\log(50)$ and $\log(500)$. This portion of the logarithm is called the *mantissa*. For any two numbers that differ only in that one is some multiple of 10 more or less than the other (in our case, 500 is 10 times 50), the mantissa of their logarithms will be the same. The reason for this will become clear later.

The portion of the logarithm to the left of the decimal point is called the *characteristic*. Notice that it differs in $\log(50)$ and $\log(500)$. For two numbers that differ only by some multiple of 10, the characteristic will differ by the number of multiples of 10 involved. Thus, since 500 is one multiple of 10 more than 50, the characteristic of $\log(500)$ is one greater than the characteristic of $\log(50)$. Once again, the reason for this is clarified later.

The logarithm associated with any specified number is developed in two steps. First, the mantissa of the logarithm is found in a table of logarithms. Such a table contains the mantissas associated with (usually) three- or four-digit sequences of numbers. Table G in the section of tables in this book shows three-digit sequences. If we wished the mantissa of the number 345, we would find the row of the table with the digits 34 in the leftmost column. Reading across that row to the column headed 5 (the third digit of 345), we read the mantissa as 5378. The logarithm of 345 is, thus, of the form c.5378, where the letter "c" to the left denotes the characteristic of the logarithm.

We have noted that the mantissa of 345 would be the same as the mantissa of 3.45, or 0.0345, or any other number with the sequence of digits 345 followed or preceded by zeroes. The logarithm of these numbers are different, however. They differ in the value of the characteristic. Written out fully, the logarithms of the numbers mentioned above are:

Number	*Logarithm*
345.0	2.5378
3.45	0.5378
0.0345	8.5378 − 10

Notice that the mantissa is the same in all three cases. The characteristic changes from 2 to 0 to −2. Logarithms for fractional numbers are written as shown for computational convenience. The characteristic is expressed as $8 - 10 = -2$. If one were to carry out fully the subtraction indicated $(8.5378 - 10 = -1.4622)$ the mantissa of the result would differ from the mantissa associated with nonfractional values with the same sequence of digits. We would then require another table of logarithms for fractional values. To determine the characteristic for a nonfractional number, a good rule is to count the number of digits to the left of the decimal point and subtract 1. Thus, 345.0 has three digits to the left of the decimal point, and the characetristic is $3 - 1 = 2$. If the number is fractional, count the number of zeroes between the decimal point and the first digit of the sequence and subtract this number from −1 to get the characteristic. In 0.0345, there is one zero between the decimal point and the first digit of the sequence. The characteristic is $-1 - 1 = -2$. For 0.345, the characteristic is $-1 - 0 = -1$, and $\log(0.345) = 9.5378 - 10$.

We can reverse the process described above to find the number associated with a given logarithm. If a is the number whose logarithm is x, we call a the antilogarithm of x and denote it as

$$\log^{-1}(x) = a .$$

Suppose $x = 7.5378 - 10$. We find the number associated with a mantissa of 5378 in the table of logarithms. This number is, of course, 345. Since the characteristic of x is $7 - 10 = -3$, there will be two zeroes between the decimal point and the first digit of the sequence. Thus

$$\log^{-1}(7.5378 - 10) = 0.00345 .$$

If $x = 4.5378$,

$$\log^{-1}(4.5378) = 34,500.0 ,$$

since there will be one more digit to the left of the decimal point than the size of the characteristic $(4 + 1 = 5)$.

Having reviewed the meaning of logarithms and how to find the logarithm of a given number, let us consider their use.

Our interest in logarithms lies in the fact that they facilitate the process of multiplication and division. This fact follows from three rules of exponents. Noting that we can express any number as 10 raised to some power, consider the product of the numbers a and b. Let $a = 10^x$ and $b = 10^y$. Then

$$a \cdot b = 10^x \cdot 10^y .$$

The first rule states that

$$L\text{-}1: \quad 10^x \cdot 10^y = 10^{x+y} .$$

Since x and y are the logarithms of a and b, this rule says the logarithm of the product of a and b is the sum of $\log(a)$ and $\log(b)$. Consequently, we can find the product of two numbers by:

1. Looking up the logarithms of the numbers in a table of logarithms.
2. Adding these logarithms.
3. Finding the number whose logarithm is equal to the sum calculated in (2).

Some examples of the use of Rule $L\text{-}1$:

1. To evaluate the product $(50)(34.5)$:

$$\log(50) = 1.6990$$
$$\log(34.5) = 1.5378$$
$$\log(50) + \log(34.5) = 3.2368$$
$$\log^{-1}(3.2368) = 1725.0[1]$$

---

[1] The fourth digit in the sequence, 5, was evaluated by interpolation.

2. To evaluate the product $(5)(0.0345)$:

$$\log(5) = 0.6990$$
$$\log(.0345) = 8.5378 - 10$$
$$\log(50) + \log(.0345) = 9.2368 - 10$$
$$\log^{-1}(9.2368 - 10) = 0.1725$$

At this juncture, we can see why the logarithms of numbers that differ by some multiple of 10 have the same mantissa but varying characteristics. Consider the number 0.0345, which has a logarithm of $8.5378 - 10$. Multiplying that number by 10, we have

$$(.0345) \cdot (10) = .345$$

and

$$\log(.0345) + \log(10) = (8.5378 - 10) + 1.0000$$
$$= 9.5378 - 10 .$$

We see that multiplying a number by 10 corresponds to adding 1 to the logarithm of that number. The effect is to increase the characteristic by 1 and to leave the mantissa unchanged.

Two other rules useful in calculations are actually extensions of Rule L–1. In the case of divisions, we recognize that

$$L\text{–}2: \quad 10^x/10^y = 10^x \cdot 10^{-y} = 10^{(x-y)} .$$

In other words, the logarithm of a quotient is equal to the difference between the logarithms of the dividend and divisor. Consequently, we can find the quotient resulting from a/b by:

1. Looking up $\log(a)$ and $\log(b)$.
2. Calculating the difference, $\log(a) - \log(b)$.
3. Determining the number whose logarithm is equal to the difference calculated in (2).

Some examples of the use of Rule L–2:

1. To evaluate the quotient $50/34.5$:

$$\log(50) = 1.6990$$
$$\log(34.5) = 1.5378$$
$$\log(50) - \log(34.5) = 0.1612$$
$$\log^{-1}(0.1612) = 1.449^2$$

2. To evaluate the quotient $5/.0345$:

$$\log(5) = 10.6990 - 10^3$$
$$\log(.0345) = 8.5378 - 10$$
$$\log(5) - \log(.0345) = 2.1612 - 0$$
$$\log^{-1}(2.1612) = 144.9$$

---

[2] The last digit, 9, was found by interpolation.

[3] Notice that if we had expressed $\log(5)$ as 0.6990, the subsequent subtraction by $8.5378 - 10$ would have yielded a negative mantissa, for which we have no table of logarithms. To avoid this result we write $\log(5)$ as $10.6990 - 10$. The result of subtraction is then positive, and we look up the mantissa, 0.1612, in a table of logarithms.

The last rule of value to us follows from noting that

$$(10^x)^2 = 10^x \cdot 10^x = 10^{2x},$$
$$(10^x)^3 = 10^x \cdot 10^x \cdot 10^x = 10^{3x},$$

and, generally,

$$L\text{-}3: \quad (10^x)^n = 10^{nx}.$$

This rule gives us a convenient method to evaluate the result of raising a number to some power. We merely multiply the logarithm of the number by the exponent and look up the antilogarithm of this result. Some examples follow:

1. To evaluate $(5)^2$:

$$\log(5) = 0.6990$$
$$2 \cdot \log(5) = 1.3980$$
$$\log^{-1}(1.3980) = 25$$

2. To evaluate $(5)^{-2} = \dfrac{1}{(5)^2}$:

$$\log(5) = 0.6990$$
$$(-2)(\log(5)) = -1.3980$$

Since this result has a negative mantissa, we adjust by adding 10.0000 to the result and carrying a value of -10 to the right:

$$
\begin{array}{r}
+10.0000 - 10 \\
-\ 1.3980 \\
\hline
8.6020 - 10
\end{array}
$$

Finally, $\log^{-1}(8.6020 - 10) = 0.04$.

3. To evaluate $(.0345)^3$:

$$\log(.0345) = 8.5378 - 10$$
$$3 \cdot \log(.0345) = 25.6134 - 30$$
$$\log^{-1}(25.6134 - 30) = .00004106$$

4. To evaluate $(.0345)^{-2} = \dfrac{1}{(.0345)^2}$:

$$\log(.0345) = 8.5378 - 10$$
$$(-2)(\log(.0345)) = -17.0756 + 20$$

Once again, the mantissa is negative, so we adjust:

$$
\begin{array}{r}
20.0000 - 20 \\
-17.0756 + 20 \\
\hline
2.9244 + 0
\end{array}
$$

We find: $\log^{-1}(2.9244) = 840.2$.

The three rules outlined and illustrated above will serve many needs where large products or quotients are developed. Let us illustrate the solution in the text for the probability that the purchaser will accept a lot with 10 percent of the items defective if he uses the sampling plan: $N = 50$, $n = 10$, $a = 1$. We noted in the text that:

and $P(\text{"lot is accepted"}) = P(r = 0) + P(r = 1)$,

$$P(r = 0) = \frac{(C_{45,10})(C_{5,0})}{C_{50,10}},$$

$$P(r = 1) = \frac{(C_{45,9})(C_{5,1})}{C_{50,10}}.$$

To evaluate $P(r = 0)$:

$$P(r = 0) = \frac{\dfrac{45!}{35! \, 10!} \cdot \dfrac{5!}{5! \, 0!}}{\dfrac{50!}{40! \, 10!}} = \frac{45! \, 5! \, 40! \, 10!}{35! \, 10! \, 5! \, 0! \, 50!}.$$

Noting that the values 5! in the numerator and denominator will cancel, as will the values 10!, and that $0! = 1$, we ignore these values and proceed to sum, in separate sums, the logarithms of the factorial numbers in the numerator and the denominator. One requires a special table for the logarithms of factorial numbers, and one is supplied as Table H in the section of tables in this book.

Numerator		Denominator	
Term	*Log*	*Term*	*Log*
45!	56.0778	35!	40.0142
40!	47.9116	50!	64.4831
	103.9894		104.4973
	+10.0000 − 10		
	113.9894 − 10		

Noting that the logarithm of the numerator is smaller than the logarithm of the denominator, we add and subtract 10 in the usual manner. We now find

$$P(r = 0) = \log^{-1}[(113.9894 - 10) - 104.4973]$$
$$= \log^{-1}(9.4921 - 10) = 0.3105$$

The value for $P(r = 1)$ is left as an exercise for the student.

chapter 3

Random
variables and
probability
distributions

Random variables

The discussion in Chapter 1 of the rules of probability was developed with reference to an experiment of tossing two dice. The events used to illustrate the rules were given names such as A, B, C, etc.; but these events were describable in terms of numbers. Some of the events and their descriptions were:

A—"the toss of two dice results in a one or a two on the first die."
B—"the toss of two dice results in a four on the second die."
E—"the toss of two dice results in a five on the first die."
F—"the toss of two dice results in a value less than five on the first die."

With x_1 denoting the value of the first die and x_2 denoting the value of the second die, these descriptions can be stated more succinctly as follows: $A = (x_1 \leq 2)$; $B = (x_2 = 4)$; $E = (x_1 = 5)$; and $F = (x_1 < 5)$. Statements such as these will be used in subsequent discussion.

It is obvious that the value of x_1 is variable, depending on the outcome of the toss of the two dice. It also is true that each possible value of x_1 has a probability assigned to it. Because x_1 has these properties, it is called a *random variable*. The variable x_2 also has these properties, and it also is a *random variable*. Generally, a *random variable* is a set of values unambiguously[1] assigned by some rule to the set of points constituting

---

[1] By "unambiguously" we mean that any point in the sample space will have only one value, under the given rule for assigning values. There may be more than one point in the sample space with any given value, however.

the sample space. It is evident that more than one random variable may be defined on a given sample space. Thus, x_1 and x_2 both are defined on the sample space for the experiment of tossing two dice. Some other possibilities are the sum of the values of the two dice (this seems to be one of the more popular random variables defined on this particular sample space), the minimum value showing on the two dice, and the maximum value of the two dice. Which random variable is of importance to the experimenter depends on his interest in the experiment. Nathan Detroit (the gambler of "Guys and Dolls"), for instance, would be more inclined to show an interest in the sum of the two dice than he would their average value.

In the toss of two dice, it is the natural thing to describe the events in terms of numbers. This is not always the case. To illustrate, suppose the experiment is the production of a painted panel to be used in the manufacture of an automobile. Our concern with the outcome might be whether or not the panel is "satisfactory." It is useful to translate the events "satisfactory" and "unsatisfactory" into a random variable. This can easily be done by letting, say, the value 0 represent the event "satisfactory" and the value 1 represent the event "unsatisfactory." Then, for a sample of five panels selected from the production of a given period, these values can be summed to yield another random variable. For example, if the sample of five showed the first three panels "satisfactory" and the last two "unsatisfactory," the result can be expressed as the random variable, $r = 0 + 0 + 0 + 1 + 1 = 2$. The interpretation is easy: there are two defective panels in this sample of five.

The student may remember that a random variable of this last type was discussed in Chapter 1, where we were concerned with the number of defective parts in a sample of five taken from the production of a machine. That discussion led to a probability distribution for r, the number of defective parts, which appears in Table 1–2. Also in Chapter 1, a discussion of the random variable X, the number of aces in your partner's bridge hand (given that yours contained no aces), led to another probability distribution as given in Table 1–1. It was indicated that the distribution of Table 1–2 is a binomial distribution, and the distribution in Table 1–1 is a hypergeometric distribution. In Chapter 2, the Wilcoxon distribution was introduced. It is the distribution associated with the random variable $(W_s - \text{Min. } W_s)$. Generally, any random variable defined on a given sample space will have a probability distribution associated with it. There are an indefinite number of probability distributions. Only a small part of these have been found useful in application to business and economic problems. We shall be able to devote attention only to a reduced group of these.

A proper understanding of much of the discussion that follows will depend heavily upon knowledge of some of the basic properties of probability distributions. It behooves us at this point, therefore, to develop some of these fundamental notions. Perhaps the first point to be made is that when one speaks of a certain probability distribution, in most instances the reference is to a family of distributions. Consider, for example, the probability distribution of x_1 as we defined it in the discussion of the toss of two dice. You will recall that x_1 is the number of dots showing on the first of the two dice tossed. The probability distribution of the random variable x_1 is given in Table 3–1.

Table 3–1

x_1	$P(x_1)$
1	$\frac{1}{6}$
2	$\frac{1}{6}$
3	$\frac{1}{6}$
4	$\frac{1}{6}$
5	$\frac{1}{6}$
6	$\frac{1}{6}$

If one were not cautious, he might conclude that this distribution is "one of a kind." That is, he might believe that in an experiment involving the toss of two dice, the distribution of x_1 must always be as the one that appears in Table 3–1. Notice, however, that the particular distribution shown there is the result of the assumption, implicit or explicit, that the die in question is a fair die. Suppose, now, that the die were "loaded," so that the probability of the number 6 appearing is twice as likely as any of the other five numbers. In that case, $P(x_1 = 6) = 2/7$, while $P(x_1 = i) = 1/7$ for $i = 1, 2, 3, 4, 5$. This new distribution is just another member of a family of distributions for the random variable x_1. An infinite number of such members is possible, just by varying the assumed probabilities for the various faces of the die.

The point can be made with respect to any probability distribution. Thus, the probability distribution which was derived in Chapter 1 for the number of defective parts in a sample of five owed its particular form to the assumption that the probability was 0.25 that any given part would be defective. It is only one member of a family with an infinite number of members, the binomial distribution.

The student will find that much of the solution to many problems in statistical inference is a matter of answering two questions: What is the relevant probability distribution to apply? and What member of the family should be used? An answer to the first question depends on the type of "experiment" being studied. Discussion of the points involved in arriving at the proper answer is reserved for later chapters, where we consider various important distributions. An adequate answer to the second question requires specification of certain characteristics of the distribution, which serves to single out one member of the family of distributions decided on in the first question. This chapter is devoted to the concepts required to answer the second question.

Problem Set 3–1

1. In a poker game there are several different types of hand that can be described. Some of these descriptions relate to the occurrence or nonoccurrence of matches in the cards of the hand. Listed below are some of these commonly used descriptions, and the number of such hands (combinations) that are possible. For the hands given in the table define the random variable, c the maximum number of cards in each hand of a given face. For example, for the hand "a pair" there are two cards in one face, and only one card in each of three other faces. Thus, the value of c will be $c = 2$. Set down the probability distribution of c. What are the features of c that make it a random variable?

Type of Hand	Characteristics of Hand	Number of Such Hands
No-match hand	Five cards all with different faces	1,317,888
"A pair"	Two cards matched in the same face and three cards with nonmatching faces	1,098,240
"Two pairs"	Two cards of same face, two more cards matching in a second face, fifth card nonmatching	123,552
"Three of a kind"	Three cards matching in one face and two nonmatching cards	54,912
"Full house"	Three cards matching in one face and two cards matching in another face	3,744
"Four of a kind"	Four cards in one face and a nonmatching card	624
Total Number of Hands Possible		2,598,960

2. In the experiment of tossing three coins, we wish to count the number of tails resulting from each trial.
   a) List the sample space as in problem 8, Problem Set 1–1.
   b) Letting t equal the number of tails appearing in each outcome, set down the value of t associated with the outcomes of the sample space as you have listed them in (a).
   c) Is t a random variable? Explain.
   d) Set down the probability distribution of t.
3. In problem 3 of Problem Set 1–4, the experiment is to draw, without replacement, two chips from a bag containing five chips which are numbered serially from one to five. The sum, s, of the numbers appearing on these two chips is then noted.

a) Is *s* a random variable? Why?

b) Set down the sample space of the experiment and indicate the value of *s* associated with each outcome.

c) Construct the probability distribution of *s*.

4. Perform the steps of problem 3, only this time with respect to problem 4 of Problem Set 1–4.

5. In problem 7 of Problem Set 1–4, we were concerned with the number of different-type toys which Jimmy might find in the first four boxes of cereal his mother bought. Let *t* be the number of types of toy and answer the following.

a) Explain why *t* is a random variable.

b) What are the possible values of *t?*

c) Construct the probability distribution of *t*. (The probabilities that Jimmy will receive only one type of toy and all four types of toy are available as results of the exercises in problem 7, Problem Set 1–4. We state here that the probabilities that Jimmy will get two or three types of toy in the first four boxes are $84/256 \cong 0.328$ and $144/256 \cong 0.563$, respectively.)

6. In problem 13 of Problem Set 1–4, the two boys were to divide eight pieces of toffee, two of which were chocolate, between them. Let *y* be the number of pieces of chocolate toffee that the younger boy might receive.

a) What is a useful way of viewing the sample space in this problem?

b) What are the possible values of *y?*

c) Can *y* be viewed as a random variable? Why?

d) Set up a table showing the probability distribution of *y*.

7. In Chapter 1, we considered the experiment of drawing four marbles from a bag containing four red and six green marbles. Let *r* denote the number of red marbles among the four drawn from the bag.

a) Construct the probability distribution of *r* under the assumption that the four marbles are drawn with replacement.

b) Construct the probability distribution of *r* under the assumption that the marbles are drawn without replacement.

c) Complete the following statement: "The two distributions of parts (*a*) and (*b*) are particular_____of two different_____of probability distributions."

8. In the experiment consisting of the toss of two dice, define the random variable *g* as the greater of the values appearing on the two dice (if the two dice have the same value, *g* is to be this common value). Construct the probability distribution of *g*.

Expected values

It has already been noted that in the case of the random variable x_1, specification of the probabilities on the six faces of the die is required in order to single out a particular probability distribution that is relevant. Also, in the case of the binomial distribution for number of parts defective in a sample, one will get a different distribution for each possible specification of the values of n, the number of trials, and p, the probability that any one trial of the experiment will result in a defective part.

For another family of probability distributions, the characteristics to be specified may differ from those indicated in the above cases. Generally, however, there will be some characteristic(s) of the probability distribution for which a numerical value or numerical values must be specified before one can proceed to a solution for the particular problem confronting him. These characteristics are usually referred to as the *parameters* of the probability distribution.

Two parameters play a particularly important role in most statistical applications: the arithmetic mean (which will be referred to simply as the mean, hereafter) and the variance. These two parameters are from a class of measures defined for probability distributions, called *expectations* or *expected values*. We therefore proceed to a discussion of expected values for probability distributions of *discrete*[2] random variables. Roughly speaking, a *discrete* random variable is one for which there are "gaps" in the values the variable may take. They often are the result of counting operations. The random variables which have been mentioned in connection with the toss of two dice were all *discrete* random variables. The possible values of x_1, for example, were 1, 2, 3, 4, 5, 6; but it was not possible for x_1 to have a value between, say, 3 and 4.

For any discrete random variable, the *expected value* of the random variable is defined as the sum, over all possible values the random variable can take, of the products formed by multiplying each of these values by the probability that value will occur. If we let x denote the random variable and $E(x)$ its expected value, we can shorten this definition considerably by stating:

$$E(x) = \Sigma x P(x), \text{ for all values of } x.$$

An example will make the definition clear. Suppose that $x = x_1 + x_2$ is the sum of the values of two fair dice tossed randomly. Then x is a random variable defined on the sample space consisting of the 36 possible outcomes in the toss of two dice. This sample space appears in Figure 1–1 and is reproduced here as Figure 3–1(a). The number appearing above each point is the value of x for that point. Thus, the point circled is for $x_1 = 2$, $x_2 = 6$, and $x = x_1 + x_2 = 8$. The probability distribution

---

[2] In later discussions, we shall consider probability distributions for two general classes of random variables, discrete and continuous. A continuous random variable has the characteristic opposite to a discrete random variable. Whereas a discrete random variable has "gaps," a continuous random variable does not. Some examples of continuous random variables might be the distance an automobile is driven between successive blowouts, or the volume of rainfall in a particular locale for a particular period of time, or the length of a bolt produced by an automatic machine. A definition of expected value for continuous distributions requires the calculus, so that we are forced to dispense with such definition. This will not be a handicap in later applications, however, since the continuous case is quite analogous to the discrete case.

for the random variable x is easily derived by examination of Figure 3–1(a). It appears in the first two columns of Figure 3–1(b). For $x = 7$

Figure 3–1(a)

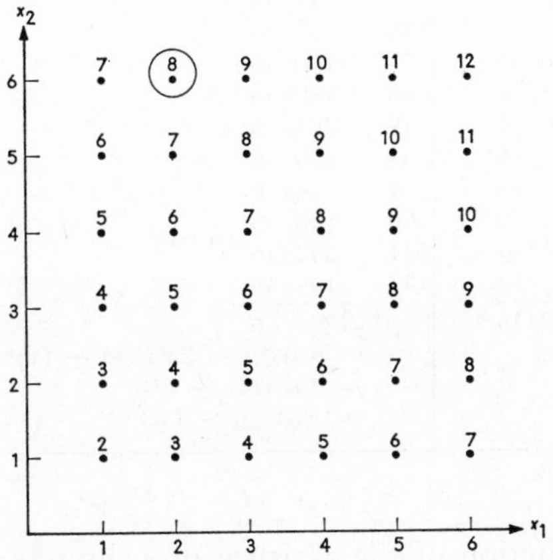

Figure 3–1(b)

x	$P(x)$	$xP(x)$
2	1/36	2/36
3	2/36	6/36
4	3/36	12/36
5	4/36	20/36
6	5/36	30/36
7	6/36	42/36
8	5/36	40/36
9	4/36	36/36
10	3/36	30/36
11	2/36	22/36
12	1/36	12/36
	36/36	252/36 = 7

in the first column, the value of $P(x)$ is 6/36, since 6 of the 36 equiprobable points in Figure 3–1(a) are associated with the value $x = 7$. The third column of Figure 3–1(a) contains the products, for each row, of x and $P(x)$. The last figure in the third column is the sum of these products, that is, $\Sigma\ xP(x)$ for all x. It is, therefore, the *expected value of x*. The *mean* of a random variable is just its expected value, and it is denoted by placing a bar over the letter that represents the random variable. Thus, $\bar{x}$ denotes the mean of x; and $\bar{x} = E(x) = \Sigma\ xP(x) = 7$.

It was noted earlier that one can define many different random variables on a given sample space. We arrive at the variance of the distribution of x given in Figure 3–1(b) by defining another random variable in terms of x and $\bar{x}$. For each value of x we determine the amount by which it differs from $\bar{x}$, and square this difference. The result is a set of values, $(x - \bar{x})^2$, one for each value of x. These values, themselves, represent a random variable, for which we can determine the expected value. Substituting $(x - \bar{x})^2$ for x in the definition of expected value given above, we get

$$E[(x - \bar{x})^2] = \Sigma(x - \bar{x})^2 P[(x - \bar{x})^2] .$$

Notice, however, that $\bar{x}$ is a fixed value for the given distribution. This means that the probability of getting a particular x will determine the probability of getting the corresponding value of $(x - \bar{x})^2$. That is, $P[(x - \bar{x})^2] = P(x)$. Making the substitution, we denote the variance of x as var(x) and note that

$$\mathrm{var}(x) = E[(x - \bar{x})^2] = \Sigma(x - \bar{x})^2 P(x) .$$

Table 3-2

x	$P(x)$	$(x - \bar{x})$	$(x - \bar{x})^2$	$(x - \bar{x}^2)P(x)$	x^2	$x^2P(x)$
2	1/36	2−7 = −5	25	25/36	4	4/36
3	2/36	3−7 = −4	16	32/36	9	18/36
4	3/36	4−7 = −3	9	27/36	16	48/36
5	4/36	5−7 = −2	4	16/36	25	100/36
6	5/36	6−7 = −1	1	5/36	36	180/36
7	6/36	7−7 = 0	0	0/36	49	294/36
8	5/36	8−7 = +1	1	5/36	64	320/36
9	4/36	9−7 = +2	4	16/36	81	324/36
10	3/36	10−7 = +3	9	27/36	100	300/36
11	2/36	11−7 = +4	16	32/36	121	242/36
12	1/36	12−7 = +5	25	25/36	144	144/36

$$\text{var}(x) = 210/36 \simeq 5.83$$

$$1974/36$$
$$\text{var}(x) = \Sigma x^2P(x) - (\bar{x})^2$$
$$= 1974/36 - 7^2$$
$$= 210/36 \simeq 5.83$$

This last expression constitutes a definition of the variance of a discrete random variable, x. For purposes of calculation it is often more convenient to use the equivalent expression[3]

$$\text{var}(x) = \Sigma x^2P(x) - (\bar{x})^2 .$$

The use of these two expressions and their equivalence is demonstrated in Table 3–2, for the random variable x of Figure 3–1.

What the mean and the variance tell us

The mean and the variance were defined in the preceding section, and methods of calculating them were illustrated for a particular probability distribution. Unfortunately, neither the definition nor the method of calculation gives a very clear impression of what these two measures tell us. This section is intended to give a first answer to that question in terms of *relative frequency*. In a later section, the explanation will run in slightly different terms.

It was noted in an earlier chapter that the probability of an event is linked rather closely to the ratio of the number of trials that resulted in that event to the total number of trials, where the experiment has been repeated over a long sequence of trials. As the number of trials increases, there is a strong tendency for the ratio of times the event occurred (which will be referred to hereafter as the *relative frequency* of the event) to approach the probability of that event. Now suppose that the experiment of tossing two dice had been performed enough times that

---

[3] In Appendix C, two programs which will accomplish the calculations for $\bar{x}$, var (x), σ, sk(x), and kur(x) appear. One of these is in BASIC language, and one is in FORTRAN language.

the relative frequencies for the sum on the dice had worked out to be exactly the probabilities associated with the values of this random variable. That is, in the long sequence of tosses, there were exactly 1/36 of the tosses that yielded $x = 2$; and all other values of x had relative frequencies equal to $P(x)$ as it appears in Figure 3–1(b). Then, if one were to "average"[4] the value of x as it appeared in all of the trials that had been made, he would find the value to be seven. This is, of course, the value that we calculated as $\bar{x}$, the expected value of x. As it turns out, then, the technical term in this case has a meaningful interpretation. The *expected value* of the random variable, the sum of two (fair) dice, is the value that one would "expect the sum to average out to" in a long sequence of tosses.[5]

Although the expected value of x is seven, we would not expect each toss to come up with that value. As a matter of fact, we have already noted that in a long sequence we would expect each of the possible values for x to occur with a relative frequency approaching its probability. That is, we would expect to note a variation, or dispersion, in the values of the dice resulting from successive tosses. It is this variation that the variance of the random variable measures. The variation is measured with reference to the mean of the random variable. This can be seen by examining the definition of the variance of x: $\text{var}(x) = \Sigma\ (x - \bar{x})^2\ P(x)$. Notice that each possible value of x enters the calculation in a manner that indicates how widely it varies from $\bar{x}$. Obviously, the more widely the possible values of x are dispersed about the mean, the larger will be the variance of x. Notice, also, that this expression will always result in a positive value for the variance of a random variable, no matter what the possible values of the random variable might be. This is true because the deviation of each value from the mean is squared, making all values in the expression positive. Large positive values of the variance of a random variable, then, indicate wide variation or dispersion in the values one can expect that random variable to take; and small values indicate less variation.

The standard deviation

The variance is a good measure of variation in a random variable, and there are applications where it is used directly. For some applications, it has one drawback, however. This is the fact that the value one gets

---

[4] The term "average" is placed in quotation marks because we will find later that there is more than one way to get an average. The term here is used in its most common, everyday connotation: the series of values taken by x are summed, and the sum is divided by the number of trials.

[5] The phrase "average out to" can be given another interpretation which relates to an important property of the mean. This is the fact that the expected deviation of a random variable from its mean is zero. Thus, if $\bar{x}$ is the mean of x, then $E(x - \bar{x}) = \Sigma\ (x - \bar{x})P(x) = \Sigma\ xP(x) - \Sigma\ \bar{x}P(x) = \bar{x} - \bar{x}\ \Sigma\ P(x) = \bar{x} - \bar{x} = 0$.

for the variance of a random variable is in units of the random variable, squared. Perhaps this will make more sense if we modify the experiment we have been discussing slightly. Suppose that on the toss of the two dice you are to receive a number of dollars equal to the sum on the dice. The only change this makes is that the random variable now is x dollars. The mean of the distribution is still 7, and this indicates that you can expect your average prize to be 7 dollars, if you play the game long enough. What variation can you expect in your winnings? Well, the value of the variance was determined to be 5.83 in Table 3–2. This measure of variation in your winnings is 5.83 dollars-squared. It was found by taking the difference between each possible winning and the mean winnings (which difference would be in dollars) and *squaring* it, multiplying each of these squared terms by $P(x)$, and summing these products. The result, of course, is dollars-squared.

In some later problems, we shall need to have a measure for dispersion which we can relate easily to the mean of the distribution. Since the mean is in unsquared units, we should like the measure of dispersion also to be in unsquared units. This is easily accomplished by taking the (positive) square root of the variance. The value which results from this operation is called the *standard deviation* of the distribution, and it is usually denoted by the Greek letter σ. Thus, the *standard deviation* of a random variable x is defined as:

$$\sigma = \sqrt{\operatorname{var}(x)} = \sqrt{\Sigma(x - \bar{x})^2 P(x)}.$$

For the winnings at dice, the standard deviation is $\sigma = \sqrt{5.83}$ dollars-squared $= \$2.41$.

Tchebycheff's Inequality

At this point, the student's mind is still undoubtedly somewhat clouded with mystery concerning the standard deviation—what it is, what is its use. The mystery will be dispelled gradually, as applications of the standard deviation are explained and become familiar. For the moment, it can be said that the standard deviation of a random variable is a measure of the dispersion, or variation, to expect in that random variable. One of its important uses is in determining intervals about the mean of a distribution for which probability statements can be made. For particular probability distributions, such probability statements related to these intervals about the mean can be very precise. We shall come to examples of these later. It may be helpful to illustrate what is meant, by stating a theorem due to a Russian mathematician, Tchebycheff.

Tchebycheff proved that for any distribution, be it discrete or continuous, of whatever form, the following amazing fact is true. If one sets up an interval about the mean whose lowest value is the mean minus a multiple, m, of the standard deviation and whose highest value is the mean plus m standard deviations, the probability is at least $(1 - 1/m^2)$ that the value taken by the random variable on any trial will fall within that interval. In more concise language, the theorem says, for any random variable x with mean $\bar{x}$ and standard deviation σ:

$$P(\bar{x} - m\sigma \leq x \leq \bar{x} + m\sigma) \geq 1 - 1/m^2.$$

The theorem can be illustrated by applying it to the winnings in the dice game. It has already been determined that the mean winnings for this game is $7 and the standard deviation is $2.41. We can set up a table showing what the Tchebycheff Inequality predicts for different values of m, say $m = 1, 2, 3$, and verifying the correctness of the prediction by

Table 3–3

m	*Interval Is:* $(\bar{x} - m\sigma)$ *to* $(\bar{x} + m\sigma)$	$P(\bar{x} - m\sigma \leq x \leq \bar{x} + m\sigma)$ *Tchebycheff* *(At Least)*	*Actual*
1	$7 - 1($2.41) to $7 + 1($2.41) or $4.59 to $9.41	$1 - 1/1^2 = 0$	24/36*
2	$7 - 2($2.41) to $7 + 2($2.41) or $2.18 to $11.82	$1 - 1/2^2 = 3/4$	34/36
3	$7 - 3($2.41) to $7 + 3($2.41) or −$0.23 to $14.23	$1 - 1/3^2 = 8/9$	36/36

* The values of x that fall within the interval $4.59 to $9.41 are $x = 5, 6, 7, 8, 9$. The probability that the random variable will take one of these values is the sum of the probabilities of the values: $4/36 + 5/36 + 6/36 + 5/36 + 4/36 = 24/36$.

noting the actual probabilities associated with each interval. The actual probabilities are found by reference to Figure 3–1b, where the values of $P(x)$ are summed within each of the intervals. Table 3–3 summarizes these comparisons.

Examination of the last two columns of Table 3–3 indicates that the prediction from Tchebycheff's Inequality was indeed correct in each instance. One cannot help but be struck by the apparent conservatism of the predictions. In each of the cases presented, the lower limit on the prediction was considerably below the actual probability. In the first case, as a matter of fact, the prediction was only that the probability would be "at least zero." We knew that before we started, of course, because of the nature of probabilities. The reason for this conservatism relates, once again, to the amount of information available. The Tchebycheff Inequality is true for *any* distribution.[6] No matter what the form

---

[6] So long, that is, as the distribution has a finite mean and standard deviation.

of the distribution, if the only information known concerning it is its mean and standard deviation, we are assured that the inequality holds for any given value of m. Thus, for all probability distributions, the probability is at least $1 - 1/5^2 = 0.96$ that a value taken by the random variable will be within five standard deviations of the mean of the distribution. This is, to repeat, an amazing assurance. We need not be surprised that with more information available (in the case illustrated, we knew the exact probability distribution), the actual probabilities depart from the Tchebycheff statements.[7]

Problem Set 3–2

1. For the probability distributions listed below, calculate the mean, variance, and standard deviation of the random variable.

   a) The distribution of g, the greater value appearing on two dice (see problem 8, Problem Set 3–1).

   b) The distribution of t, the number of tails appearing in the toss of three coins (see problem 2, Problem Set 3–1).

   c) The distribution of y, the number of pieces of chocolate toffee that the younger boy might receive (see problem 6, Problem Set 3–1).

2. In problem 1(b), the toss of three coins might result in none, one, two, or three tails. In one sense of the word, then, we can *expect* one of these values to occur. But in your computations for problem 1(b), the *expected value* of t is one particular value—and one that cannot occur, at that. How do you reconcile these facts?

3. If the probability is 0.1 that any given part produced by a machine is defective, and if the results occurring for different parts are independent, then the random variable r, number of defective parts in a sample of four parts, has the distribution given in the table below. Find the value of var (r) by the two formulas given in the text. Also calculate the value of $\bar{r}$.

r	$P(r)$
0	0.6561
1	.2916
2	.0486
3	.0036
4	.0001
	1.0000

---

[7] A brief pedagogic aside may be in order at this juncture. Illustrations such as the one just completed often lead to confusion for some students. They are inclined to ask, for example, "Why did you show that the Tchebycheff Inequality indicates a probability of at least ¾ for the interval $2.18 to $11.82 in Table 3–3? Why go to the trouble? We already know from Figure 3–1(b) that the probability is ³⁴⁄₃₆, which is obviously 'at least ¾.'" The answer is that the illustration was not intended to show something we did not know about the experiment we had already discussed. Its purpose was twofold: to illustrate the meaning of the Tchebycheff Inequality, and more importantly, to illustrate the manner in which one can make use of the standard deviation of a distribution. It was noted above that, for distributions which we shall discuss later, more exact probability statements are possible for intervals constructed in the manner employed in Table 3–3.

4. If four marbles are drawn from a bag containing five red and five green marbles, the probability distribution associated with the number of red marbles among the four marbles drawn varies with the assumption of whether or not drawing takes place with replacement. Letting x_w denote the number of red marbles where the draws are made with replacement and x_{wo} denote the number without replacement, the two parts of the table below give the relevant probability distributions. Calculate $\bar{x}_w$, var (x_w), $\bar{x}_{wo}$, and var (x_{wo}). How does comparison of these values indicate similarities and differences between the random variables x_w and x_{wo}?

x_w	$P(x_w)$	x_{wo}	$P(x_{wo})$
0	0.0625	0	0.024
1	.2500	1	.238
2	.3750	2	.476
3	.2500	3	.238
4	.0625	4	.024
	1.0000		1.000

5. In problems 3 and 4 of Problem Set 1–4, the student was asked to consider an experiment consisting of drawing two chips from a bag containing five chips which are numbered serially from one to five. The student was asked to construct the probability distributions for s, the sum of the numbers on the two chips drawn, under the assumptions that draws are made without replacement and with replacement. For those two distributions, calculate the values of the mean, variance, and standard deviation, and comment on similarities and differences between the two distributions, as reflected in these values.

6. A game involving wins and losses of money is called a *fair* game if the player can expect to receive a return of zero. Suppose that the possible amounts a player of a certain game can win or lose are win $0.50, $0.25, or nothing and lose $0.25 or $0.50. Letting w denote the random variable "winnings on any one play of the game" and expressing losses by a negative value of w, suppose that the probability distribution for w is as given in the table below. Is this game a *fair* game? Why?

w	$P(w)$
$-0.50	0.05
$-.25	.25
0	.40
.25	.20
.50	.10
	1.00

7. How many defective parts can be expected in a sample of five parts drawn randomly from a production process in which the probability of a defective part being produced is 0.25 (see Table 1–2)? What variability can be expected in the number of defective parts in such samples?

8. Calculate measures for the number, and variation in the number, of aces

you might expect in your bridge partner's hand, given that your hand contains no aces (see Table 1-1).

9. In the text, we considered an experiment in which a person was to get $2 for every dot appearing on a tossed die. The random variable in this case is $d = 2x_1$. Find the values of $\bar{d}$, var (d), and σ_d.

10. In the text, the random variable $d = 2x_1$ was defined as the number of dollars a person was to get on the toss of a die, where he was to be paid $2 for each dot appearing on the die. Suppose, now, he is to receive 50 cents ($0.50) for each dot. Define the random variable $f = 0.5x_1$ as the dollar amount he receives and find the values $\bar{f}$, var(f), and σ_f.

11. In the cases of random variables listed below, demonstrate the validity of the Tchebycheff Inequality, in the manner that this was done in Table 3-3.
    a) t, the number of tails in the toss of three coins [problem $1(b)$].
    b) r, the number of defective parts in a sample of five parts (problem 7).
    c) X, the number of aces in your bridge partner's hand (problem 8).
    d) x_w, the number of red marbles in four marbles drawn with replacement from a bag containing five red and five green marbles (problem 4).
    e) w, the winnings in a game (problem 6).
    f) g, the greater value appearing on two dice [problem $1(a)$].

12. Suppose that a certain brand of automobile battery is known to have a mean life of 25 months and a standard deviation in life of 3 months.
    a) What statement can you make concerning the probability that a battery of this brand will have a life somewhere between 19 and 31 months?
    b) What is the probability that a battery of this brand will have a life less than 16 months?
    c) What is the probability that a battery of this brand will have a life longer than 31 months?

13. Suppose that it has been determined that a person betting $10 on a whirl of the roulette wheel can expect to lose 50 cents and that variation in winnings is measurable by a standard deviation of $5.
    a) What is the probability that he will lose more than $20.50 on a given play?
    b) What is the probability that his winnings on any given play will fall between −$10.50 and $9.50?
    c) What is the probability that he will win more than $9.50 on a given play?

Graphs of discrete probability distributions

It will help to gain added perspective in understanding the concepts developed thus far if we can visualize the ideas we have been discussing. This is easily accomplished by constructing a graph of the probability distribution(s) of interest. In such a graph, distance on the vertical axis represents probability, and distance on the horizontal axis represents the random variable. The usual procedure is to erect a vertical bar, *centered* on each possible value that random variable might take, whose *area* is equal to the probability of that value occurring. If the area of the bar is to equal the probability, the dimensions of the bar must be in units so that the product of the height and the width will be in probability units.

The width of the bar represents the difference between successive possible values, and these values are usually counting numbers for discrete random variables. The values of x_1, for example, were the number of dots on the faces of die: 1, 2, 3, 4, 5, and 6. The random variable r, whose distribution is summarized in Table 1–2, was the number of defective parts in a sample of five. Its values also were count numbers: 0, 1, 2, 3, 4, and 5. For the random variable x, the sum of two dice, the possible values were also count numbers: 2, 3, 4, 5, 6, 7, 8, 9, 10, 11, 12. The point is that often, though not always, the possible values taken by a discrete random variable are expressible as successive digits. In these cases, the width of the bars in the graph will represent the difference between successive digits and will thus have a value of one. Since the area of the bar is to equal the probability of the particular value, say x_0, of the random variable, we have: area of bar $= P(x_0) =$ (width)(height) $=$ (1)(height), which leads to "height of bar" $= P(x_0)$. We denote the height of the bars by P'.

Suppose, to illustrate another possibility, that one were playing a game with dice in which he was to receive $2 for every dot appearing on the first die. The random variable of interest in this case is easily related to x_1. Its possible values are the dollar amounts one gets from the products, $2x_1$. The possible values of this random variable are 2, 4, 6, 8, 10, and 12, and the width of the bars centered on these values would be two. In order to graph this distribution properly, the bar for each particular value would be erected with a height equal to one half the probability of that value. Generally, the height of each bar in the graph must equal the probability per unit width for that value, so that area $=$ (height)(width) $=$ (probability/unit width)(width) $=$ probability.

Three graphs appear in Figure 3–2, for the random variables x_1, r, and x as mentioned earlier in this section. In all three cases, the scales on the vertical and the horizontal axis have been drawn the same so that the figures can be readily compared. Since the width of the bars for all three of these graphs is one, the heights of the bars, as well as their areas, are equal to the probabilities of the corresponding values. With the graphs before us, it is easy to give a graphical interpretation to such probability statements as $P(x_1 \leq 2) = 2/6 = 1/3$. This statement can be verified from Table 3–1 by noting that the sum of the probabilities associated with $x_1 = 1$ and $x_1 = 2$ is 2/6. Graphically, $P(x_1 \leq 2)$ is the sum of the areas of the two bars erected over the values for $x_1 = 1$ and $x_1 = 2$ in Figure 3–2(*a*). In the same manner, the probability that the random variable r will be greater than two is interpreted as the sum of the area of bars associated with $r = 3$, 4, and 5, in Figure 3–2(*b*).

Figure 3–2

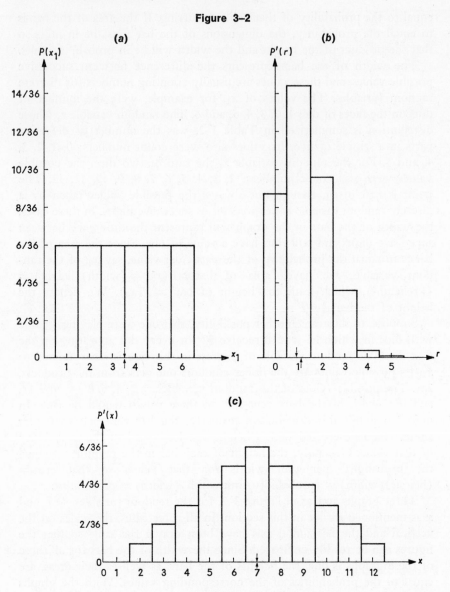

On each of the graphs, a small pointer (↑) has been set on the horizontal axis to indicate the value of the mean for that distribution. It was determined in Figure 3–1(*b*) that the mean of the sum of two dice is $\bar{x} = 7$. The student can verify that $\bar{r} = 1.25$ and that $\bar{x}_1 = 3.5$. Comparison of the locations of these three pointers on their respective graphs offers a clue to the sort of information one learns concerning a probability distribution when he learns the value of its mean. In ascending order of distance from the origin of their graphs, the means are $\bar{r}$, $\bar{x}_1$, and $\bar{x}$. This order corresponds with the fact that is obvious from visual inspection of the graphs: the center of the mass of the distribution of r is closer to the origin of its graph, while the center of mass for x_1 is somewhat farther removed from its origin, and the center of mass for x is farthest removed of the three from its origin.[8] The function of the mean of a distribution is clear. It is a measure which gives us information concerning the *central location* of the distribution, relative to zero.

It is evident that the mean does not tell the whole story concerning a probability distribution. Although the three distributions illustrated in Figure 3–2 do vary in central location, as indicated by their means, there are other differences apparent among them. One obvious difference is the "spread" of the three distributions. The total probability of 1.0 represented by the areas underlying the graphs is spread over a greater range in one case than in another. We would say that the random variable x exhibits greatest dispersion, or variation, x_1 the next greatest, and r the least. The variance and the standard deviation were noted as measures of variation, and we find that for the distributions illustrated these measures have the proper order of magnitude: $\text{var}(x) = 5.83$, $\sigma_x = 2.41$; $\text{var}(x_1) = 2.92$, $\sigma_{x_1} = 1.71$; and $\text{var}(r) = 0.94$, $\sigma_r = 0.97$. [$\text{Var}(x)$ was determined to be 5.83 in Table 3–2. The other values stated above are left as an exercise for the student.]

The mean and the variance, or standard deviation, of a probability distribution yield quite a lot of information about the distribution. The student may be aware of other ways in which the three distributions of Figure 3–2 differ, ways not touched on by the mean and the standard deviation. Two other characteristics of probability distributions will be mentioned, and methods of measuring them set down, in a later section. At this point, however, it seems advisable to introduce two other measures of central location that are sometimes used in place of the mean.

The median and the mode

The mean is a measure of the central location of a probability distribution, but it sometimes performs this function rather poorly. The reason for this is that the mean is especially sensitive to extreme values in the distribution. Suppose, for example, that the bar associated with $x = 12$ in Figure 3–2(c) were moved from its present position further to the right, to be centered over a value for x of, say, 24. This shift in the mass

---

[8] The word "mass" has a physical connotation that it may be helpful to exploit. To continue the analogy, if the bars of the graphs were considered to be made of a homogeneous metal of uniform thickness and density, so that the weights of the bars were proportional to their areas, then the means of the distributions would represent the center of gravity of the distribution along the horizontal direction.

of the distribution would cause the mean of the distribution to shift to the right of its present position, from a value of 7 to 7 1/3. But in some ways of looking at it, this small change in the location of one outlying bar of the distribution should not be looked upon as a shift in the central location of the distribution. Consequently, when such an interpretation of central location is required, more suitable measures of central location are the median and the mode. Each of these measures has its own particular interpretation, which may lead the user to prefer one over the other.

The median of a probability distribution may be defined in various ways. Probably the most suitable for our purposes is to say that the median of a random variable x [let us denote it by $med(x)$] is the value of x for which half of the area underlying the graph of the distribution is to the left and half of the area is to the right.[9] The positions of the medians on the horizontal axes of the graphs in Figure 3–2 are indicated by a small pointer ($\downarrow$). For graphs (a) and (c), the position of the median is the same as that of the mean. For graph (b), however, the

Table 3–4

r	$P(r)$	$P(r \leq r_0)$
0	0.24	0.24
1	0.40	0.64
2	0.26	0.90
3	0.09	0.99
4	0.01	1.00
5	0.00	1.00

median lies slightly to the left of the mean. This difference in relative positions is due to the fact that the graphs for x_1 and for x are symmetrical and the graph for r is not. In a symmetrical distribution, the mean and the median, as defined here, will have the same value. In the case of an asymmetrical distribution, the median may be above or below the mean, depending on the direction of the asymmetry.

The median of a random variable has been defined with reference to the graph of its probability distribution. For purposes of computation, however, this is not very satisfactory. The median is easily computed using a table of the probability distribution and interpolating where required. The process is illustrated with the random variable r depicted in Figure 3–2(b) and in Table 1–2. The table is reproduced above as

---

[9] An alternative definition, which is perhaps better formally, relates to the cumulative distribution of a random variable, which we shall discuss in the next section. The practical difficulty with this definition is that it admits the possibility of an infinite number of values for the median, as we shall see.

Table 3–4, with the values of $P(r)$ rounded to the nearest one hundredth. The entry on each row of the third column indicates the probability that the random variable r will take a value less than or equal to r_0, where r_0 is the value of r corresponding to that row. We need the value for r which corresponds to the position on Figure 3–2(b) that bisects the area of that graph. This value will be med(r).

An examination of the entries in the third column of Table 3–4, as well as examination of Figure 3–2(b), indicates that this value must fall somewhere within the interval corresponding to $r = 1$, that is $0.5 <$ med(r) < 1.5. For purposes of locating the median, we treat r as if it were a continuous random variable, and interpolate to a point within this interval. In traversing the interval, the value of $P(r \leq r_0)$ increases by 0.40 from 0.24 to 0.64. We find the fraction of the interval at which the value would have increased to 0.50, assuming a uniform rate of increase across the interval, to be $(0.50 - 0.24)/0.40 = 0.26/0.40 = 0.65$. Thus, the median of r is located above the lower boundary of the interval a distance equal to $65/100$ of the interval. Since the lower boundary is 0.50 and the width of the interval is in this case 1, the median is: med(r) $= 0.50 + (0.65)(1) = 1.15$.

The median as we have defined it measures the central location of a probability distribution by bisecting the area of the graph of the distribution. It is a measure of central location less sensitive than the mean to extreme values. It was noted earlier that through a hypothetical shift of the bar centered over $x = 12$ in Figure 3–2(c), the value of the mean could be made to change. Suppose, once again, that this bar were relocated at $x = 24$. The effect on med(x) would be nil; its value would still be seven. This is true because it is only the location of the interval for x_0 in which $P(x \leq x_0) = 0.50$—and the probability associated with that interval, relative to the sum of the probabilities on the intervals preceding it—that determines the value of med(x).

Another measure of central location is the mode. It is defined simply as the value which the random variable of concern is most likely to take. Graphically, the mode is located by finding the bar with the largest area (or height, if the bars have uniform widths). The mode of the random variable r is seen from Figure 3–2(b) to be, mod(r) $= 1$. Using a table of the probability distribution, one locates the mode simply by locating the row with the largest probability. Once again, mod(r) $= 1$ because examination of Table 3–4 indicates that $P(r = 1) = 0.40$, which is the largest value of $P(r)$. As a measure of central location, the mode identifies the center of the distribution with the most probable value of the random variable. This usually works well, but there are exceptions. The mode will be insensitive to extreme values, for example, unless the mode happens to be an extreme value. Also, the mode often may not exist. The random variable x_1 has no mode, as is evident from noting its graph or its table. Sometimes a probability distribution will have two or more "peaks" in its graph. Such distributions are sometimes referred to as bimodal, trimodal, etc.

The three measures of central location discussed, commonly called averages, are all useful. The mode indicates the value that should be expected most frequently as the outcome of an experiment. The median may be interpreted (roughly, and for some distributions, very roughly) as the value such that the probability is about 0.5 the experiment will yield an outcome with a smaller or equal value. As indicated earlier (footnote 5), the mean is the value such that the expected deviation of the outcome of the experiment from the mean is zero. Of the three, the mean is much more important in terms of frequency of application in traditional statistical methods. This will become clear as we proceed through subsequent discussion.

Problem Set 3–3

1. It was mentioned in the text that the graphs of Figure 3–2 are all scaled so as to have the same width on the vertical bars.

   a) Find the area, in square inches, of each of the bars of Figure 3–2(*a*) and Figure 3–2(*b*) and sum these areas to find the total area in each graph.

   b) In terms of probability, what do the (equal) areas in each of these graphs represent?

   c) Using the relevant values from your work above, express the probability that $x_1 = 4$ and the probability that $r = 1$, in each case as the ratio of two areas.

2. Construct a graph of the probability distributions for the following random variables:

   a) g, the greater value appearing on two dice [see problem 1(*a*) of Problem Set 3–2].

   b) t, the number of tails appearing in the toss of three coins.

   c) w, the winnings in the game described in problem 6 of Problem Set 3–2.

3. Recalling that x_1 is the number of dots appearing on one tossed die and that $d = 2x_1$, and $f = 0.5x_1$ (see problems 9 and 10 of Problem Set 3–2), construct the graph of the probability distribution of each of these three random variables. Scale the horizontal axis in the graph of x_1 so that the width of each bar is one half inch. Then be sure to scale the horizontal axes in the graphs of d and f—and the vertical axes of $P'(d)$ and $P'(f)$—so as to be consistent with the scales of x_1 and $P'(x_1)$.

4. In the graphs constructed for problem 3, shade in the areas corresponding to the following probabilities:

   a) $P(2 < x_1 \leq 4)$.

   b) $P(4 < d \leq 8)$.

   c) $P(1 < f \leq 2)$.

   What relationship exists among these areas? Explain the existence of this relationship in commonsense terms.

5. On the graphs which you constructed in problem 2, shade in the areas corresponding to the following probabilities:
   a) $P(g < 3)$.
   b) $P(t \geq 2)$.
   c) $P(g = 4)$.
   d) $P(w < 0)$.
   e) $P(w = 0.50)$.

6. Determine the values of the median and the mode for the following random variables:
   a) g, the greater value on two dice (see problem 8, Problem Set 3–1).
   b) t, the number of tails in the toss of three coins (see problem 2, Problem Set 3–1).
   c) r, the number of defective parts in a sample of four (see problem 3, Problem Set 3–2).
   d) x_w, the number of red marbles drawn with replacement (see problem 4, Problem Set 3–2).

7. In previous problems, you have found the values of the means for the random variables listed in problem 6, above. Comparing for each random variable the mean value to the values of the median and mode found in problem 6, comment on the advantages or disadvantages of each value as a measure of central tendency.

Cumulative probability distributions

We had occasion, in the calculation of med(r), to compute $P(r \leq r_0)$ for successive values of r_0 (see Table 3–4). These probabilities are referred to as *cumulative* probabilities because they sum up, or cumulate, the probabilities for all values of r less than or equal to r_0. For a discrete random variable x, the cumulative probability $P(x \leq x_0)$ has a minimum value of zero, for values of x_0 smaller than the minimum value of x. It proceeds stepwise through successively higher values as x_0 is increased, until it reaches a maximum value of 1.0 when x_0 has become as large as the maximum value of x.[10] The cumulative probability distribution for the random variables x_1, r, and x of Figure 3–2 are presented graphically in Figure 3–3.

Perhaps the two most important practical applications of cumulative probability distributions are in Monte Carlo procedures and in the construction of probability tables. Monte Carlo procedures, which will be introduced in a later chapter, consist of methods which arrive at a solution to a problem involving random variables by simulation of a series of experiments with those random variables. As regards the second area of application, many probability tables are constructed so as to give cumulated, rather than single, probabilities. Table A which was used in

---

[10] One can cumulate the probabilities in the other direction as well. In that case, the values would be $P(x \geq x_0)$ and they would range from 1.0 to zero as x_0 increased.

Figure 3–3

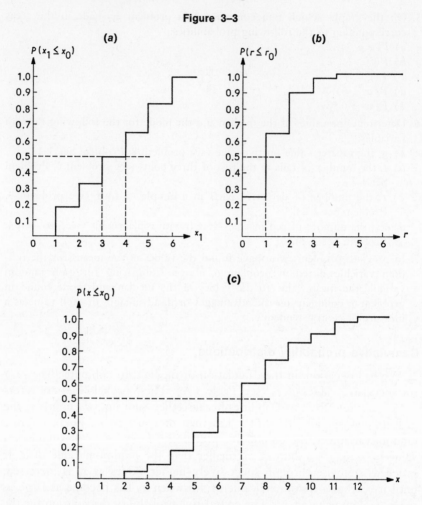

conjunction with Chapter 2 is an example. More examples will appear later.

It was mentioned earlier that an alternative definition of the median was possible. This definition relates to the cumulative distribution, and so it is given here. In this definition, the median of a random variable x is the value(s) of x underlying the intersection of the graph of the cumulative distribution with a straight line projected horizontally from the vertical axis at the value $P(x \leq x_0) = 0.50$. This definition becomes clear upon inspection of Figure 3–3. On each graph, a broken line has been projected horizontally from the vertical axis at a value 0.50, until this line intersects the cumulative distribution. Vertical lines projected downward from the point(s) of intersection meet the horizontal axis at the value(s) of the median. For the random variables r and x, there is a unique value for the median: $\text{med}(r) = 1$, and $\text{med}(x) = 7$. Notice, however, that there are an infinite number of values for the median of x_1. $\text{Med}(x_1)$ is any value from three to, but not including four: $3 \le \text{med}(x_1) < 4$.

Problem Set 3–4

1. In problem 6 of Problem Set 3–3, you were asked to find the median values of g, t, r, and x_w. Now, plot graphs of the cumulative probability distribution of each and find the median value by the graphical definition. What differences appear in the values for the medians found by the two different methods?

Skewness and kurtosis

For a random variable x, the mean of x measures its distribution's central location. The dispersion of the distribution is measured by $\text{var}(x)$, or alternatively, by σ. These two measures are the most important characteristics of a probability distribution for purposes of practical application. There are two other characteristics which are found useful, however. These are the *skewness* of the distribution and its *kurtosis*. Of the two, skewness is much more frequently of application than kurtosis. Because of this, a measure of skewness will be discussed in some detail while a measure of kurtosis will be mentioned only briefly for completeness.

In the earlier discussion of the median of a distribution, it was noted that two of the distributions of Figure 3–2 were symmetrical but one was not. If a distribution is not symmetrical, it is said to be *skewed*. Departures from symmetry can occur in either of two directions. Consequently, a distribution may exhibit negative skewness or positive skewness. A distribution in which the more extreme values are below the mean is *negatively skewed*. Since this corresponds graphically to a longer "tail" of the distribution appearing on the left, the phrase "skewed to the left" also describes this condition. A distribution is *positively skewed*, or skewed to the right, if the more extreme values are above the mean. The distribution of r, shown in Figure 3–2 (b), is positively skewed.

A measure of skewness for a random variable x relies on $E[(x - \bar{x})^3] = \Sigma(x - \bar{x})^3 P(x)$.[11] The cubes of the deviations, $x - \bar{x}$, will preserve the sign

---

[11] Note the parallel to the variance of x, which is $E[(x - \bar{x})^2] = \Sigma(x - \bar{x})^2 P(x)$. $E[(x - \bar{x})^2]$ is one of a group of measures of a probability distribution called the *central moments* of the distribution, in this case the second moment. $E[(x - \bar{x})^3]$ is the third central moment, and generally $E[(x - \bar{x})^n]$ is the nth central moment. The modifying term "central" is included because the central moments are measured relative to $\bar{x}$, a measure of central location for the distribution. It will be noted later that a measure of kurtosis is developed in terms of the fourth central moment, $E[(x - \bar{x})^4]$.

of the deviations, and larger deviations will receive greater emphasis than smaller deviations. If the distribution is skewed to the left, for example, the larger negative deviations will receive more emphasis and $\Sigma(x - \bar{x})^3 P(x)$ will be negative. If the distribution is skewed to the right, the sum will be positive. If the distribution is symmetrical, the sum will be zero. Consequently, the sign of $E[(x - \bar{x})^3]$ indicates the direction of the skewness in the distribution.

$E[(x - \bar{x})^3]$ by itself does not provide a satisfactory measure of the magnitude of skewness, however. This is due in part to the fact that, just as the variance of x is in terms of squared units of x, $E[(x - \bar{x})^3]$ is in terms of cubed units of x. Another defect is that $E[(x - \bar{x})^3]$ does not indicate the degree of skewness relative to the dispersion of the distribution. The procedure for removing these defects is to divide $E[(x - \bar{x})^3]$ by the cube of the standard deviation of x. Since the standard deviation is a measure of the dispersion of the distribution, in units of x, this process of division "cancels out" the units in which x is measured and provides a ratio of skewness relative to dispersion. Letting $\text{sk}(x)$ denote the coefficient of skewness for the random variable x, the result is:

$$\text{sk}(x) = \frac{E[(x - \bar{x})^3]}{\sigma^3} = \frac{\Sigma(x - \bar{x})^3 P(x)}{\sigma^3}.$$

The expression above represents a definition of the coefficient of skewness. An easier expression to use for computing it is:

$$\text{sk}(x) = (\Sigma x^3 P(x) - 3\bar{x}\Sigma x^2 P(x) + 2(\bar{x})^3)/\sigma^3.$$

Calculation of the coefficient of skewness is illustrated in Table 3–5,[12] where the value of $\text{sk}(r)$ is obtained. The results are approximate, since the values of $P(r)$ have been rounded to nearest hundredths. Notice that the entries for the third column are the products of the corresponding entries in the first two columns. The entries of the fourth and fifth columns are obtained by successively multiplying the entries of the third column by the entries of the first column. The sums of the last three columns provide the values of $\Sigma r P(r)$, $\Sigma r^2 P(r)$, and $\Sigma r^3 P(r)$ to be used in the formulas for computing $\bar{r}$, $\text{var}(r)$, and $\text{sk}(r)$.

A measure of kurtosis is designed to measure the relative height, or "peakedness" of a probability distribution. It is evident from inspection of the graphs in Figure 3–2 that the distribution for x_1 is "flatter" than either of the other two distributions, and the distribution for r appears to be most "peaked." The absence or presence of this characteristic is signaled by $E[(x - \bar{x})^4] = \Sigma(x - \bar{x})^4 P(x)$. As the relative height of a distribution increases, the magnitude of $E[(x - \bar{x})^4]$ increases relative to

---

[12] The probability distribution of Table 3–5 reproduces that of Table 1–2, where r was the number of defective parts in a sample of $n = 5$, given a probability of $p = 0.25$ that a given part will be defective. The values of $p(r)$ have been rounded to hundredths.

Table 3–5

r	$P(r)$	$rP(r)$	$r^2P(r)$	$r^3P(r)$
0	0.24	0.00	0.00	0.00
1	.40	.40	0.40	0.40
2	.26	.52	1.04	2.08
3	.09	.27	0.81	2.43
4	.01	.04	0.16	0.64
5	.00	.00	0.00	0.00
	1.00	1.23	2.41	5.55

$$\bar{r} = \Sigma rP(r) = 1.23$$
$$\mathrm{var}(r) = \Sigma r^2P(r) - (\bar{r})^2 = 2.41 - (1.23)^2 \simeq 0.8971$$
$$\sigma = +\sqrt{\mathrm{var}(r)} = +\sqrt{0.8971} \simeq 0.9471$$
$$\mathrm{sk}(r) = \frac{\Sigma r^3P(r) - 3\bar{r}\Sigma r^2P(r) + 2(\bar{r})^3}{\sigma^3}$$
$$= \frac{5.55 - 3(1.23)(2.41) + 2(1.23)^3}{(0.9471)^3}$$
$$= +0.4459$$

the value of the standard deviation. Consequently, the measure of kurtosis, denoted $\mathrm{kur}(x)$, for a random variable x parallels in form the measure of skewness: $\mathrm{kur}(x) = \dfrac{E(x - \bar{x})^4}{\sigma^4}$. An equivalent computational formula is:

$$\mathrm{kur}(x) = \frac{\Sigma x^4P(x) - 4(\bar{x})\Sigma x^3P(x) + 6(\bar{x})^2\Sigma x^2P(x) - 3(\bar{x})^4}{\sigma^4}.$$

Computation of the coefficient of kurtosis will not be illustrated at this point, but it can be seen from the second expression above that it can be calculated by an extension of the procedure illustrated in Table 3–4. There is required in addition to the values appearing in that table a sixth column whose entries would be $r^4P(r)$.

The main task of this chapter was to familiarize the student with the concepts of random variable and probability distribution. It was noted that probability distributions come in families and that successful application of statistical methods requires one to be able to pick, at least approximately, the right member of the right family. Questions of identifying the family are reserved for later consideration, but some of the answer lies in being able to describe the relevant characteristics of the distribution. A proper description of the distribution is also required to know which member of the family is appropriate. The most important descriptive measures of a distribution are its mean and variance, or standard deviation. Two other measures that are often useful are the coefficients of skewness and of kurtosis. These measures have been developed at this point so that they will be available when they are required in an application. Our next point of concern, to be aired in the next chapter, is to gain some familiarity with two families of probability distributions that have played a peculiarly important role in traditional statistical method.

Problem Set 3–5

1. For the following random variables, defined in earlier problems and in the text, calculate the coefficient of skewness and write a sentence explaining what the value arrived at tells you concerning the relevant probability distribution:

   a) g [see problem 1(a), Problem Set 3–2].
   b) d (see text).
   c) x_1 [see text and Figure 3–1(a)].
   d) r (see problem 3, Problem Set 3–2).

2. Explain why $sk(x_1)$ equals $sk(d)$, as calculated in problem 1 above.

3. Which random variable, g or r, has the greater *degree* of skewness? What aspect of the probability distributions of g and r is reflected in the signs of $sk(g)$ and $sk(r)$?

Appendix A

Some rules for summation:
Suppose we have a set of values for some variable, X.

$$X: \quad 10, 25, 15, 63$$

We can *index* X by a subscript, *i:*

i	X_i
1	$X_1 = 10$
2	$X_2 = 25$
3	$X_3 = 15$
4	$X_4 = 63$

This allows us to express the sum of the values of X very compactly as:

$$\sum_{i=1}^{4} X_i = X_1 + X_2 + X_3 + X_4$$

$$= 10 + 25 + 15 + 63 = 113$$

If we are sure of the values taken by the index, we can specify the sum as:

$$\sum_i X_i \text{ or just } \Sigma X .$$

Some rules for summation:
   S–1: For a constant, a,

$$\Sigma aX = a\Sigma X ,$$

for example, if $a = 2$, and the values of X are as below (here, $\Sigma X = 113$ and $\Sigma 2X = 226$ and $\Sigma 2X = 2\Sigma X$ as rule S–1 states):

X	$aX = 2X$
10	20
25	50
15	30
63	126
113	226

S–2: For a constant, a,

$$\Sigma(X + a) = \Sigma X + na,$$

where n is the number of terms summed over. For example, with the same values as above for a and X (here $\Sigma X = 113$, and $n(2) = 4(2) = 8$, and $\Sigma(X + 2) = \Sigma X + 8$, as rule S–2 states):

X	$X + a = X + 2$
10	12
25	27
15	17
63	65
$\Sigma X = 113$	121

S–3: If X and Y are two variables with the same number of values,

$$\Sigma(X + Y) = \Sigma X + \Sigma Y.$$

For example (here $\Sigma(X + Y) = 145 = \Sigma X + \Sigma Y$, as rule S–3 states):

X	Y	$X + Y$
10	4	14
25	7	32
15	9	24
63	12	75
113	32	145

S–4: At times we may wish to specify an array or table of values, X, for which we wish the sum. We can describe the array by two indexes, i and j. For example, suppose the array is as below, and we let the value of i indicate the row and j the column:

i \ j	1	2	3
1	10	15	12
2	4	18	20
3	51	16	7
4	8	24	9

There are four rows and three columns. We can specify any value in the array as X_{ij}, where the value of i indicates the row in which it appears and j the column. Thus $X_{11} = 10$, $X_{23} = 20$, $X_{42} = 24$. Now, the sum of the values in the array can be obtained in more than one way. One pos-

sibility is to sum the values in each row and then add up those sums. We would have:

Row	Sum	"Σ Notation"
1	$10 + 15 + 12 = 37$	$\sum_{j} X_{1j}$
2	$4 + 18 + 20 = 42$	$\sum_{j} X_{2j}$
3	$51 + 16 + 7 = 74$	$\sum_{j} X_{3j}$
4	$8 + 24 + 9 = 41$	$\sum_{j} X_{4j}$

Adding these sums, we get a total of 194. This last summation occurs over the range of i and can thus be written

$$\sum_{i} \left(\sum_{j} X_{ij} \right) = \sum_{i} \sum_{j} X_{ij} .$$

We could just as well have found the sum of the array by summing columns first and then adding these sums. In this case, the operation is described as:

$$\sum_{j} \sum_{i} X_{ij} .$$

Use of rules for summation, an illustration:

In the text, it is stated that the value of var(x) may be calculated as

$$\text{var}(x) = \Sigma(x - \bar{x})^2 \cdot P(x)$$

or as

$$\text{var}(x) = \Sigma x^2 \cdot P(x) - (\bar{x})^2 .$$

Let us show the equivalence of these two expressions for the variance of x:

$$\Sigma(x - \bar{x})^2 P(x) = \Sigma(x^2 - 2\bar{x}x + \bar{x}^2) P(x)$$
$$= \Sigma[x^2 \cdot P(x) - 2\bar{x}x \cdot P(x) + \bar{x}^2 P(x)]$$

which, by S–3,

$$= \Sigma x^2 \cdot P(x) - \Sigma 2\bar{x}x \cdot P(x) + \Sigma \bar{x}^2 P(x) .$$

Noting that $2\bar{x}$ in the second term and $\bar{x}^2$ in the third term are constants, we use Rule S–1 to get:

$$= \Sigma x^2 \cdot P(x) - 2\bar{x}\Sigma x \cdot P(x) + \bar{x}^2 \Sigma P(x) .$$

But, in the second term, $\Sigma x \cdot P(x) = \bar{x}$, by definition, and, in the third term, $\Sigma P(x) = 1$, by the probability axiom, P–2: $P(S) = 1$. Thus, we have

$$= \Sigma x^2 \cdot P(x) - 2\bar{x} \cdot \bar{x} + \bar{x}^2 \cdot 1$$
$$= \Sigma x^2 \cdot P(x) - (\bar{x})^2 ,$$

which was to be shown.

Appendix B

Some rules for expected values.

There are certain relationships between expected values that it is useful to know. We consider the more important ones here.

For a random variable, x, we have $E(x) = \Sigma(x) \cdot P(x)$. Suppose all possible values of x are multiplied by some constant, a. Then,

$$E(ax) = \Sigma(ax) \cdot P(x) = \Sigma a(x \cdot P(x))$$
$$= a\Sigma x \cdot P(x)$$
$$= aE(x) .$$

That is,

$$E\text{–1}: \ E(ax) = aE(x) .$$

In the same manner, it is easy to show that:

$$E[(ax)^2] = a^2 E(x^2) .$$

We anticipate a rule derived later in the appendix: *E*–6,

$$\text{var}(Z) = E(Z^2) - [E(Z)]^2 .$$

Thus,

$$\text{var}(ax) = E[(ax)^2] - [E(ax)]^2 .$$

But, noting rule E–1 and the result directly above,

$$\text{var}(ax) = a^2 E(x^2) - [aE(x)]^2$$
$$= a^2 E(x^2) - a^2 [E(x)]^2$$
$$= a^2 \{E(x^2) - [E(x)]^2\} .$$

The term in braces is var (x), so we arrive at a second rule.

$$E\text{–2}: \ \text{var}(ax) = a^2 \cdot \text{var}(x) .$$

The standard deviation of a random variable is the square root of its variance. This leads to, for a random variable x and some constant a,

$$\sigma_{ax} = \sqrt{\text{var}(ax)} = \sqrt{a^2 \, \text{var}(x)}$$
$$= a\sqrt{\text{var}(x)} = a\sigma_x .$$

This leads to a third rule:

$$E\text{–3}: \ \sigma_{ax} = a\sigma_x .$$

At times we are concerned with more than one random variable and the result of some operation by which these variables are combined. Restricting our attention to two random variables, x and y, for example, we might wish to know the characteristics of the distribution of the sums, $x + y$, where values of x and y are independently selected from their respective distributions. We shall consider here the mean and variance of the distribution that would be generated in this manner.

It should be apparent that if x and y are random variables, then so is the sum $x + y$. The probability of any particular pair of values, x_i and y_j, appearing together to form a sum is $P(x_i)P(y_j)$, since the values are independent. The expected value of $x + y$ is just the sum of the products, $(x_i + x_j)P(x_i)P(y_j)$. If there are m values of x and n values of y, the expected value of $x + y$ is, then:

$$E(x + y) = \sum_{i=1}^{m} \sum_{j=1}^{n} [(x_i + y_i)P(x_i)P(y_i)] .$$

For any given value of i, say, $i = 2$,

$$\sum_{j=1}^{n} [(x_2 + y_i)P(x_2)P(y_i)]$$

$$= \sum_{j=1}^{n} [x_2 P(x_2)P(y_i) + y_i P(x_2)P(y_i)] ,$$

which, by Rule S–3,

$$= \sum_{j=1}^{n} x_2 P(x_2)P(y_i) + \sum_{j=1}^{n} y_i P(x_2)P(y_i) ,$$

which, noting that x_2 and $P(x_2)$ are constant in this sum, yields by Rule S–1,

$$= x_2 P(x_2) \sum_{j=1}^{n} P(y_i) + P(x_2) \sum_{j=1}^{n} y_i P(y_i)$$

$$= x_2 P(x_2) + P(x_2)E(y) .$$

Returning, now, to the general index, i, we have:

$$E(x + y) = \sum_{i=1}^{m} [x_i P(x_i) + P(x_i)E(y)]$$

$$= \sum_{i=1}^{m} x_i P(x_i) + \sum_{i=1}^{m} P(x_i)E(y)$$

$$= E(x) + E(y) \sum_{i=1}^{m} P(x_i)$$

$$= E(x) + E(y) .$$

Thus, for x and y independent,

$$E\text{-4}: \quad E(x + y) = E(x) + E(y) .$$

Actually, this result holds even if the values of x and y are not independently selected.

Before proceeding to find the value for var $(x + y)$, we need the value of $E(xy)$. By manipulations parallel to those above,

$$E(xy) = \sum_i \sum_j (x_i y_i) P(x_i) P(y_i)$$

$$= \sum_i x_i P(x_i) \sum_j y_j P(y_j)$$

$$= E(x) E(y) .$$

That is,

$$E\text{-5}: \quad E(xy) = E(x)E(y), \text{ for } x \text{ and } y \text{ independent} .$$

Turning to the variance, now, we note that, for any random variable, say $\mathcal{Z}$,

$$\text{var}(\mathcal{Z}) = E[(\mathcal{Z} - E(\mathcal{Z}))^2]$$
$$= E[\mathcal{Z}^2 - 2\mathcal{Z}E(\mathcal{Z}) + (E(\mathcal{Z}))^2] ,$$
which, by $E\text{-4}$,
$$= E(\mathcal{Z}^2) - 2E[\mathcal{Z}E(\mathcal{Z})] + E[(E(\mathcal{Z}))^2] .$$

Noting that $E(\mathcal{Z})$ is a constant term appearing in each of the terms $E[\mathcal{Z}E(\mathcal{Z})]$ and $E[(E(\mathcal{Z}))^2]$, we have, by $E\text{-1}$,

$$\text{var}(\mathcal{Z}) = E(\mathcal{Z}^2) - 2E(\mathcal{Z})E(\mathcal{Z}) + [E(\mathcal{Z})]^2$$
$$= E(\mathcal{Z}^2) - [E(\mathcal{Z})]^2$$

Thus, the rule,

$$E\text{-6}: \quad \text{var}(\mathcal{Z}) = E(\mathcal{Z}^2) - [E(\mathcal{Z})]^2 .$$

Now, for the sum $x + y$,

$$\text{var}(x + y) = E[(x + y)^2] - [E(x + y)]^2 \text{ by } E\text{-6} .$$

Expanding the squared terms and using Rules $E\text{-1}$ and $E\text{-4}$ leads to,

$$\text{var}(x + y) = E(x^2) + 2E(xy) + E(y^2) - (E(x))^2 - 2E(x)E(y) - (E(y))^2$$

which, rearranging,

$$= E(x^2) - (E(x))^2 + E(y^2) - (E(y))^2 + 2E(xy) - 2E(x)E(y) .$$

Note that $2E(xy) - 2E(x)E(y) = 0$ by $E\text{-5}$. Then

$$\text{var}(x + y) = [E(x^2) - (E(x))^2] + [E(y^2) - (E(y))^2]$$
$$= \text{var}(x) + \text{var}(y) \text{ by } E\text{-6} .$$

That is:

$$E\text{-7}: \quad \text{var}(x + y) = \text{var}(x) + \text{var}(y) \text{ for } x \text{ and } y \text{ independent} .$$

Use of rules for expected values, an illustration:

For a binomial distribution with parameter values n and p, what is the mean and variance of the distribution?

Consider, first, one trial of the experiment (to make the illustration concrete, let the experiment be drawing a part from a production process in which the probability is p that the part will be defective). Let us define a random variable, x, which is assigned a value of zero if the part is not defective and a value of one if the part is defective. Then $P(x = 1) = p$ and $P(x = 0) = 1 - p$. We can set down the distribution of x and find $\bar{x} = E(x)$ and $\text{var}(x)$:

x	$P(x)$	$x \cdot P(x)$	$x^2 \cdot P(x)$
0	$1 - p$	0	0
1	p	p	p
		p	p

The sum of column three indicates that:

$$E(x) = \bar{x} = p .$$

The sum of column four indicates that:

$$E(x^2) = p .$$

By Rule E–6,

$$\begin{aligned}
\text{var}(x) &= E(x^2) - [E(x)]^2 \\
&= p - p^2 \\
&= p(1 - p) .
\end{aligned}$$

The work above shows that on one draw, the random variable x has a mean, $\bar{x} = p$, and variance, $\text{var}(x) = p(1 - p)$. Now suppose that n draws are made. The results of the n draws can be written as a series of 0's and 1's, corresponding to the nonappearance and appearance, respectively, of a defective part in each of the n draws. If we were to sum the values in this sequence of 0's and 1's, the resulting sum would just be the number of defective parts, which we have denoted by r. That is:

$$r = \Sigma x .$$

The result of each draw is assumed independent of the results of other draws, so we can use the rules for expectations developed earlier. Noting, once again, that $r = \Sigma x$, we have:

$$\begin{aligned}
E(r) &= E(\Sigma x) \\
&= \Sigma E(x) \text{ by Rule } E\text{–4} , \\
&= nE(x), \text{ since } E(x) \text{ is summed over } n \text{ values} , \\
&= np, \text{ since } E(x) = p .
\end{aligned}$$

Also,

$$\begin{aligned}
\text{var}(r) &= \text{var}(\Sigma x) \\
&= \Sigma \text{var}(x) \text{ by Rule } E\text{-}7 , \\
&= n \cdot \text{var}(x) \\
&= np(1 - p) .
\end{aligned}$$

Problem Set 3–6

1. Show that the values for $\bar{r}$ and $\text{var}(r)$ calculated in Table 3–5 demonstrate the general relationships between n and p on the one hand and $\bar{r}$ and $\text{var}(r)$ on the other, as developed at the end of Appendix B.

2. In problem 9 of Problem Set 3–2, you found the values of $\bar{d}$, $\text{var}(d)$, and σ_d. In the text, it was shown that $\bar{x}_1 = 3.5$, $\text{var}(x_1) = 2.92$, and $\sigma_{x_1} = 1.71$, Noting, also, that $d = 2x_1$, show how these results support the rules for expected values, E-1, E-2, and E-3 of Appendix B.

3. In problem 10 of Problem Set 3–2, you were to find the values of f, and $\text{var}(f)$, and σ_f. Noting the facts stated in problem 2 above, and noting also that $f = 0.5x_1$, show how these results support rules E-1, E-2, and E-3 of Appendix B.

4. Suppose that there are two populations designated as A and B. We select values of X_a from A and X_b from B (one pair at a time, randomly), and calculate the value $Y = X_a + X_b$.
   a) If $\text{var}(X_a) = 10$ and $\text{var}(X_b) = 30$, what is the value of $\text{var}(Y)$?
   b) If we calculate the mean of each pair, X_a and X_b, what is the variance of these means?

Appendix C

Two computer programs are listed in this appendix. The first appears as Figure 3–C–1 here, and is reproduced from Figure 1 of the Appendix to the book, *Statistical Analysis and the Computer*, where it is described in detail. It is written in FORTRAN language and can be used, with some possible minor modifications to allow for variation in computer facilities, as it appears here.

Each line of the program must be punched on a separate 80-punch computer card, with the first column of the card corresponding to the relative location of the "C's" which appear to the left of the first two statements. The statements themselves all begin in the seventh column of the card. The several numbers that appear to be left of various statements are punched in the fifth column of the card.

The data of the probability distribution are viewed as occurring in pairs: X, $P(X)$. When viewed in this way, each line of a probability distribution can be punched on a separate data card. The first four columns of the card are for the value of X for that row, and the value of $P(X)$ is punched in the next four columns. For example, the first row

Figure 3–C-1

```
C          A PROGRAM TO CALCULATE THE MEAN, VARIANCE, STANDARD DEVIATION,
C          AND COEFFICIENT OF SKEWNESS FOR A DISCRETE PROBABILITY DISTRIBUTION
     1 FORMAT (F4.0, F4.4)
     7 SUMX = 0.0
       SUMX2 = 0.0
       SUMX3 = 0.0
     5 READ 1, X, PX
       IF (PX − 0.9999) 2, 3, 2
     2 SUMX = SUMX + X*PX
       SUMX2 = SUMX2 + (X**2)*PX
       SUMX3 = SUMX3 + (X**3)*PX
       GO TO 5
     3 XMEAN = SUMX
       VARX = SUMX2 − XMEAN**2
       STDEVX = SQRTF(VARX)
       SK1 = SUMX3
       SK2 = (XMEAN*SUMX2)
       SK3 = XMEAN**3
       SKX = (SK1 − 3.0*SK2 + 2.0*SK3)/STDEVX**3
       PRINT 6, XMEAN, VARX, STDEVX, SKX
     6 FORMAT (3F11.4, F9.4)
       PAUSE
       GO TO 7
       END
```

of the probability distribution of Table 3–5 has $r = X = 0$ and $P(r) = P(X) = 0.24$. The data card for this row will be punched 00002400 in the first eight columns. The second data card will be punched 00014000 in the first eight columns, to record the values of the second row: $r = X = 1$, $P(r) = P(X) = 0.40$. The set of data cards will be placed at the end of the set of program cards, for processing by the computer. Following the cards containing the data for the probability distribution, there must be a "signal" card punched with 00009999 in the first eight columns. This card is not processed, but serves merely to signal the computer that it has received all data in the preceding cards.

Upon processing the data according to the instructions of the program, the computer will print out, in the following order, the values of the mean, variance, standard deviation, and coefficient of skewness for the random variable. These values will appear on one line of the printer, with blank spaces separating them.

The second program, listed in Figure 3–C–2, is written in BASIC language for use on a time-sharing computer facility. The programming technique used here is somewhat more sophisticated than that of the first program, but is readily accessible to the student who has studied the appendix on the computer.[1] Some minor modifications may be required in the program to accommodate variations in computer facilities.

In the time-sharing mode, the program may be entered to computer storage by typing on the terminal keyboard, by use of a punched paper

---

[1] It should be noted that all arithmetic operations are designated by the same symbols in BASIC as they are in FORTRAN, with the exception of exponentiation. In FORTRAN, for example, $X**2$ designates the square of X, X^2, whereas in BASIC the designation is $X \uparrow 2$.

Figure 3–C-2

```
100  REMARKS: A PROGRAM TO ANALYZE A DISCRETE PROBABILITY DISTRIBUTION
110  READ N
120  LET T1 = 0
130  LET T2 = 0
140  LET T3 = 0
150  LET T4 = 0
160  FOR I = 1 TO N
170  READ X(I), P(I)
180  LET X1 = X(I)*P(I)
190  LET X2 = X(I)*X1
200  LET X3 = X(I)*X2
210  LET X4 = X(I)*X3
220  LET T1 = T1 + X1
230  LET T2 = T2 + X2
240  LET T3 = T3 + X3
250  LET T4 = T4 + X4
260  PRINT X(I); P(I);X1;X2;X3;X4
270  NEXT I
280  PRINT
290  PRINT "                    ";T1;T2;T3;T4
300  PRINT
310  PRINT
320  LET V = T2 − T1 ↑ 2
330  LET S = SQR(V)
340  LET W = (T3 − 3*T1*T2 + 2*T1 ↑ 3)/S ↑ 3
350  LET K = (T4 − 4*T1*T3 + 6*T1 ↑ 2*T2 − 3*T1 ↑ 4)/S ↑ 4
360  PRINT "MEAN = "T1; "S = "S; "VAR = "V; "SK = "W; "KUR = "K
370  DATA 9
380  DATA 2,.0004,3,.0031,4,.0162,5,.0584,6,.1460,7,.2530,8,.2816
390  DATA 9,.1877,10,.0563
400  END
```

tape, or by other possible alternatives. Note that the data to be processed are entered as a part of the program—see lines 370–390. The first DATA line contains the number of $X, P(X)$ pairs in the probability distribution. The remaining DATA lines contain the values of X and $P(X)$, in that order, for the nine pairs included in this particular probability distribution. Note that successive values are separated by commas.

If a set of data with a larger number, say 15, of $X, P(X)$ pairs must be analyzed, this requires only slight modification of the program format. The obvious changes are to replace the value of 9 in statement 370 with the value 15. Then as many DATA lines must be written as are required to contain the 15 $X, P(X)$ pairs. These may be numbered 380, 390, 400, and so forth. If the statement number 400 is used for a DATA line, then it is necessary to enter a new END statement with a statement number larger than the number of the last DATA line. Finally, because the program is written to operate on the $X, P(X)$ pairs as subscripted variables, and because there will be more than 10 values in each variable, enter a new statement: 105 DIM $X(15), P(15)$.

The program is written to give output as it appears in Figure 3–C-3. First, a table is printed, giving the values of X, $P(X)$, $XP(X)$, $X^2P(X)$, $X^3P(X)$, and $X^4P(X)$. Then a separate line indicates the sums, $\Sigma XP(X)$, $\Sigma X^2P(X)$, $\Sigma X^3P(X)$, and $\Sigma X^4P(X)$, under the appropriate columns. Finally, the values for various characteristics of the distribution are given in the last two lines of output. Notice, in particular, the value of the

Figure 3–C-3

2	.0004	.0008	.0016	.0032	.0064
3	.0031	.0093	.0279	.0837	.2511
4	.0162	.0648	.2592	1.0368	4.1472
5	.0584	.292	1.46	7.3	36.5
6	.146	.876	5.256	31.536	189.216
7	.253	1.771	12.397	86.779	607.453
8	.2816	2.2528	18.0224	144.179	1153.43
9	.1877	1.6893	15.2037	136.833	1231.5
10	.0563	.563	5.63	56.3	563.
	7.519	58.2578	464.051	3785.51	

MEAN = 7.519 S = 1.31242 VAR = 1.72244 SK = 4.81132 E-2
KUR = .578567

coefficient of skewness, SK = 4.81132 E–2. The E–2 designation indicates that the value preceding it must be multiplied by $10^{-2} = .01$. Therefore, the value of SK is $(4.81132)(10^{-2}) = (4.81132)(.01) = .0481132$.

The binomial distribution and the normal distribution

Introduction

The point was made in the preceding chapter that a large part of problem solving in statistical methods involves identification of the family of distributions that is relevant to the problem, if indeed there is one. The ability to make such identifications grows with experience, and proficiency in this phase of problem solving requires a level of experience much beyond that achieved in an introductory course. A fundamental prerequisite for developing proficiency is a knowledge of the basic families of distributions and their important characteristics. Successful application of statistical methods requires that the practitioner be able to recognize situations in which a particular family of distributions is (either exactly or approximately) applicable, and perhaps more importantly, where it is not. The beginning of proficiency is made, then, by acquainting the student with some of these families of distributions, enumerating their characteristics, and noting some situations in which their use may be applicable. We begin with the binomial distribution, one member of which family the student has already met.

Characteristics of the binomial distribution

In Chapter 1, the general formula for the binomial distribution was shown to be:

$$P(r) = \frac{n!}{(n-r)!r!} p^r (1-p)^{n-r}.$$

This expression contains three terms: r, n, and p. The term r is, of course, just a description of the event for which the probability is required. For any given value of r which might be of interest, the probability of its occurrence is determined by the values of n and p. A change in either or both of these values will change the probability associated with any specified r, as will be made clear by example in subsequent discussion. Thus, n and p are the parameters of the binomial distribution. Specifying particular values for n and p singles out one member of the family of distributions. There are obviously an infinite number of members in the family.

The discussion of the preceding paragraph can be given substance

Figure 4–1

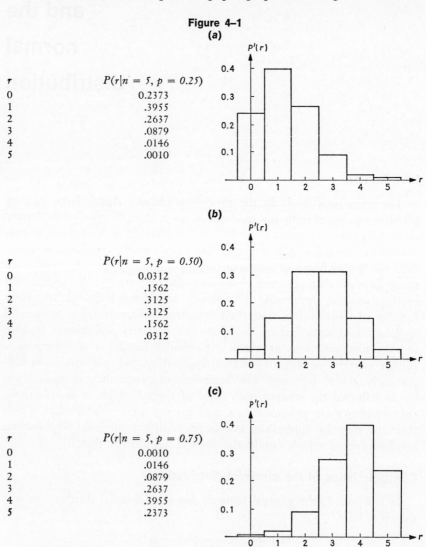

(a)

r	$P(r\|n = 5, p = 0.25)$
0	0.2373
1	.3955
2	.2637
3	.0879
4	.0146
5	.0010

(b)

r	$P(r\|n = 5, p = 0.50)$
0	0.0312
1	.1562
2	.3125
3	.3125
4	.1562
5	.0312

(c)

r	$P(r\|n = 5, p = 0.75)$
0	0.0010
1	.0146
2	.0879
3	.2637
4	.3955
5	.2373

through consideration of the particular binomial distribution which was discussed in earlier chapters and through a comparison of it with some other members of the family. The student will recall that this particular distribution was introduced in the context of a production process in which a machine produced a certain part. The probability that any given part selected from the production stream would be defective was assumed to be 0.25. If a random sample of five parts was selected from the production stream, the problem was to determine the probabilities that the sample would contain varying numbers of defective parts.

The table and the graph for this probability distribution were presented earlier. They are reproduced here as the top third of Figure 4–1. Two other members of the family, which differ from the first in respect to the value of p, appear in Figure 4–1. Since the value of $P(r)$ for any r is conditional on the values assigned to n and p, this fact is reflected in the headings for the probability columns of the tables: $P(r|n, p)$.

Comparison of the three graphs makes it clear that variation in the value of p leads to considerable difference in the appearance of the distribution. These differences can be summarized by stating the value of the measures which characterize a distribution: the mean, variance, standard deviation, coefficient of skewness, and coefficient of kurtosis. It would be a laborious procedure to calculate all these measures for the three distributions if one had to do so by the procedure laid out in the previous chapter. Fortunately, it is not necessary in this case, since these measures can be calculated from general formulas that are applicable to any binomial distribution.

It can be shown (see Appendix B in Chapter 3, for some of these results) that, for a binomial distribution with particular values of n and p, the following relationships hold, where r is the random variable of interest: $\bar{r} = np;$ $\quad \text{var}(r) = np(1 - p);$ $\quad \sigma = \sqrt{np(1 - p)};$ $\quad \text{sk}(r) = \dfrac{1 - 2p}{\sqrt{np(1 - p)}}$ $\quad \text{kur}(r) = 3 + \dfrac{1 - 6p + 6p^2}{np(1 - P)}$. By the use of these formulas, the measures have been calculated for the three distributions of Fig. 4–1. The information is summarized in Table 4–1.[1]

Relating visual comparisons of the graphs in Figure 4–1 to a comparison of the numerical values appearing in Table 4–1, there are several points that are worth considering. Note, first, that taking the graphs in the order *a, b, c,* there is a shift of the mass of the distribution from the left to the right. This is due to the fact that for values of p less than 0.5, the most likely value of r will be smaller than half the sample size (in this case, 2.5), while for values of p greater than 0.5, the opposite will be

---

[1] The student can verify that the formulas work for $p = 0.25$ by comparing the first four values calculated in the second column of Table 4–1 with the corresponding values calculated in Table 3–5. The slight disagreements between corresponding values are due to rounding of the values of $P(r)$ which appear in Table 3–5.

Table 4-1

Measure	Figure 4-1(a): $p = 0.25$	Figure 4-1(b): $p = 0.50$	Figure 4-1(c): $p = 0.75$
$\bar{r} = np$	$5(0.25) = 1.25$	$5(0.50) = 2.5$	$5(0.75) = 3.75$
$\text{var}(r) = np(1-p)$	$5(0.25)(0.75) = 0.9375$	$5(0.50)(0.50) = 1.25$	$5(0.75)(0.25) = 0.9375$
$\sigma = \sqrt{np(1-p)}$	$\sqrt{0.9375} \simeq 0.97$	$\sqrt{1.25} \simeq 1.12$	$\sqrt{0.9375} \simeq 0.97$
$\text{sk}(r) = \dfrac{1-2p}{\sqrt{np(1-p)}}$	$\dfrac{1-0.50}{0.97} \simeq +0.51$	$\dfrac{1-1}{1.12} = 0$	$\dfrac{1-1.5}{0.97} \simeq -0.51$
$\text{kur}(r) = 3 + \dfrac{1-6p+6p^2}{np(1-p)}$	$3 + \dfrac{1-1.5+0.375}{0.9375} \simeq 2.87$	$3 + \dfrac{1-3.0+1.5}{1.25} = 2.6$	$3 + \dfrac{1-4.5+3.375}{0.9375} \simeq 2.87$

true. This shift in the mass of the distribution is summarized in the numerical values of Table 4–1. As one considers the columns of the table corresponding to the three distributions, for example, one finds that the mean moves from a low position, $\bar{r} = 1.25$, through a middle position, $\bar{r} = 2.5$, to a high position, $\bar{r} = 3.75$. In the same sequence, the coefficient of skewness moves from a positive value, $+0.51$, through zero, to a negative value of -0.51. Notice, also, that while the variances (and standard deviations) for the distributions of Figures 4–1(a) and 4–1(c) are the same, the values of these measures are different for the distribution of Figure 4–1(b). Finally, the measure of kurtosis has the same value for 4–1(a) and 4–1(c), but differs for 4–1(b).

The particular similarities that exist between distributions 4–1(a) and 4–1(c) are not there by accident. The numerical values of all the measures of Table 4–1 are the same for these two distributions with the exception of the means (the coefficient of skewness differs only in sign). The mean of 4–1(a) lies as much below the mean of the symmetrical distribution, 4–1(b), as the mean of 4–1(c) lies above it. All of these similarities are due to the fact that the two distributions are "mirror images" of one another.

The explanation lies in the values of p assigned to the distributions. For the first distribution, $p = 0.25$; for the second, $p = 0.75$. Identifying these values by subscripts as $p_1 = 0.25$ and $p_2 = 0.75$, the relation between the two is $p_1 = 1 - p_2$. It is a characteristic of the binomial distribution that when two values of p_1 and p_2 are related in this fashion the following equality of probabilities holds: $P(r|n, p_2) = P(n - r|n, p_1)$. An illustration from the tables of Figure 4–1 will clarify the meaning of this equality. The table of probabilities for 4–1(c) indicates that $P(r = 3|n = 5, p_2 = 0.75) = 0.2637$. To transform this, we find $p_1 = 1 - p_2 = 0.25$ and $(n - r) = 5 - 3 = 2$. Entering the table for 4–1(a), we find $P(r = 2|n = 5, p = 0.25) = 0.2637$, which agrees with the former probability. The practical import of this relationship has to do with the manner in which probability tables for the binomial distribution are constructed. In order to economize on space in these tables, it is typically the case that probabilities are listed only for values of p less than or equal to 0.50. If one wishes the probability for a given value of r, for a binomial distribution in which the value of p_2 is greater than 0.50, he must look up the probability of $(n - r)$ in the table for $p_1 = 1 - p_2$.

Tables of the binomial distribution

One can always find the probability of a particular value of r, for given values of n and p, through the use of the general formula presented above. For large values of n, the calculations become quite lengthy, however. There are tables available for these probabilities, for an extensive range of the value of n and many values of p. These tables are usually of the cumulative probabilities, as discussed in the preceding chapter. Table B of the section of tables in this book comprises examples of these tables for selected values of n and p.

The use of Table B is best explained by example. Suppose that for the machine that produces defective parts with probability of 0.25, we require the probability that a random sample of five parts would have three defective parts. In more succinct notation, we wish the value for $P(r = 3 | n = 5, p = 0.25)$. Table B is not constructed in a manner that allows us to read this value directly. We find it by taking the difference between the probability that there will be three or fewer defective parts and the probability that there will be two or fewer defective parts. That is:

$P(r = 3 | n = 5, p = 0.25)$
$$= P(r \leq 3 | n = 5, p = 0.25) - P(r \leq 2 | n = 5, p = 0.25)$$
$$= 0.9844 - 0.8965 \text{ (values read from Table B)}$$
$$= 0.0879 .$$

The student may check to see that this value agrees with the corresponding value given in the table of Figure 4–1(*a*).

Sometimes the probability is required that r will be within a certain range of values. We might wish to know, for example, the probability that the number of defective parts in the sample would be between two and four, inclusive. The answer is found in the following way, where the designations of $n = 5$ and $p = 0.25$ have been omitted:

$$P(2 \leq r \leq 4) = P(r \leq 4) - P(r \leq 1)$$
$$= 0.9990 - 0.6328 \text{ (from Table B)}$$
$$= 0.3662 .$$

Once again, the student may check this value against the table of Figure 4–1(*a*), by noting that $P(2 \leq r \leq 4) = P(r = 2) + P(r = 3) + P(r = 4)$.

As a final illustration, suppose that the machine in question has undergone a radical change, so that the probability that a part produced by it will be defective has jumped from 0.25 to 0.75. Let us use Table B to find the probability, in these circumstances, that the number of defective parts in a sample of five will be between two and four, inclusive. We wish the value of $P(2 \leq r \leq 4 | n = 5, p = 0.75)$, but Table B does not contain entries for p greater than 0.50. It is necessary to transform the problem so that the answer can be found using the table for $p = 1 - 0.75 = 0.25$. To do this, it will be remembered, we must find for each value of r in the original problem the value of $n - r$. For $r = 2$, $n - r = 5 - 2 = 3$. For $r = 4$, $n - r = 5 - 4 = 1$. Substituting these values of $n - r$, the problem set out above translates as follows:

$P(2 \leq r \leq 4|n = 5, p = 0.75)$
$= P(1 \leq r \leq 3|n = 5, p = 0.25)$
$= P(r \leq 3|n = 5, p = 0.25) - P(r \leq 0|n = 5, p = 0.25)$
$= 0.9844 - 0.2373$ (Table B)
$= 0.7471$.

We check by the table of Figure 4–1(*c*): $P(2 \leq r \leq 4) = P(r = 2) +$
$P(r = 3) + P(r = 4) = 0.0879 + 0.2637 + 0.3955 = 0.7471.$

Problem Set 4–1

1. Using Table B, set down the probability distribution of the random variable *r*, in the case where $n = 10$ and $p = 0.25$.
2. Having set down the probability distribution for *r*, with $n = 10$ and $p = .25$ (in problem 1 above), use the relation, $P(r|n,p) = P(n-r|n,1-p)$, to set down the distribution for *r* with $n = 10$, $p = 0.75$.
3. For the distribution of problem 1 and 2, do the following:
   a) Graph each one.
   b) Calculate, for each, $\bar{r}$, σ_r, sk(*r*), and kur(*r*).
   c) Comment on similarities and differences in the values calculated in (*b*) and note how these characteristics relate to the appearances of the two graphs in (*a*).
4. Noting that $P(r = 3) = P(r \leq 3) - P(r \leq 2)$, write down the two entries required from Table B, and perform the indicated arithmetic to find $P(r = 3)$ in the situations specified below:
   a) $n = 10, p = .5.$
   b) $n = 10, p = .1.$
   c) $n = 10, p = .9.$
   d) $n = 20, p = .5.$
   e) $n = 20, p = .1.$
   f) $n = 20, p = .9.$
5. You will have noted, in working problem 4 above, that $P(r = 3|n=10, p = 0.5) \neq P(r = 3|n = 10, p=0.1)$ and that $P(r = 3|n = 10, p=0.5) \neq P(r = 3|n = 20, p = 0.5)$. Relate these two facts to the statement that "*n* and *p* are the parameters of the binomial distribution."
6. Determine the probabilities of the events as listed below. Be sure to state in notational form the equality which will allow you to use Table B, to write in the required values as found in Table B, and then to carry out the arithmetic to arrive at the required answer. An example:
$$P(r > 5|n = 10, p = 0.25) = 1 - P(r \leq 5)$$
$$= 1 - 0.9803 = 0.0197.$$
   a) $P(r = 15|n = 20, p = 0.4).$
   b) $P(1 \leq r < 3|n = 5, p = 0.5).$
   c) $P(r \geq 4|n = 10, p = 0.25).$
   d) $P(r = 5|n = 10, p = 0.25).$
   e) $P(r = 5|n = 10, p = 0.75).$
   f) $P(r \geq 4|n = 10, p = 0.4).$
   g) $P(6 \leq r \leq 8|n = 10, p = 0.75).$

7. In problem 6, parts (*d*) and (*e*), the answers you gave should have been the same. Indicate why this is so,
   a) By reference to the appropriate equation given in the text, and
   b) In terms of the commonsense nature of the relationship between the two events of 6 (*d*) and 6 (*e*).
8. In Table B, in the column corresponding to $n = 20$, $p = .10$, the entries for all values of r above $r = 8$ are 1.0000. This indicates that is is not possible to get a value of $r \geq 9$, when $n = 20$, $p = 0.10$. Or does it? Explain.

Appropriateness of the binomial distribution: The Bernoulli model

Having gotten some idea of the characteristics of the binomial distribution, it is time to ask in what situations it is applicable. We can get a generalized answer to that question if we look carefully at the problem which first led us to a formulation of the binomial probability and the asumptions which underlay that formulation.

The binomial probability,

$$P(r) = \frac{n!}{(n - r)!r!} p^r (1 - p)^{n - r},$$

was developed in conjunction with the machine-part example of Chapter 1. In considering that example, it was assumed that each and every part produced by the machine could be classified as being either defective or not defective. Furthermore, it was (implicitly) assumed that the probability of a part being defective was stable. The possibility was not considered that the machine might suddenly or gradually change so that the probability attached to a defective part would also shift. Finally, and once again implicitly, it was assumed that the outcome for any one part was independent of the outcomes for all other parts produced. That is, in a given sequence of defective parts and good parts—*DDGGG*, for example—the fact that the first part is defective has no influence on the probabilities that succeeding parts will be defective or not.

The Bernoulli model is the name sometimes given to the idealized experiment which has these three characteristics: dichotomy (two classes of outcome), stability, and independence. Any actual experiment or process in which these conditions are met is said to fit the Bernoulli model. It is important to ask if actual processes do have these characteristics. The answer is that probably no process has these characteristics exactly, but many may come close enough to make it practical to use the model. The last statement will take on substance through considering three different experiments, or processes, to see how well the three assumptions of dichotomy, stability, and independence fit them. The first example is chosen to give a good fit, in the sense that it comes about as close as a real-life situation can be expected to come to the Bernoulli model. The second is our old friend, the machine-part example; and the third illustrates another important area of practical application, marketing surveys.

Tossing a die: A first example

In an experiment consisting of the tossing of a die, we can easily create a dichotomy by definition. One possibility would be to look on the outcome of the toss as being an ace[2] or a nonace, for example. Another is to dichotomize the outcome as "less than three" and "three or more." There are obviously a number of other possibilities. In this example, the dichotomy is very real and quite unambiguous. With well-constructed dice, one should always be able to tell if the outcome is an ace or a nonace. The real-life situation fits the model very well in this respect.

Once the two classes of outcomes have been suitably defined to produce a dichotomy, a pair of probabilities can be assigned to the two outcomes: p and $(1 - p)$. Notice that, although this assignment can always be made in principle, it may be difficult, as a practical matter, to know what the actual probabilities are. That is, we feel sure that there *is* a pair of probabilities that are the correct ones, but we may not be so sure what their values are.[3] This fact need not cause dismay. It is the fundamental statistical problem, once again, that we never have full knowledge. Our use of the model will be precisely in those areas where we are uncertain —in testing hypotheses and in estimation. A more important question is: Are the probabilities stable?

The dice-tossing experiment provides a rather good fit to the Bernoulli model in respect to stability, but not so good as it did in respect to dichotomy. Even if we grant that there is some pair of probabilities that can be assigned to the outcomes "ace" and "nonace" at the outset of the experiment, we cannot in principle assume that these probabilities are stable. As the experiment is repeated time after time, it is certain to be true that the die will be modified somewhat. As the shape, size, and weight of the die is modified, of course, so are the probabilities that attach to the events "ace" and "nonace." "But," it may be protested, "such wear as might occur would be so small as to be inconsequential!" If one makes such a protest, he really is saying that the departure of the real-life situation from the model is so small as to make no practical

---

[2] An ace is said to occur in the toss of a die if the die comes to rest with the one spot up.

[3] If we plead that for "true" dice the probabilities are known, we really are making a plea that the idealized Bernoulli model applies exactly. Actually, there probably is no such thing as "true" dice, and if there were, we would have no way of recognizing them.

difference. Probably everyone would agree with him, but it is important to understand what the agreement is.[4]

The third characteristic of the Bernoulli model is that the outcome of any trial of the experiment is independent of outcomes on any preceding trials. In the toss of a die this characteristic seems to be pretty well fulfilled, unless the tosser has a knack for learning from practice how to toss a particular result. It is this characteristic that is sometimes summarized by the statement that "the dice have no memory."[5]

The toss of a die is an experiment that fits closely the Bernoulli model. The advantage of discussing it is in seeing in concrete terms what the Bernoulli model implies. In judging a practical situation to see if it departs too widely from the model, one must have a god idea of what is to serve as the reference for the departure. Another advantage is that the student recognizes from the first that the model *is an idealization* and that its realization is impossible, or at least beyond our ability to recognize it if it were realized. There is no help for it. We are stuck with approximations of reality when we attempt to solve problems in statistics (or anywhere else, for that matter). The proper attitude should be to choose models that are good enough, not to suppose that we can find an exact model.[6] Bearing that in mind, let us turn our attention to the machine-part example.

The machine-part problem: A second example

How well does the machine-part situation fit the Bernoulli model? As before, the three characteristics of the model can be considered separately. In respect to dichotomy, the machine-part situation is not as satisfactory as the dice experiment. The problem in this case is to recognize a part as "defective" or "not defective." There can be varying degrees of ambiguity involved in this classification, depending on the criteria by which a part is judged to be defective or not. If, for example, a part is judged to be defective if its width is outside a specified range,

----

[4] When a group of cardplayers agree to open a new deck of cards, they are recognizing that the assumption of stability in the probabilities is wide enough of the mark in the real-life situation that it does make a practical difference.

[5] We need to distinguish between lack of stability and independence. It may be true that the wear produced by an "ace" occurring on a toss may alter slightly the probability of an "ace" on the next throw. But the critical test from the point of view of independence is, given that an "ace" has occurred on this trial, does that lead us to decide on a different probability for an "ace" on the next trial? If the answer is no, then the outcomes are effectively independent.

[6] This is not an agnostic attitude. Because we recognize that we are bound to use approximate models does not mean that we cannot improve the models. As a matter of fact, we must recognize that the models are approximations or we will not look for improvements. For many practical applications, the models available will be adequate.

a fairly accurate classification of the part in a sample is possible by the use of go and no-go gauges. Ambiguity will be at a minimum in such a case. On the other hand, it may be that the color of the part is the criterion by which the part is to be judged. If the judgments as to whether a part is defective or not is to be made by inspectors who visually test the color of the part, there may be much room for ambiguity. A part may be defective or not, depending on which inspector happens to pick it up, or depending on the time of day a particular inspector examines it. In such cases as this, the probability that a part will be "defective" or not depends on the inspection procedure as well as the state of the machine producing the part. This is true in varying degrees of any inspection scheme, and it points up the need for well-trained inspectors and carefully planned inspection procedures in quality control work.

It is clear that the machine-part situation lacks stability, although this may be true to a greater or a lesser extent. In a painting operation, there may be a tendency for the paint to change color somewhat as the time the paint has been in the vat lengthens, or as the level of the paint in the vat is drawn down. This can be combated by choice of the quality of the paint, by careful mixing, by constant stirring, and so forth. In a machine operation where a part is punched from a metal blank, the problem of lack of stability is much greater. As successive parts are punched, cutting edges are subjected to increasing wear and deterioration. This deterioration will lead to increasing probability with successive parts that the parts will be defective. Another possibility arises in the case where material from which the part is made is itself subject to variation in quality. With one batch of this material, the probability of a defective part may be low and with the following batch it may jump considerably.

One should recognize these possibilities for lack of stability and set up safeguards against them. As a matter of fact, techniques of statistical quality control are designed as one such safeguard. They provide a basis for determining when a process lacks stability, as we shall see later.

The last characteristic of the Bernoulli model is independence of outcomes, and here once again the machine-part situation may depart from the model in varying degree. There are a number of possibilities in which the assumption of independence would not be fulfilled. In the part-punching example, there would be a distinct possibility that if the machine punched a part with a small burr on its edge, there would be an increase in the probability that the next part punched would also be defective. Another example of lack of independence is the situation in which the operator of the machine adjusts the machine according to his judgment of the quality of the parts. If upon noting a defective part the operator adjusts the machine, the property of independence is destroyed. It obviously depends on the particular situation as to whether the assumption of independence seems a reasonable approximation.

Throughout the foregoing discussion, emphasis was placed upon departures of the real-life situation from the model. This was done in order to instill an attitude of caution in the student and to point up the things to look for in assessing a given situation. If at this juncture the student has thrown up his hands in despair, then the point has been overdone. There are many production situations in which the Bernoulli model serves admirably. The evidence lies in a long list of outstanding firms in which the model is used in quality control procedures. Postponing further discussion of the machine-part example until later, we turn now to a marketing example.

Marketing surveys: A third example

Suppose that the sales manager of a firm wishes to determine the proportion of the population in a particular sales region, say, a certain large city, who purchase a product distributed by his firm. As a means of accomplishing this, he has a questionnaire distributed to a random sample of 400 residents of the city.[7] The question to be considered here[8] is if it would be reasonable to treat the results of the sample as if it were the outcome to 400 trials of a Bernoulli experiment.

Without going into great elaboration and repeating the basic cautions introduced in the former example, the answer is yes. The 400 returned questionnaires will divide into two groups, one group containing the answer, "Yes, I purchase Brand X," the other group saying, "No, I do not purchase Brand X." If the questionnaire was well written, there should be little ambiguity present in this dichotomy. Relative stability will be present, if the survey was conducted in a relatively short time during which no events occurred which might tend to raise or lower the favor of Brand X in the eyes of the city's population. The proportion of individuals in the population who buy Brand X at the time of the survey becomes the probability that a given individual asked will answer yes on the questionnaire.

Finally, although the assumption of independence is violated, the violation is so small in a case such as this as to be of little significance. The reason for this can be easily seen in an example. Suppose that the city boasts a population of 1,000,000 residents and that 500,000 of these buy Brand X. For the first person to answer the questionnaire, the

---

[7] In order to avoid unnecessary complications at this point, we shall assume that all 400 questionnaires are returned, properly answered.

[8] The manner in which the sales manager might use the sample result to estimate the proportion of the population favoring his product will be explained in a later chapter.

probability is 0.5 $(= 500{,}000/1{,}000{,}000)$ that he will say yes. Suppose, now, that his answer is indeed yes. Then the probability that the second person to answer the question will say yes is no longer 0.5, but exactly $499{,}999/999{,}999$. If the first person had answered no, then the probability that the second person would answer yes would have been exactly $500{,}000/999{,}999$. It is clear, then, that the outcome on each successive trial of the experiment is not independent of the preceding outcomes. It is equally clear that with a large population and a sample that is small relative to the population size, the modification that occurs in the initial probability as the sample is collected will be too small to have practical significance. If the sample has been collected randomly in such a situation, the binomial distribution can be used with assurance that it will give good results.

Problem Set 4–2

1. Suppose that in an experiment consisting of the toss of two dice, we are interested in the number of occurrences of the event "$x_1 + x_2 \leqq 3$" in a total of ten tosses of the dice.
   a) Can this experiment reasonably be considered to fit the Bernoulli model? If so, indicate how the characteristics of the Bernoulli model are met. If not, indicate how the characteristics of the Bernoulli model are not met.
   b) Assuming that we were to treat this experiment as a Bernoulli model, what are the relevant values of n, p, and r?

2. Suppose that a large city (over a million inhabitants) wishes to estimate the proportion of its citizens who live in conditions of poverty. As a preliminary step in the investigation, a random sample of 100 households are mailed a questionnaire in which they are asked to state their income level and the number of persons in the household. Suppose that all households to whom the questionnaire is mailed respond with the required information. Looking upon the collection of the sample data as an experiment in which the outcomes (the respondents' answers) are to be classified as indicating conditions of poverty or no poverty, would it seem reasonable to regard this experiment as conforming to the Bernoulli model? Why, or why not?

3. In the text, we talked of a machine process in which a part was produced as conforming to the Bernoulli model, under certain assumptions. Discuss different conditions, or characteristics, of such a machine process which might invalidate an assumption of conformity to the Bernoulli model.

4. In an earlier problem, it was noted that a certain professor was fond of giving tests consisting of 20 multiple-choice questions each with four alternatives. Suppose that a student was completely ignorant of the material to be covered on one of these tests. He accordingly decides to select answers to the questions on a random basis. Suppose, further, that he is successful at randomizing his selection of answers.
   a) Would it be reasonable to consider his taking the test as an experiment which conforms to the Bernoulli model? Why or why not?

    b) What is the probability that this student will pass the test if "to pass" means he must answer at least half of the questions correctly?

    c) What number of questions can this student be "expected" to answer correctly?

Approximating hypergeometric probabilities with binomial probabilities

The distinction was made, in Chapter 1, between a situation in which the hypergeometric distribution is relevant and one in which the binomial distribution may be used. This distinction is that in the former situation, withdrawal of items from a finite population, without replacement, causes the probability associated with a given class of outcome to change. In situations where withdrawal does not change the probability (i.e., with replacement), the binomial distribution is appropriate.

If the finite collection of items from which the draws are being made is large, however, and if the number of items to be drawn is a small proportion of the total collection, the practical difference between the results of these two distributions becomes small. To illustrate this point, consider the problem discussed earlier (problem 6, Problem Set 1–4) of the boy who must cull defective golf balls from a bucket containing 100 balls. We considered a bucket containing 20 defective balls and 80 good ones, and found the probability that the boy would find 2 defective balls in the first 10 inspected to be:

$$P(2 \text{ defective in } 10) = \frac{C_{80,8} \cdot C_{20,2}}{C_{100,10}} \simeq 0.3182 .$$

Now, with only 10 balls drawn from the total of 100, the effective change in the probability of getting a defective ball is not very great, even though the balls drawn are not replaced. One can anticipate that the probability one would get by using the binomial distribution might approximate rather closely the correct probability calculated above. To check this, we find the relevant binomial probability. Since 10 balls are drawn, $n = 10$. Also, since 20 of the 100 balls are defective, the proper value for p is $p = 0.2$. Using the formula for the binomial probability, we find:

$$P(r = 2 | n = 10, p = .2) = \frac{10!}{8!2!} (.2)^2 (.8)^8 \simeq 0.3020 .$$

The differences between the correct probability, 0.3182, and the value found through using the binomial distribution, 0.3020, is not great. In many situations, so small a difference might not be considered important. If that is the case, the statistician may decide to use the binomial distribution. It is much easier to find binomial probabilities from a table than it is to calculate the correct hypergeometric distribution, so that using the former to approximate the latter can be very advantageous.

Problem Set 4–3

1. In the preceding section, the binomial distribution was used to get an approximation of the probability that 10 balls, drawn from a bucket containing 20 defective and 80 good balls, would include 2 defective balls. Suppose the bucket contained 40 balls, 8 of which were defective and 32 good.
   a) Find the correct probability that 2 of the 10 balls drawn would be defective.
   b) Approximate the correct probability by using the binomial distribution.
   c) Compare your answers to (a) and (b) with the analogous values in the example of the text. On the basis of this comparison, what do you conclude concerning the role of total number of balls in the bucket?

2. In Chapter 2, some consideration was given to acceptance sampling techniques. In problem 4, Problem Set 2–1, you were asked to complete a table showing the operating characteristics of four different sampling plans. The various values of $P(\text{Accept})$ stated there are based on the hypergeometric distribution. Using the binomial distribution, find approximately the values of $P(\text{Accept})$ for the following situations:
   a) $(N = 20, n = 5, a = 1)$, at a fraction defective rate of $p = 0.1$.
   b) $(N = 100, n = 5, a = 1)$, at $p = 0.1$.
   c) $(N = 20, n = 5, a = 1)$, at $p = 0.5$.
   d) $(N = 100, n = 5, a = 1)$, at $p = 0.5$.
   e) Compare the approximate values found in (a), (b), (c), and (d) with the exact values of the table in problem 4, Problem Set 2–1. Comment on the results of these comparisons.

3. In the table below, probability distributions are given for r, number of defectives to be found in samples of size $n = 5$ taken from lots of two different sizes, $N = 40$ and $N = 100$. For each lot size, two possible rates of fraction defective are considered, $p = 0.1$ and $p = 0.25$. The leftmost column of probabilities in the portion of the table corresponding to a fraction defective of $p = 0.1$ is the distribution for the binomial probabilities, $P_b(r|n = 5, p = 0.1)$. The leftmost column in the portion of the table corresponding to $p = 0.25$ are the values of $p_b(r|n = 5, p = 0.25)$. The other columns of the table give the exact hypergeometric probabilities, $p_h(r)$, corresponding to the designated values of N and p.

r	$p = 0.1$			$p = 0.25$		
		$N = 40$	$N = 100$		$N = 40$	$N = 100$
	$P_b(r)$	$P_h(r)$	$P_h(r)$	$P_b(r)$	$P_h(r)$	$P_h(r)$
0	0.5905	0.573			0.216	0.230
1		.358	0.341	0.3955	.418	.403
2	.0729	.065	.070	.2637		.268
3	.0081	.004			.078	.085
4		.000	.000	.0146		.013
5	.0001	–0–	.000	.0010	.000	.001
	1.0000	1.000	1.000	1.0000	1.000	1.000

a) Calculate and fill in the missing entries of the table.

b) Study the completed table and make a judgment as to the effects of the influence of the factors, p and N, on the appropriateness of the binomial distribution as an approximation of the hypergeometric distribution.

4. In problem 3 above, we see that the binomial probabilities, $P(r|n=5, p=0.1)$ are close approximations to the correct hypergeometric probabilities for the case where $n=5$, $N=40$, and there are 4 defective items among the collection of 40 items. In Chapter 1, we had occasion to set down the hypergeometric distribution for X, the number of aces in your bridge partner's hand, given you have no aces. The differences in the two situations are that in the latter case $N=39$ and $n=13$. Since there are four aces to be considered, $p = 4/39 \simeq 0.1$.

a) Using this approximate value of p, find $P(r|n=13, p=.1)$ for $r=0$, 1, 2, 3, and 4, and compare to the correct probabilities which are given in the table below.

b) Having made the comparisons asked for in (a), compare the goodness of the approximations provided by the binomial probabilities there, with the approximations provided in the case of problem 3 where $N=40$, $n=5$, $p=0.1$. To what conclusion does this comparison lead you?

Probabilities for r, number of aces in bridge partner's hand, given that your hand contains none:

r	$P(r)$
0	0.182
1	.411
2	.308
3	.090
4	.009
	1.000

Large samples and the binomial distribution

It has been indicated in the preceding sections that there are many situations in which it is practical to use the binomial distribution. In order to use the binomial distribution, however, one must have available a table related to the exact values of n and p which appear in the problem. In the marketing problem discussed earlier, for example, a table of binomial probabilities would be required for $n=400$ and $p=0.50$. Other problems requiring the binomial distribution would almost certainly require differing values for n and p.

It has already been noted that each pair of values for n and p requires a separate table of probabilities. The task of providing a set of tables to meet all possible situations is an impossible one. Although very extensive tables of the binomial distribution do exist, they are for only relatively small values of n.

At first glance, the lack of comprehensive tables for the binomial distribution might appear to cripple its usefulness. Fortunately, this is not the case. It turns out that for given values of n and p, where n is sufficiently large, the particular binomial distribution associated with those values of n and p is well approximated by a specifiable member of another family of distributions, the *normal* distributions. Generally, the larger the value of n contemplated, the better the appropriate normal distribution approximates the binomial distribution.

The student can get some feeling for this tendency by examination of the graphs in Figure 4–2. Each graph depicts a binomial distribution for specific values of the parameters n and p, as specified to the right of each graph. The smooth curves superimposed on each graph is the appropriate member of the family of normal distributions. The normal distribution is a two-parameter family, just as the binomial distribution is. That is, any member of the family of normal distributions is specifiable by assignment of values to two parameters—in this case, the mean and the standard deviation.

Each normal curve depicted in Figure 4–2 was selected by setting its mean, which will be denoted by μ (the Greek letter mu), equal to the mean of the corresponding binomial distribution, and by setting its standard deviation, denoted by σ, equal to the standard deviation of the binomial distribution. Since the mean of a binomial distribution has a value equal to np and the standard deviation is $\sqrt{np(1-p)}$, the relevant values for the normal distributions of Figure 4–2 are: for 4–2(a), $\mu = np = 10(0.5) = 5$ and $\sigma = \sqrt{np(1-p)} = \sqrt{10(0.5)(0.5)} \simeq 1.58$; for 4–2($b$), $\mu = np = 20(0.5) = 10$ and $\sigma = \sqrt{np(1-p)} = \sqrt{20(0.5)(0.5)} \simeq 2.23$; and for 4–2($c$), $\mu = np = 20(0.25) = 5$ and $\sigma = \sqrt{np(1-p)} = \sqrt{20(0.25)(.075)} \simeq 1.94$. Notice that although the means and standard deviations of the three distributions are not the same, the graphs of Figure 4–2 have been scaled so that they present about the same appearance with respect to location and dispersion. This was done to emphasize the similarities that are evident in the three situations.

In a comparison of graphs 4–2(a) and 4–2(b), the important point to notice is that the normal curve is a better approximation of the corresponding binomial in the latter case. The difference is that $n = 20$ in 4–2(b), while $n = 10$ in 4–2(a). The comparison illustrates the tendency for the normal approximation to improve with increasing values of n.

A second comparison, between 4–2(b) and 4–2(c), serves to illustrate another important feature of the normal approximation to the binomial distribution. It has been pointed out earlier that the binomial distribution will be skewed if the value of p is not equal to 0.5. The skewness becomes more pronounced as the value of p departs further from 0.5. A normal distribution, on the other hand, is always a symmetrical curve.

Figure 4–2

(a)

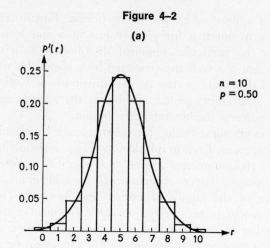

(b)

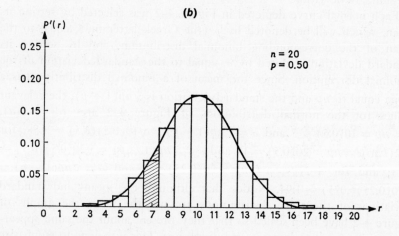

(c)

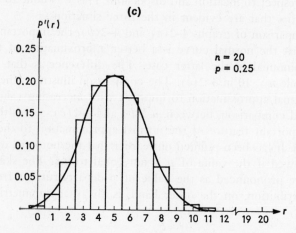

It follows that the normal curve will not be as good an approximation of the binomial in cases where p is not equal to 0.5. This fact is easily perceived from inspection of graphs 4–2(b) and 4–2(c).

Now compare graph 4–2(c) with the graph in Figure 4–1(a). The difference between the two binomial distributions depicted in these graphs is that $n = 5$ for 4–1(a) and $n = 20$ for 4–2(c). It is evident that the distribution of 4–2(c) is much closer to being symmetrical than the one of 4–1(a). It is also true that the normal curve of 4–2(c) is a much better approximation of its binomial than would be the appropriate normal curve for 4–1(a). Once again, even in the case of a binomial distribution for which p is not equal to 0.5, the normal approximation to the binomial distribution improves as the value of n increases.

The practical import of the foregoing discussion is that if one requires certain values for a binomial distribution but tables are not available which would give these values, or if the labor of using the tables seems too arduous, he may get approximate values for these probabilities by using the appropriate normal distribution. These approximations will be better, the closer p is to 0.5 and the larger the value of n. In most practical applications, one can feel safe with the approximations if the values of n and p are such that $np \geq 5$ and $n(1 - p) \geq 5$. It is much easier, as will become apparent later, to use the normal distribution than it is to use the binomial distribution.

The force of the discussion to this point has been to persuade the student of the similarity of the binomial distribution and the normal distribution. There may be a strong predilection for the student to decide that the two distributions are "much the same thing." Such an impression would be harmful and should be dispelled. The normal distribution is not a special case of a binomial distribution. It just happens to be a distribution that gives good approximations to the binomial under certain conditions.[9]

The two distributions differ in many ways, some of which should be apparent from the discussion above. One further difference should be emphasized before subsequent discussion is concentrated solely on the normal distribution. The binomial distribution is a distribution for a *discrete* random variable, as was pointed out in the first discussion of it. The random variable r may take integral values, but there are no possible values of r between the integers: it has "gaps." A random variable whose distribution is normal, however, would be a *continuous* random variable. There are an indefinite number of possible values in an interval on the domain of a continuous variable. The difference is indicated graphically

---

[9] Technically, the normal distribution is derivable from a limiting process applied to the binomial distribution as the value of n increases indefinitely and p is held constant.

by representing the binomial distribution with a series of vertical bars and the normal distribution with a smooth curve.

An important practical consideration follows from this difference. It was agreed earlier that graphs of probability distributions should be constructed so that the area underlying a certain portion of the graph would represent the probability that the random variable would have a value falling in the corresponding interval. Because of the special nature of the binomial distribution (the width of each bar is unity), it turned out that the height of the bars also represented the probabilities. This is not the case for continuous distributions. In a distribution for a continuous variable, the height of the distribution does not indicate the probability that the value of the random variable associated with that height will occur. Strictly, probability statements cannot be associated with particular values of a continuous random variable, but only with some interval, or range, of the variable. This follows from the agreement that the probability of an event is represented by the area underlying the graph. If some *point* on the horizontal axis of the graph is specified (some particular value of the random variable is specified), there is no *area* associated with this point. Because of this distinction, the curves of the normal distribution depicted in Figure 4–2 should not be referred to as probability distributions. Such curves for a continuous variable are usually referred to as *density* functions.

This point can be illustrated by reference, once again, to Figure 4–2. In graph 4–2(b) the area of the bar centered on $r = 7$ is the probability that the random variable will take that value, and the height of the bar also happens to have a value equal to this probability. Suppose for the moment that r is a continuous variable with a normal distribution as depicted by the smooth curve. Then the probability that $r = 7$ is not the height of the smooth curve at that point. As a matter of fact, since there is no area associated with a vertical line extended to the curve from this point, there is no probability associated with the event $r = 7$.

If we wish to approximate the probability that the *discrete* random variable r will take the value seven with a *continuous* normal distribution, we can do so by using the proper area. The probability that $r = 7$ is approximately equal to the area of the normal curve that has been shaded in 4–2(b). That is, the probability that $r = 7$ is approximately equal to the probability that a continuous random variable with the normal distribution shown will have a value between 6.5 and 7.5. A correction of this sort is always required when one approximates a probability for a discrete random variable by use of a continuous distribution.

Characteristics of the normal distribution

Most of the important characteristics of the normal distribution have been treated, implicitly or explicitly, in the preceding section. Perhaps an examination of the formula for the normal distribution will serve to give added perspective. For a continuous random variable *x with a normal distribution and a mean of* μ *and a standard deviation of* σ,[10] the *density* function of *x* is:

$$y(x) = \frac{1}{\sigma\sqrt{2\pi}} e^{-1/2\,[(x-\mu)/\sigma]^2}.$$

There are several points to note in respect to this function. First, notice that, in addition to the constant numerical values 1, 2 and ½, the formula contains the two mathematical constants π, whose value is approximately 3.14, and *e*, whose value is approximately 2.718. The important point to notice is that, being constants, these terms will be the same for all members of the family of normal distributions. There are two other terms, other than *x* itself, which appear in the function: μ and σ. These are the parameters of the normal distribution. It is through specification of the values for these parameters that particular normal distribution is singled out. The three curves depicted in Figure 4–3 are all normal distributions. They differ from one another in respect to the values of the mean and standard deviation, as is indicated along side each graph. There is a very important relationship among these curves which will be discussed in the next section. First, however, a few more descriptive details concerning normal curves will be helpful.

It is evident that all three curves of Figure 4–3 are symmetrical, sk = 0. It has already been pointed out that this is a characteristic of all normal curves. It may not be so evident that each curve has a point of inflection (change in the slope changes signs) at a distance of one standard deviation on each side of the mean. It is this characteristic that has led to the normal distribution often being referred to as a "bell-shaped" curve.

Finally, with respect to the last of the four practical measures of distributions, the coefficient of kurtosis of all normal distributions is the same value: kur = 3.0. All normal distributions have the same relative "peakedness." Having looked at the graphs of Figure 4–3, the student may feel compelled to challenge this statement. The three curves depicted there certainly look different. Graph 4–3(*a*) appears to be most peaked and graph 4–3(*b*) the least. The secret is that kurtosis measures *relative* peakedness. It will be remembered that the coefficient of kurtosis is a ratio of the fourth moment to the fourth power of the standard deviation. In those relative terms, the three dissimilar appearing curves of Figure 4–3 have the same measure of relative height. The degree of kurtosis of the normal distribution is often used as a point of comparison for other distributions. Distributions with the same degree of kurtosis as

---

[10] The description of the random variable *x* given in the phrase *italicized* can be written more succinctly as "*x* is $N(\mu, \sigma)$." For a particular member of the normal family, the symbols μ and σ would be replaced by numbers. For example, if $\mu = 10$ and $\sigma = 2$, the distribution would be specified as $N(10, 2)$.

Figure 4–3

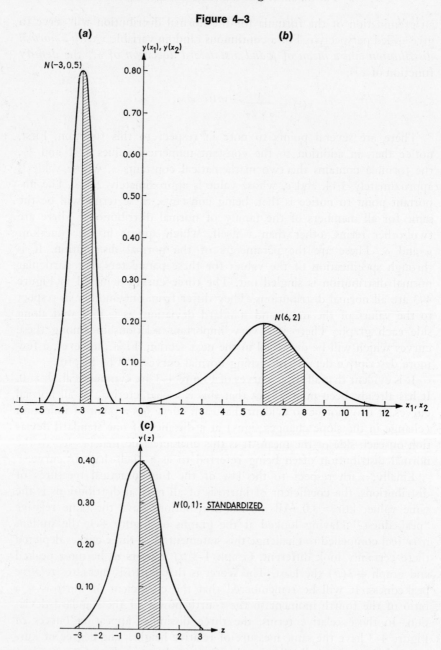

the normal distribution (kur = 3.0) are said to be *mesokurtic*. Distributions that are "flatter" than the normal curve (kur < 3.0) are said to be *platykurtic*. If a distribution is more "peaked" than the normal distribution (kur > 3.0), it is *leptokurtic*.

These features of the normal curve can be useful in practical applications to determine if use of the normal curve would be appropriate in a given situation. Although it will not always hold, if investigation of some random variable of interest indicates that its distribution is approximately symmetrical and nearly mesokurtic, this is a good first indication that the normal distribution will be successful as a model of the situation. The proposition can be put more strongly the other way around. If a random variable appears to have a distribution with the coefficients of skewness and kurtosis departing widely from zero and three, respectively, approximations of the distribution based on the normal model are almost certain to be poor.

The standardized normal distribution

The members of the family of normal distributions differ from one another with respect to the values of their means and standard deviations. There are therefore an indefinite number of members in the family. All of these curves have striking similarities, however, some of which have already been examined. Because of these similarities it is possible to reduce all normal distributions to one *standardized* curve.

The reason for this is found in the exponent of e in the formula for the density function. Notice that the exponent contains the square of the term $\dfrac{x - \mu}{\sigma}$. What this term expresses is the deviation of any given value of x from the mean of the distribution *in number of standard deviations*. When the value of a random variable is expressed in this way, it is said to be expressed in *standard units*. If all the values of the random variable are transformed in this manner, the new random variable resulting from the transformation is referred to as *standardized*.

Illustrations from the curves of Figure 4–3 will help to clarify these ideas. Graph 4–3(b) is for the normal random variable x_2 with a mean of 6.0 and a standard deviation of 2.0. One possible value of x_2 is $x_2 = 8.0$. To express this value in standard units, we divide the deviation of this value from the mean by the value of the standard deviation. Letting z denote the number of standard units, the result is $z = \dfrac{8.0 - 6.0}{2.0} = 1.0$. The result $z = 1$ indicates that the value $x_2 = 8.0$ is one standard deviation *above* (the value of z is positive) the mean of the distribution. As another example, in standard units, the value $x_2 = 2.0$ is $z = \dfrac{2.0 - 6.0}{2.0} = -2.0$, which indicates that this value is two standard deviations *below* the mean. In the same manner, for graph 4–3(a) the value $x_1 = -2.5$ has a value in standard units of $z = \dfrac{-2.5 - (-3.0)}{0.5} = 1.0$. Generally, all the values of

x_1 can be expressed in standard units, as can all the values of x_2, as can the values for any normal distribution. Through this transformation, all normal distributions can be made "to look alike."

More precisely, all normal distributions can be transformed to the *standardized normal distribution*, which is represented in Figure 4–3 by graph 4–3(c) for the random variable z. It has a mean of zero, which reflects the fact that the transformation expresses the random variable (x_1, for example) in deviations from its mean, and a standard deviation of one, which follows from the fact that these deviations are divided by the standard deviation of the original random variable. Graph 4–3(c) is for the density function of the values of z which one will get by transforming the variable x_1 in the manner described above. It also is the density function for the z values obtained by transforming x_2. It is the density function for the z values obtained by similar transformation of any normal distribution.

The importance of this fact lies in the relationship between the probabilities (the area) associated with the standardized normal distribution and any other normal distribution. The relationship is illustrated in Figure 4–3. The probability that z will take a value between 0.0 and 1.0 [the shaded area of 4–3(c)] is equal to the probability that x_1 will take a value between -3.0 and -2.5 [the shaded area of 4–3(a)] and is also equal to the probability that x_2 will take a value between 6.0 and 8.0 [the shaded area of 4–3(b)]. Similar equalities exist for any other intervals one may wish. What this means is that the probability that any normal random variable will take a value between two specified points may be found by finding the probability that z lies between the corresponding points in standard units. Thus, although there are an indefinite number of different normal distributions, all questions concerning probabilities can be answered if we have available one table of probabilities for the *standardized normal distribution*.

A table for the standardized normal distribution appears as Table C in the section of tables in this book. Because of the symmetry of the normal distribution, the probabilities have been provided for $z \geq 0$ only. The probabilities entered in the table correspond to the areas as indicated in the figure appearing above the table. Some illustrations of the use of Table C follow. We have already noted that the three shaded areas of Figure 4–3 are equal in value. Let us see what that value is. The area of concern is the area underlying the standardized curve on the interval between $z = 0.0$ and $z = 1.0$. Reading down the leftmost column to the value $z = 1.0$, we stop at that row. There are 10 entries on that row, starting with 0.3413 in the column headed 0.00, and ending on the right with 0.3621 in the column headed 0.09. We wish the area associated with $z = 1.00$, so the required value is in column 0.00. The area is 0.3413. Thus,

$$P(-3.0 < x_1 \leq -2.5) = P(6.0 < x_2 \leq 8.0) = P(0.0 < z \leq 1.0) = 0.3413 \ .$$

Suppose we wished the value for $P(8.0 < x_2 \le 10.0)$. Transforming this to the standardized distribution, this will equal $P(1.0 < z \le 2.0)$. The area we wish is between the points $z = 1.0$ and $z = 2.0$. But Table C is set up to give areas between $z = 0$ and any positive value of z. To find the required area, we find the area corresponding to $z = 2.0$ in the table (0.4772) and the area corresponding to $z = 1.0$ (which area is 0.3413). By subtracting the latter from the former, we get the desired area. Thus, $P(8.0 < x_2 \le 10.0) = P(1.0 < z \le 2.0) = 0.4772 - 0.3413 = 0.1359$. This procedure is illustrated in Figure 4–4.

Figure 4–4

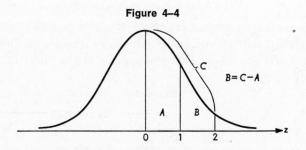

If one wishes areas associated with negative values of z, he may use the appropriate positive values of z. To illustrate, suppose we wished the value for $P(3.0 \le x_2 \le 8.0)$. First, we standardize the values of x_2:

$$\text{For } x_2 = 3.0, \ z = (3.0 - 6.0)/2.0 = -1.5 \ ;$$
$$\text{For } x_2 = 8.0, \ z = (8.0 - 6.0)/2.0 = \ \ \ 1.0 \ .$$

Thus, $P(3.0 \le x_2 \le 8.0) = P(-1.5 \le z \le 1.0)$, and we find the latter value by use of Table C. The area of the standardized normal curve which corresponds to this probability is shown in Figure 4–5. Note that the area required can be thought of as the sum of the areas designated

Figure 4–5

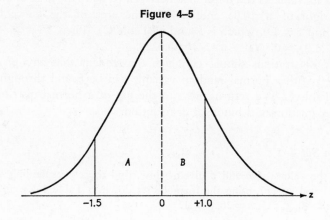

A and *B*. The area *B*, between $z = 0.0$ and $z = 1.0$, has already been determined to be 0.3413. The area *A*, between $z = -1.5$ and $z = 0.0$, is, by symmetry, equal to the area between $z = 0.0$ and $z = +1.5$. We can find the latter area in Table C. The value given in Table C is 0.4332. Combining these results, we have $P(3.0 \leq x_2 \leq 8.0) = P(-1.5 \leq z \leq 1.0) = 0.4332 + 0.3413 = 0.7745$.

As another illustration of the use of Table C, suppose we wish the value for $P(x_1 > -2.0)$. Since the mean of x_1 [of Figure 4–3(*a*)] is $\mu = -3.0$ and its standard deviation is $\sigma = 0.5$, the standardized value is:

$$z = (-2.0 - [-3.0])/0.5 = +2.0 .$$

This leads to the equality, $P(x_1 > -2.0) = P(z > +2.0)$, and the area of the standardized normal curve which we require is shown as the shaded area of Figure 4–6. The area appears in the "tail" of the curve.

Figure 4–6

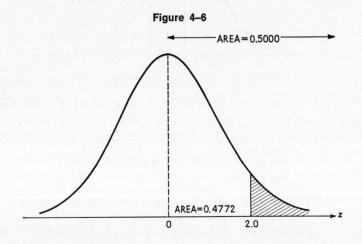

We find its value as the difference between 0.5000 (the area of the curve to the right of $z = 0.0$) and 0.4772 (the area of the curve between $z = 0.0$ and $z = 2.0$, which is found in Table C). Then, $P(x_1 > -2.0) = P(z > +2.0) = 0.5000 - 0.4772 = 0.0228$.

These illustrations should convince the student that any probability associated with a normal random variable can be found through proper use of Table C. We return, now, to the use of a normal distribution as an approximation of a binomial distribution.

Problem Set 4–4

1. For the values of *n* and *p* given below, find the corresponding values of sk(*r*) and kur(*r*), using the formulas set down in Table 4–1.
   a) $n = 20, p = .5; n = 20, p = .1$.

b) $n = 50, p = .5; n = 50, p = .1$.

c) $n = 100, p = .5; n = 100, p = .1$.

Comment on the patterns that are apparent in these values of $\text{sk}(r)$ and $\text{kur}(r)$ and how these relate to the question of using the normal distribution as an approximation for the binomial distribution.

2. Suppose that x is a random variable with a normal distribution which has a mean value, $\mu = 100$, and a standard deviation $\sigma = 4$. For the values of x given below, find the corresponding values of z, the standardized normal variable.

a) $x = 102$, b) $x = 96$, c) $x = 94$, d) $x = 107$, e) $x = 100$.

3. If r is a random variable with a binomial distribution for which the values of the parameters are $n = 100$, $p = 0.5$, express the values of r given below in standard units.

a) $r = 45$, b) $r = 53$, c) $r = 55$, d) $r = 50$, e) $r = 47$.

4. Suppose that a machine process produces bolts with a mean diameter of 0.25 inch and a standard deviation of 0.01 inch. Express the diameters given below in standard units.

a) 0.26 inch, b) 0.22 inch, c) 0.251 inch, d) 0.30 inch, e) 0.249 inch.

5. A personnel manager for a large firm has administered an examination for manual dexterity to a large number of employees. The score on this examination may range anywhere between 50 and 100. The mean score on the examinations given thus far is 76, and the standard deviation for all scores is eight. Given below are the scores of several employees. Express these scores in standard units.

a) Johnson, 80; b) Grunke, 82; c) Harrell, 62; d) Bolander, 78; e) Kent, 90.

6. Suppose that z is the standardized normal random variable, $N(0,1)$. Find the probabilities associated with the following events.

a) $z > 1.2$.

b) $z > -.8$.

c) $0 < z \leqq 0.5$.

d) $z \leqq 2.4$.

e) $-1.9 < z \leqq 0$.

f) $-1.5 \leqq z \leqq 0.75$.

g) $-1.2 \leqq z$.

h) $-2.1 < z < 1.82$.

i) $-2.6 \leqq z \leqq -1.4$.

j) $1.32 < z \leqq 2.41$.

7. Suppose that x is a random variable with a normal distribution, $N(25,5)$. Calculate the values for the probabilities given below.

a) $P(10 < x \leqq 35)$.

b) $P(x \leqq 10)$.

c) $P(x > 20)$.

d) $P(28 \leqq x \leqq 32)$.

e) $P(16 < x < 24)$.

f) $P(20 < x < 25)$.

8. The diameter of a bolt produced in the machine process described in

problem 4 is a continuous variable. If we suppose it is also a normal random variable, determine the probabilities indicated below, where d denotes the diameter in inches.

a) $P(d \leq 0.24)$.
b) $P(0.255 \leq d \leq 0.27)$.
c) $P(0.2505 < d \leq 0.252)$.
d) $P(d \geq 0.26)$.
e) $P(0.22 < d \leq 0.245)$.
f) $P(d < 0.20)$.
g) $P(0.235 \leq d \leq 0.272)$.
h) $P(d \leq 0.31)$.

9. Recalling the Tchebycheff Inequality,

$$P(\bar{x} - m\sigma_x \leq x \leq \bar{x} + m\sigma_x) \geq 1 - \frac{1}{m^2},$$

suppose that x is, in fact, a random variable with a normal distribution. Show that the Tchebycheff Inequality is consistent with the values of $P(\bar{x} - m\sigma_x \leq x \leq \bar{x} + m\sigma_x)$, for values of $m = 1, 2, 3, 4$. In what way is it advantageous, in this context, to know that the random variable x is normally distributed?

10. A ball bearing is manufactured with a mean diameter of 0.75 inch and a standard deviation in diameters of 0.001 inch. The distribution of these diameters is considered to be approximately normal. The manufacturer has set the specifications on these ball bearings so that if one has a diameter of less than 0.7485 inch or more than 0.7515 inch, it is considered defective. What is the probability that a ball bearing will be defective?

Approximating binomial probabilities by the normal distribution

Now that we have had some practice at using Table C, we can see how it can be used to approximate binomial probabilities. Let us concentrate our attention on the binomial distribution graphed in Figure 4–2(b), for which $n = 20$ and $p = 0.50$. It has already been noted that the mean of this distribution is $np = 10$, and the value of its standard deviation is 2.23. We shall therefore wish to use a normal distribution with $\mu = 10$ and $\sigma = 2.23$.

As a beginning illustration, let us first find the exact probability that r will be larger than 12. In terms of Figure 4–2(b), we wish the area of the bars for $r = 13, 14, 15, 16, 17, 18, 19$, and 20, since these are the values of r larger than 12. To find this probability, we use Table B for the binomial distribution. The table gives us cumulative probabilities, $P(r \leq r_0 | n, p)$, and we need $P(r > 12 | n = 20, p = 0.50)$. By procedures discussed earlier, we restate the probability as:

$$P(r > 12 | n = 20, p = 0.50) = 1.0 - P(r \leq 12 | n = 20, p = 0.50) .$$

Looking to Table B, we find that $P(r \leq 12 | n = 20, p = 0.50) = 0.8684$. Thus, $P(r > 12 | n = 20, p = 0.50) = 1.0 - 0.8684 = 0.1316$.

The probability derived above is an exact probability, found by using the binomial distribution. Let us now find an approximation of this probability using the normal distribution with $\mu = 10$ and $\sigma = 2.23$. We wish to approximate the area of the bars for $r = 13$ and above. Figure 4–7 shows a "blowup" of this portion of Figure 4–2(b). The area under

Figure 4–7

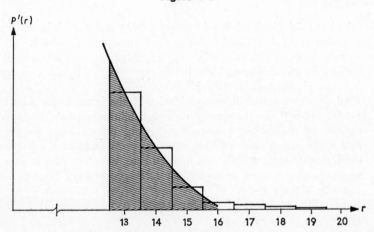

the bars shown there will be approximated by the shaded area under the "tail" of the normal distribution. This "tail" extends from the lower bound of the bar for $r = 13$ on through successively higher values. The lower bound of the bar for $r = 13$ is located at the value 12.5. We require, then, the probability that a normal random variable with $\mu = 10$ and $\sigma = 2.23$ would be larger than 12.5. As usual, we standardize this value, $z = (12.5 - 10.0)/2.23 \simeq 1.12$. From Table C we find that $P(z > 1.12) = 0.5000 - 0.3686 = 0.1314$. Comparing the two values, we find that the exact probability of 0.1316 is very closely approximated by the value from the normal distribution, 0.1314. One cannot always expect the agreement to be this close; but with large n and with p close to 0.50, the agreement should be good.

As a final example, consider the value for $P(9 \leq r \leq 14)$. To approximate this probability, we need the area under the normal curve from the value 8.5 (*lower* bound of bar for $r = 9$) to the value of 14.5 (*upper* bound of bar for $r = 14$). These values are converted to z values to give

$$P\left(\frac{8.5 - 10.0}{2.23} \leq z \leq \frac{14.5 - 10.0}{2.23}\right)$$
$$= P(-0.67 \leq z \leq 2.02)$$
$$= P(0.0 < z \leq +0.67) + P(0.0 < z \leq 2.02)$$
$$= 0.2486 + 0.4783 = 0.7269 .$$

We can compare this approximate value to the exact value derived from Table B: $P(9 \leq r \leq 14 | n = 20,\ p = 0.50) = P(r \leq 14 | n = 20,\ p = 0.50) - P(r \leq 8 | n = 20,\ p = 0.50) = 0.9793 - 0.2517 = 0.7276$. Once again, there is close agreement between the two values.

Problem Set 4–5

1. For the binomial distributions of Figures 4–2(b) and 4–2(c) in the text:
   a) Calculate $\bar{r}$, σ_r, sk(r), kur(r), using the formulas of Table 4–1.
   b) On the basis of the results in (a), which of the two binomial distributions do you think would be better approximated by the corresponding normal distribution? Why?
   c) Find the exact probabilities associated with the intervals for r indicated below, and find also the approximate probabilities based on the appropriate normal distribution (remember that one must correct for the fact that a discrete random variable is being approximated by a continuous one). Assume $n = 20$, $p = 0.5$. In each case, note by what amount the approximation is over or under the exact probability: (i) $8 \leq r \leq 11$, (ii) $r > 10$, (iii) $r < 5$.
   d) Repeat the procedure of (c) for $n = 20$, $p = 0.25$, and (i) $3 \leq r \leq 6$, (ii) $r > 5$, (iii) $r < 0$.
   e) Comment on the results of parts (a), (b), (c), and (d). Note any relevant comparisons and contrasts.

2. In problem 10 of Problem Set 4–4, you found the probability that a ball bearing would be of defective diameter. Suppose these ball bearings are packaged for shipment in lots of 1,000, with no inspection prior to packaging. Using an appropriate approximation, find the following:
   a) What is the probability that a lot will contain more than 138 defective ball bearings?
   b) What is the probability that such a lot will contain fewer than 110 defective ball bearings?
   c) What is the interval in number of defective bearings per lot within which one would expect approximately 90 percent of all lots to fall (setting the limits of this interval equidistant on either side of the mean number of defectives per lot)?

3. Suppose that a certain television program is viewed in 50 percent of homes of a certain large city. A television rating service calls 500 homes, randomly selected, to ask if the household is watching this program.
   a) What is the probability that fewer than 200 of these 500 households will be viewing the program in question?
   b) What is the probability that the number of households viewing the program will be somewhere between 235 and 275?

4. Suppose that two different brands of soft drink are equally preferred by the consumers in a large marketing area where both drinks are sold. (The meaning of "equally preferred" can be translated to mean that a consumer is as likely to prefer one as the other.) We set out with a large supply of each type of drink and offer people we meet their choice of the two drinks.

(We assume that the people we meet are met in a random manner.)

a) What is the probability that, of the first one hundred people we meet, 55 percent or more will prefer drink A?

b) What is the probability that, of the first two hundred people we meet, 55 percent or more will prefer drink A?

c) What is the probability that, of the first thousand people we meet, 55 percent or more will prefer drink A?

d) Review your answers to parts (a), (b), and (c), and comment on the significance of what you find.

Appropriateness of the normal distribution

The normal distribution has played a role more important than any other single type of distribution in the development of traditional statistical methods. There are several reasons for this. One that has been discussed already is that the normal distribution is an adequate approximation to other distributions in many practical applications. This point was brought out only with respect to the binomial distribution, but the same point holds relative to some other (not all) distributions. We shall be content to illustrate the uses made of this fact for only one or two cases, in a following chapter.

There may be some situations, to mention a second area of application, in which a process generates a random variable that is approximately normally distributed. In some applications of statistical quality control, usually dealing with the control of some dimension of a product, an assumption that the random variable is normal seems to lead to satisfactory results. The approximations one gets for the probability that the diameter of a bolt produced by an automatic machine will be within certain limits, for example, may be adequate for purposes of control. Admitting that such cases may exist, we should hasten to add that these situations will be a distinct minority.

For much business and economic data that one might collect, the distributions associated with these data are more likely to depart somewhat from normality that they are to approach it. This is not so serious a problem as it might at first appear, however, because often our interest in a particular set of data really centers on the value of a few selected parameters of the distribution—the mean, for example—rather than the overall distribution. And often we are forced to make inferences about the values of these parameters on the basis of a sample instead of the full body of data. It is in this latter area that the normal distribution has found its widest use. It is a remarkable fact that when one works with a sample taken from a larger body of data, it is often quite appropriate to use the normal distribution, even though there is no assurance that the body of data from which the sample was collected is itself normally distributed. The purpose of the next chapter is to explain why this is so.

chapter 5

Samples, frequency distributions, and sampling distributions

Introduction

The discussion in previous chapters has been couched largely in terms of probability distributions and density functions. It has dealt with random variables and the probability that they might take certain values. With few exceptions, our concern was with questions of the type, "What is the probability that a certain event *will* occur?"

In certain instances, the discussion centered on the concept of a sample result. It is important to notice that when a statement is made that a certain sample result was obtained, this is not the same sort of statement as statements involving probabilities. The sample result is a statement concerning data actually in hand. If it is found that the mean diameter of a sample of 10 bolts selected from the production of a machine has a value of 0.15 inches, this is a value that has been realized, not one that may occur in the future. It is true, however, that this particular mean of 0.15 inches can be thought of as one point in a range of values that the sample mean might have taken. Thus, actual sample results are linked to the concepts of random variable and probability distributions.

One of the purposes of this chapter is to introduce methods for properly selecting a sample and measuring the characteristics of interest in the sample. A second purpose is to provide the required conceptual link between a sample result and the considerations of probability developed in preceding chapters. This task will be facilitated with the introduction of some new terminology.

Populations and samples

In procedures of statistical inference, one wishes to make an inference about a large (perhaps infinite) set of data on the basis of a smaller set of data. For example, one might wish to test the hypothesis that the mean income of residents of New York City is $10,000. The large set of data in this case comprises the incomes of all residents of New York City. This set of data is too large for the statistician to test the hypothesis by actually calculating the true mean income. He must therefore test the hypothesis on the basis of a smaller set of data selected from the larger set. The smaller set of data, it has already been noted, is called the sample. The larger set of data is called the *population*. Strictly, the *population* is not the set of persons who are residents of New York City, it is the set of their incomes. To a statistician the term *population* refers to a set of data, not to the source of the data. Measures of the characteristics of a population are called *parameters*. Measures of characteristics of a sample are called *statistics*. Thus, the mean of a population is a *parameter*, while the mean of a sample is a *statistic*.

For a population as large as the one considered above, it is clear that there will be a very large number of possible sample results. The concept of a sample from a finite population is identical to the concept of combination which was developed in the discussion of counting methods. If two separate selections of incomes for residents of the city were to result in the incomes of exactly the same set of people in both cases, these two selections would constitute the same sample. Two samples are different in that the two sets do not contain exactly the same elements. This means that if one were to select a sample of 1,000 incomes from the incomes of the approximately 8 million residents of New York City, there would be as many different possible samples as the number of combinations of 8 million objects taken 1,000 at a time. It is this set of all possible samples from which the concept of the sampling distribution springs.

To summarize, there are *three different distributions* that enter into problems of statistical inference. There is the *population*, the distribution of values about which it is required to make some inferential statement. Second, there is the sample, a smaller set of values selected from the population. The sample data will, of course, have their own distribution. The third distribution is the *sampling distribution*. It is the distribution of all the possible sample results which might occur—all the possible sample means, for example—as a result of selecting a sample from the population. Only the sampling distribution is a probability distribution. The population is a set of values that exist but are not completely known to the statistician. The sample is a set of values which exists and is known to the statistician. Both sets are of realized values. The sampling distribution is a set of values most of which may never be realized. In this last case it is proper to talk of the probability that a certain sample result will occur.

Purpose of randomness in sample selection

A sampling distribution is a probability distribution. This means that we can make probability statements concerning the occurrence of certain sample results if we can preserve the validity of the probability distribution arising from the selection process. What this means, in essence, is that we must be careful to select our sample in such a way that the actual probabilities associated with the sampling distribution are not modified. Each sample which could possibly be selected from the population should have the same probability of being selected as any other.[1] In order to guard against selection procedures that might make some samples more likely to be selected than others, the sample usually is selected in a supposedly random manner. The element of randomness may be introduced in some cases by as simple a procedure as tossing a coin, or thorough mixing before selection if that is possible. The most common, and the best, procedure for introducing randomness is by using random numbers.

Sets of random numbers are sequences of the digits 0 through 9. These sequences have been generated in such a manner as virtually to assure that any particular sequence of digits has the same probability of being generated as any other. Large tables of random numbers are available, and there are also routines available through which a computer can be used to generate random numbers. Table D in the section of tables is an excerpt from a large table of random numbers. The procedures by which these tables are used are the subject of the next section.

Selecting a random sample

To illustrate the procedure of random selection, we shall consider an idealized situation. Further, to keep the illustration to manageable proportions, we assume that the population of interest is small. Specifically, suppose that the population consists of the 12 values that appear in the columns headed "Population Value" of Table 5–1. The first step is to

---

[1] This particular statement applies only for the case of finite populations of discrete variables. For the case of infinite populations or continuous variables, we shall have to be content with the statement that the method of selection should be chosen so as not to modify the probability distribution.

Table 5–1

Serial Number	Population Value	Serial Number	Population Value
00	10	06	12
01	10	07	12
02	11	08	12
03	11	09	13
04	11	10	13
05	11	11	14

number the values of the population serially, as indicated in the columns headed "Serial Number." Since the total number of values in the population (the *size* of the population) is 12, the largest serial number assigned, 11, has two digits. We will be required, therefore, to select random numbers in sequences of two, so we make all the serial numbers two-digit pairs. Having numbered the population values serially, we are ready to select the sample.

Suppose that we wish to select a random sample of two values from the population. We enter the table of random numbers and use a systematic procedure for reading two-digit pairs from the table until we have found two pairs in the table that fall in the range of the serial numbers 00 through 11 in Table 5–1. Looking at Table D, we note that it is divided into columns and rows, with the digits appearing in pairs. We might agree to read down the column at which we enter the table, and to start at the top of the next column to the right when we reach the bottom of the present column, continuing in this fashion until we have found two two-digit numbers that fall in the proper range. If we were to follow this procedure and if entry in Table D were at the 7th column and the 16th row, the student can verify that the resulting pair of two-digit numbers would be 11 and 07. Thus, the population values that would be included in the sample would be 14 and 12, respectively.

It bears repeating that the situation above was an idealized one meant to illustrate the role of random numbers in the selection process. It requires a list on which appears every member of the population to be sampled. In real situations there are many lists available. The telephone directory is available to all. Trade organizations have lists of members. Professional survey groups have specially prepared lists to meet their needs. Some of these lists are undoubtedly better for particular needs than are others.

Some points of caution in using such lists can be illustrated with reference to the telephone directory. If one wished to select a random sample of residents in a certain city, he might decide that the telephone directory of that city met his needs adequately. He should be aware, however, that a selection of names from a telephone directory is not a random selection of residents of the city. There are several reasons for this, some of which will be mentioned only hurriedly. An obvious problem is that not all residents' names appear in the directory. Some residents have just moved to the city, others may be too poor to afford a telephone. At the same time that the names of some residents do not appear at all, the names of others may appear more than once, in home-office listings and similar ways. Even with a list of names gleaned from the directory, there is still the problem that some people will not be at home when called. Call-backs may find them, or they may not. It is very difficult to get a completely random sample in most real situations.

Very often the person or agency collecting a sample will find it advantageous to sacrifice some small degree of randomness in order to assure that the sample will have other features, such as representativeness or economy. To assure that the sample will adequately represent the population, a *stratified random sample* is often selected. The problem can be illustrated by supposing that an investigator wishes to learn something concerning the mean life insurance coverage of the residents of a particular area. The amount of coverage which a person carries is influenced by many things, one of which is his income. To assure that the sample will contain persons from various income levels, the investigator may stratify the sample by income. He may decide, for example, to select parts of the sample from high-income, middle-income, and low-income groups. The three different income groups are the strata of the population. Such a procedure precludes the possibility that exists in a completely random sample of missing one or more income groups or giving unduly large weight to some groups. A *proportional stratified sample* is often used, which means that the proportion of the sample taken from each stratum will be approximately equal to the proportion that stratum bears to the entire population. The selection of persons from each stratum will be randomized as in the earlier illustration.

When an extensive sample survey is undertaken, questions of economy often dictate that the selection procedure be carried out in stages. In order to canvass a large city, for example, the city may be partitioned into areas in such a way that the composition of the residents of each area is relatively homogeneous with respect to certain characteristics, whereas the areas differ from one another. In terms of the previous illustration, the city might be partitioned into three areas corresponding to residents of high, middle, and low incomes. Usually, these larger areas are further subdivided into a number of smaller areas, which we shall call *primary sampling areas*. The primary sampling areas are set up so that each one has a composition similar to the larger area of which it is a part. Finally, the primary sampling areas are divided into *block clusters*, consisting of one or more city blocks, with approximately the same number of residents in each cluster. The homes in the clusters are then numbered serially.

The selection of the sample then proceeds by stages. In the first stage, a number of primary sampling areas are randomly selected from each of the larger areas they comprise. At the second stage, several block clusters are selected randomly from the primary sampling areas selected in the first stage. The third and final stage would consist of random selection of homes to be called upon within the clusters selected in the second stage.

A multistage area sample design of the type just explained has two primary advantages. First, it helps to assure representativeness in the sample. Second, it is much less expensive to send interviewers to homes concentrated in several block clusters than it would be to send them out over the city in the more or less haphazard fashion that would result from a completely random selection procedure. In the explanation above, the only characteristic of the residents that was mentioned was income. In an actual survey, it is likely that several characteristics would be considered in the partitioning process. Some of these might include age, race, family size, and nationality, to name a few.

Problem Set 5–1

1. On page 153 there appears a set of data consisting of 100 values which represent annual insurance premiums.
   a) Copy this set of data on a sheet of paper and select a random sample of 10 from this set.
   b) How many possible samples of size $n = 10$ could one select from this set of data?
   c) Suppose that the sample of 10 values were taken with the intention of using the mean of these 10 values as an estimate of the mean of the 100 values on page 153. In this context, identify the following:
      i. The parameter.
      ii. The statistic.
      iii. The sample.
      iv. The population.
      v. The sampling distribution.
2. Explain what is meant by the statement in the text that "the sampling distribution is a set of values most of which may never be realized."
3. The list on page 147 contains the weekly wages paid to 100 employees of a local firm. From this list, select a stratified random sample of size $n = 10$ (make this a *proportional* stratified sample, so that the proportion of wages from each wage group that appears in the sample equals the proportion that wage group bears to the entire group of employees).

Weekly Wages of Employees in Three Wage Groups

White Collar	Skilled		Unskilled	
$175.90	$205.20	$213.30	$138.60	$137.90
172.00	184.70	188.80	125.30	126.70
194.50	179.90	191.00	122.20	140.80
189.90	186.80	199.60	126.70	129.30
175.40	187.60	206.90	127.20	131.70
182.60	207.00	204.10	139.80	137.70
180.40	208.20	186.90	140.50	137.60
177.00	215.80	208.60	145.50	130.00
157.90	193.80	190.90	131.20	132.20
190.00	197.80	194.60	133.80	128.20
165.40	205.60		138.90	129.00
183.50	203.80		137.70	131.70
178.50	180.40		122.50	139.80
186.30	203.90		137.80	132.20
177.70	188.60		127.80	128.40
172.00	216.20		145.80	133.00
186.70	211.60		142.80	135.00
186.70	192.40		130.30	135.40
171.30	193.30		130.90	141.40
193.50	184.40		125.10	137.90
			143.90	150.10
			128.00	144.80
			129.40	125.30
			135.00	128.00
			139.70	137.00

4. It often is economical to select a multistage sample. The multistage area sampling technique discussed in the text has as one advantage the fact that the sample ultimately collected will not require interviewers to move randomly throughout the area (city, county, state) in order to collect the data. Rather, the actual interviews conducted will tend to occur in geographical "clusters." One can arrive at an appreciation of the economy of multistage sampling by considering the following model.

Using your local telephone directory, interpret it in the following way:

a) Let the first 5 pages represent persons with high income, the next 10 pages those with middle income, and the next 5 pages those persons with low income.

b) Treat the columns of each page as if they were primary sampling areas.

c) Look on each column on a page as if it consisted of, say, four block clusters, with each cluster containing as close as possible to the same number of persons.

(Some adaptation of this model may be required, of course, to allow for local variations in directory format.)

a) For this model, select a sample of $n = 24$ names from the directory by randomly choosing, in stages:

   i. Two primary sampling areas from the upper-income group, four from the middle-income group, and two from the lower-income group.

ii. One "cluster" from each of the primary sampling areas selected in (i).

iii. Three names from each of the "clusters" selected in (ii).

b) Compare the method used in (*a*) with the method one would have used to get a random sample from the first 20 pages of the directory if these pages had not first been divided into groups and clusters. Make the comparison in terms of:

i. Effort in gathering names.

ii. Effort in conducting the survey of persons (remembering that contiguity in the directory represents geographical closeness in the model).

iii. Representativeness of the samples drawn in both methods.

5. The workers in a large manufacturing plant are issued identification cards which are numbered serially from 1 through 250. Select a random sample of 10 workers from the roster.

6. It often happens that a list of interest to the statistician will have a corresponding list of numbers assigned to it. The identification card numbers assigned to employees in problem 5 above is an example. In such a situation, the statistician may select a *systematic* random sample. For example, suppose that the statistician wished a sample equal in size to $n = 10$. Then, to select a systematic random sample, he would enter a random number table, to find a two-digit number lying between 01 and 25, inclusive. The number so chosen becomes the "starting point" of the sample. The remainder of the sample is found by adding, successively, 25 to each preceding value until 10 numbers have been generated and the corresponding sample of $n = 10$ has therefore been specified.

To illustrate, if the "starting" number selected from a random number table had been 11, then the sample would consist of the 10 employees with the identification numbers: 11, 36, 61, 86, 111, 136, 161, 186, 211, 236. One determines the "period" within which each successive item is to be selected for the sample by dividing the total number of items in the list, N, by the size of sample desired, n. In this case, $N = 250$, $n = 10$, and $N/n = 25$, so that each successive 25th item was selected.

It should be noted that a systematic random sample should not be taken if there is a known or suspected relationship between the serial numbers assigned to the values in a list and the values themselves. In the identification numbers example of problem 5, to illustrate, suppose that the numbers ending with the digit, 1, are reserved for supervisory personnel. Then, if a systematic sample is taken using every 10th value in the list, the sample will contain only supervisory or nonsupervisory personnel, depending on the random starting point. This is an exaggerated example; the relationship can be more subtle than this.

Suppose, now, that you wish a sample of $n = 20$ from the one hundred values in the list of page 153. Select a systematic random sample. (In this case, of course, a set of numbers is not naturally assigned to the annual premiums listed. One can assign serial numbers to these values, however.)

7. The various sampling procedures discussed in the text and in the problems above lead to samples with varying degrees of randomness. Suppose we refer to a sample as a *completely* random sample if the method of selection is such that,

- *a*) Each item in the population has the same chance (equal probability) of being selected, and,
- *b*) Each *possible* sample of the specified size has the same chance of being selected.

If the sample selected does not have both of these properties, it is referred to as an *incompletely* random sample, so long as randomization occurs at some point in the selection process. For the samples designated below, indicate whether each is completely or incompletely random, and why:

- *a*) The sample selected in problem (1).
- *b*) The sample selected in problem (3).
- *c*) The sample selected in problem (4).
- *d*) The sample selected in problem (6).

Sample statistics

The sample collected by one of the procedures outlined in the preceding section is a set of data with characteristics which are analogous to, and which can be measured in much the same fashion as, the characteristics of a probability distribution. These characteristics—mean, standard deviation, and so forth—are called *statistics*, as noted earlier. Generally, the statistician wishes to make inferences concerning the parameters of a population on the basis of values of various statistics in the sample he has collected. The function of this section is to indicate how these values are calculated for a sample. Although the calculations are analogous to those explained earlier for the characteristics of a probability distribution, some differences in terminology and procedure do arise.

The discussion proceeds by stages, in order to develop several conceptual and computational points in the most convenient manner. First concern is with definition of terms, followed by explanation of calculating procedures. The procedures most convenient to use depend on the computational aid available to the investigator. If a computer is available, a convenient procedure for calculation involves only slight elaboration of the definitional formulas. If the calculations must be performed on a desk calculator, or with paper and pencil, some additional elaboration of the procedure is an expense well worth undertaking for the consequent saving in computational labor.

The mean of a sample is defined as the sum of the values divided by the number of values. If x denotes the values of the sample, the formula is $\bar{x} = \dfrac{\Sigma x}{n}$. If we suppose the sample consists of the five values appearing

Table 5–2

x	$x - \bar{x}$	$(x - \bar{x})^2$	x^2
20	−23.2	538.24	400
35	− 8.2	67.24	1,225
42	− 1.2	1.44	1,764
51	7.8	60.84	2,601
68	24.8	615.04	4,624
216		1,282.80	10,614

$$\bar{x} = \frac{216}{5} = 43.2$$

$$s = \sqrt{\frac{1,282.80}{4}} = \sqrt{320.7} \simeq 17.91 \qquad\qquad s = \sqrt{\frac{10,614}{4} - \frac{(216)^2}{(5)(4)}}$$

$$= \sqrt{2,653.5 - 2,332.8}$$

$$= \sqrt{320.7} \simeq 17.91$$

in the leftmost column of Table 5–2, the calculation in that table shows the mean of the sample to be 43.2.

The standard deviation of a sample will be denoted by s, and it is defined by $s = \sqrt{\dfrac{\Sigma(x - \bar{x})^2}{n - 1}}$. This calculation is performed in Table 5–2, below the calculation of the mean. The sample standard deviation is approximately 17.91.

The fact that the denominator in the formula for the sample standard deviation is $n - 1$ rather than n requires some explanation. Our purpose in computing the standard deviation of a sample will be to use it in estimating the standard deviation of the population from which the sample has been selected. For purposes of this estimate, a sample of size n is said to have $n - 1$ *degrees of freedom*. The meaning of this phrase can be explained in two different ways.

First, notice that since the sample of Table 5–2 has $n = 5$ values, it has $n - 1 = 4$ degrees of freedom. It should be obvious that the best estimate of the population standard deviation which we could get using the five values of the sample would use the deviations of these values *from the population mean*. Since the population mean is unknown, however, the next best thing is to use the deviations of the values *from their own mean*, $\bar{x}$, which is what has been done in Table 5–2. Notice, however, that since these deviations must have a sum equal to zero,[2] once any four of the deviations are specified, the fifth is automatically deter-

---

[2] For any set of data, the mean of the data will be the value such that the sum of the deviations from it will equal zero. Noting that, for a set of values denoted by x, their mean is $\bar{x} = \Sigma x/n$, we have:

$$\Sigma(x - \bar{x}) = \Sigma x - \Sigma\bar{x} = \Sigma x - n\bar{x} = \Sigma x - n(\Sigma x/n) = \Sigma x - \Sigma x = 0.$$

The same result is easily demonstrated for probability distributions.

mined. If, for example, one were to specify the first four deviations as they appear in Table 5–2 (-23.2, -8.2, -1.2, 7.8) we would know without being told that the fifth deviation must be 24.8 in order for the sum of all five to equal zero. Thus, the sample has only four degrees of freedom for purposes of estimating the population standard deviation, and the sum of the squared deviations is "averaged" only over four, not five, points.

A second explanation can be made graphically and may be clearer intuitively. To illustrate, suppose that the distribution of the population from which a sample of five values was selected is distributed approximately as depicted in Figure 5–1, and that the population mean, denoted by $m(X)$, is located as shown.

Suppose also that the sample values are located as depicted by the points

Figure 5–1

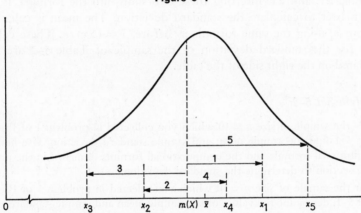

x_1, x_2, x_3, x_4, and x_5. Then the mean of the sample would be located approximately as depicted by the point $\bar{x}$. We should like to base our estimate on deviations of the sample points from the population mean, as shown in Figure 5–1 by the numbered arrows. We are forced to base it on deviations from the sample mean. There is a consequent loss of one degree of freedom.[3]

The discussion above of the calculation of the sample mean and standard deviation was employed to define the two terms. The parallel between these measures for a set of data and the corresponding measures for a probability distribution should be evident. For computational pur-

---

[3] A more precise, but somewhat technical, explanation is made in terms of the fact that an estimate of variance based on the number of values, n, in the sample is *biased* downward. This means, roughly, that such estimates are too small "on the average." The *expected value* of these estimates is smaller than the variance of the population. Estimates of variance using $n - 1$ are unbiased. See Appendix A.

poses, the calculations can be performed much more easily by other methods.

An improved computational procedure for the standard deviation which would be useful if one were to use a computer to provide the answers is based on the formula

$$s = \sqrt{\frac{\Sigma x^2}{n-1} - \frac{(\Sigma x)^2}{n(n-1)}}.$$

The advantage of using this formula lies in the fact that it is not necessary first to compute the mean, $\bar{x}$, in order to find the deviations of each value of x from $\bar{x}$. Instead, as each value of x is "read in" to the computer, the computer is made to generate the two sums appearing in the formula, Σx^2 and Σx. Inserting these two sums into the formula, it is an easy matter to calculate the standard deviation. The mean is calculated, of course, using the same formula as before, $\bar{x} = (\Sigma x)/n$. These calculations for the standard deviation of the sample of Table 5–2 are demonstrated on the right side of the table.

Problem Set 5–2

1. For the sample of size $n = 10$ which you collected in problem 1 of Problem Set 5–1 find the sample mean and sample standard deviation. Use both the definitional formula and the computational formula discussed in the preceding section to determine the standard deviation.
2. For the sample of size $n = 10$ which you selected in problem 3 of Problem Set 5–1, determine the values of the sample mean and sample standard deviation. Determine the sample standard deviation by the two formulas developed in the preceding section.
3. For the sample of size $n = 20$ selected in problem 6 of Problem Set 5–1 determine the values of the sample mean and the sample standard deviation. In the case of the sample standard deviation, find the value by both of the formulas developed in the preceding section.
4. Treating the 20 values which appear in the list of wages for the white-collar workers in problem 3 of Problem Set 5–1 as a sample, calculate the values of the mean and the standard deviation for these data.

Frequency distributions

A desk calculator or paper and pencil can be used to calculate the mean and standard deviation in the manner described for the computer. If the set of sample values is large, this method will probably involve less effort than using the earlier, definitional, formulas. If one must make the calculations by calculator or pencil and paper, however, considerable effort can be saved in the case of a large set of data if the data are first grouped into a frequency distribution. The frequency distribution is useful not only because of laborsaving computational procedures based on it. It also is helpful in allowing the statistician to get a visual representation of the data.

An explanation of the frequency distribution is best made by example. Suppose that a sample of 100 persons yields the following 100 values for annual insurance premiums paid by those persons, rounded to the nearest dollar:

171	156	166	178	227
164	179	216	181	177
161	185	175	184	162
193	208	172	201	166
183	206	183	196	200
197	177	155	171	221
194	186	150	203	166
224	180	175	197	183
188	173	165	147†	206
173	176	182	230	189
175	181	181	153	167
158	174	173	171	163
186	177	187	179	181
220	165	180	182	191
202	168	181	185	179
180	184	168	203	185
199	200	174	216	198
187	234	169	168	190
178	162	190	213	179
188	243†	205	210	206

For a set of data as large as this, it is not apparent what the characteristics of the data are. One cannot be very sure, for example, if the data exhibits a tendency to concentrate in a central location, or just what the dispersion of the data is. The computational procedures already discussed can be used to find the mean and the standard deviation, but the calculations are lengthy.[4]

A remedy to these problems is to group the data into a frequency distribution. The first step is to determine the range of the data by locating the lowest and the highest values. For the data illustrated, these have been marked with daggers (†). The second step is to construct a series of *classes* which partition the range of the data into equal[5] intervals.

---

[4] There are listed, in Appendix B, four computer programs which can be used in computing several characteristics of a set of data, both in grouped (set in a frequency distribution) and ungrouped form.

[5] It is not actually necessary that the intervals be equal, but shortcut computational procedures to be illustrated later depend on this being the case. If the class intervals are not equal, the second computational procedure illustrated below cannot be accomplished, as will be evident.

The smallest class should contain the lowest value in the data and the largest class should contain the highest value. All possible values of the data should fall in one of the classes, and the classes must not overlap. A series of classes which meet these requirements appear in the leftmost column of Table 5–3. The two values associated with each class are called the *class limits*. The third step is to assign each of the 100 values above to its proper class by a tallying procedure. The results of the tally will be the number of values falling in each class. These numbers are called the *class frequencies* and will be denoted by the letter f. The second column of Table 5–3 contains the class frequencies for the given data.

Table 5–3

Class	f	Midpoint (x)	$f \cdot x$	$f \cdot x^2$
145–154	3	149.50	448.50	67,050.75
155–164	8	159.50	1,276.00	203,522.00
165–174	19	169.50	3,220.50	545,874.75
175–184	28	179.50	5,026.00	902,167.00
185–194	15	189.50	2,842.50	538,653.75
195–204	11	199.50	2,194.50	437,802.75
205–214	7	209.50	1,466.50	307,231.75
215–224	5	219.50	1,097.50	240,901.25
225–234	3	229.50	688.50	158,010.75
235–244	1	239.50	239.50	57,360.25
	100		18,500.00	3,458,575.00

$$\bar{x} = \frac{\Sigma f \cdot x}{n} = \frac{18,500.00}{100} = 185.00$$

$$s = \sqrt{\frac{\Sigma f \cdot x^2}{n-1} - \frac{(\Sigma f x)^2}{n(n-1)}} = \sqrt{\frac{3,458,575.00}{99} - \frac{(18,500.00)^2}{(100)(99)}}$$

$$\simeq \sqrt{34,935.10 - 34,570.71} = \sqrt{364.39}$$

$$= 19.09$$

The two leftmost columns of Table 5–3 constitute the frequency distribution for the data. It is much more evident from inspection of these columns what the central tendency and dispersion of the data are. If one wished a clearer picture, he might graph the frequency distribution as in Figure 5–2. Two vertical scales appear with Figure 5–2. The scale on the left indicates the *frequency* of each class. The scale on the right indicates the proportion, or *relative frequency*, of each class. It has been denoted by f'. The purpose in presenting both scales is to indicate that either one may be used. Obviously, the scale for relative frequency is derived by dividing the scale for frequency by the number of values in the set of data. Thus, since there are 100 values in the present example, the scale on the right is one hundredth of the scale on the left.

It should be noted that the class limits of the distribution in Table 5–3 are not the values which appear on the horizontal scale of Figure 5–2. In Figure 5–2, for example, the values associated with the leftmost bar are 144.5 and 154.5, not 145 and 154. The reason for this is that the values in the set of data are rounded to the nearest dollar. This means that all values reported between \$144.50 and \$154.50 would have been rounded so as to fall in the class with the limits 145–154. The values 144.50 and 154.50 are called the *class bounds*, since actually the class extends from the one bound to the other (not from one class limit to the other). It is evident that the *width* of a class (to be denoted by w) may be found as the difference between successive class bounds or as the difference between successive lower (or upper) class limits.

Figure 5–2

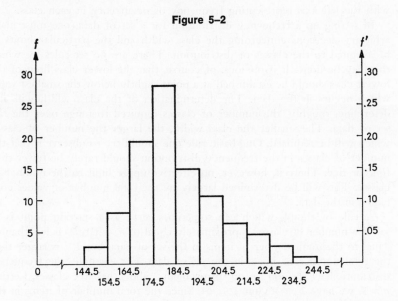

Notice that having constructed a frequency distribution of the data, we have lost a certain amount of information. For example, the frequency distribution tells us that there are three values in the set of data which fall in the interval 145–154, but it does not tell us the exact values. Since we are not able to use the exact values in the frequency distribution, we assign new values to the items appearing in each class. Specifically, we say that the three values in the first class have a value equal to the *midpoint* of that class. The *midpoint* of a class is found by taking the mean of its class limits. Thus, the midpoint of the first class is $\dfrac{145 + 154}{2} = 149.50$. In a similar manner, the eight items of the second class are assigned values of 159.50, and so on through the distribution.

Problem Set 5-3

1. Treating the weekly wages listed for white-collar workers in problem number 3 of Problem Set 5-1 as a sample, set up a frequency distribution for these data with the width of the classes equal to 10 and the lower class limit of the lowest class equal to 155. Graph the resulting distribution with the left scale representing frequency in each class and the right scale indicating relative frequency in each class.

2. Look upon the data for the weekly wages of unskilled workers set out in problem 3 of Problem Set 5-1 as a sample and set up the frequency distribution for these data with a class width of 7 and the lower class limit of the lowest class equal to 120. Graph the frequency distribution which results with the left axis representing frequency of occurrence in each class.

   In setting up a frequency distribution for a set of data, one must make arbitrary decisions concerning the class width and the particular limits to be assigned to the classes of distribution. There are no set rules by which this may be done. It is obvious, of course, that the lower class limit of the lowest class should be established at a point slightly below the smallest value which occurs in the data. The determination of the class width will also determine, roughly, the number of classes required to range over the full set of data. The smaller the class width, the larger the number of classes which will be required. One basic rule one should try to observe is that the number of classes in the frequency distribution should rarely be fewer than four or five. There is, however, no effective upper limit to the number of classes. This will be determined largely by the total number of values contained in the data.

   A rule of thumb which can sometimes serve as a starting point is to select a number of classes approximately equal to n, where 2^n is less than or equal to the total number of items in the set of data, but 2^{n+1} is larger than the total number of items in the set of data. For example, the frequency distribution which you set out in problem 2 above has five classes. Letting $n = 5$, we have $2^5 = 32$, but $2^6 = 64$. Since the total number of items in the frequency distribution is 50, the value of $n = 5$ was selected in this case. Since the lower class limit of the lowest class has been set at 120, and since the maximum value appearing in the list of wages for unskilled workers is $150.10, we find that a class width of $7 produced a set of five classes which summarizes the data rather nicely.

   Beyond these considerations, however, the statistician must finally choose the frequency distribution on the basis of how it "looks" to him. A fundamental consideration here is that if the data truly are representative of one source, one would expect them usually to have a central tendency indicated by a class for which the frequency is larger than the other classes and a tendency for the frequencies on either side of this class to fall off in a relatively smooth succession as the end classes of the distribution are approached. The following problems are included to give the student some appreciation of the difficulties involved in setting up the frequency distribution.

3. For the data concerning wages of white-collar workers in problem 3 of Problem Set 5–1, set up two frequency distributions. The first distribution is to have a lower class limit of 155 for the lowest class and a class width of 8. The second distribution is to have a lower class limit for the lowest class of 158 and a class width of 6. Graph both of these distributions and compare with the distribution which you set down in problem 1 above. Which of the three seems best and on what features of the distributions do you base this valuation?

4. For the data on the weekly wages of unskilled workers set out in problem 3 of Problem Set 5–1, construct two frequency distributions. The first frequency distribution is to have a lower limit for the lowest class of 120, and the class width is to be 5. The second distribution is to have a lower limit of 122, and the class width is to be 7. Graph the two distributions and compare with the distribution which you constructed in problem 2 above. Evaluate these three distributions and indicate which you feel is the best of the three, giving your reasons therefor.

The student will have noticed in problem 4 above that the first distribution set down was a bimodal distribution. That is, there were two classes which had class frequencies larger than the class frequencies on either side of them. The class of 125–129 had a frequency of 14, and the class 135–139 had a class frequency of 12. When this occurs with a set of data, one must usually look to one of two causes. It may be the case that through the accidental grouping of the values into the classes assigned, this bimodality occurs in the distribution, although the underlying data actually reflect no dual central tendency. The second possibility is that the data included in the distribution actually reflect two different sources or types of data.

Given the results for the first distribution of problem 4, for example, one might wish to consider the possibility that the category of wage earners which were classified as unskilled might actually include more than one category of worker. If there were two categories of unskilled labor, one with a lower general wage scale than the other, this would tend to cause a bimodality in the distribution. If the statistician is reasonably sure that his categories of data have been set up properly in the first place, his first step upon finding that a distribution has a bimodality would be to try regrouping the data in new classes. With the data for unskilled workers we see that although one method of grouping the data results in a bimodal distribution, two other ways of grouping the data do not lead to a bimodality. This gives a strong indication that the bimodality was an accident arising from the grouping in the one case. If in repeated attempts to regroup the data the bimodality continues to develop in the distributions, this is a strong indication that the statistician should reconsider his categories for that set of data. Problem 5, which deals with the data for the wages of skilled workers presented in problem 3 of Problem Set 5–1, exemplifies this sort of difficulty.

5. For the data on weekly wages paid to skilled workers which are presented in problem 3 of Problem Set 5–1, set up three different frequency distributions. In the first distribution set the lower limit of the lowest class at 180 and make the class width 6; in the second distribution set the lower class

limit of the lowest class at 180 and make the class width 10; in the third
distribution set the lower limit of the lowest class at 175 and make the class
width 10. Examine these three frequency distributions and comment on their
characteristics. As a statistician, what course of action do you feel is indicated by the characteristics which you see in the three distributions?

Calculating the mean and standard deviation of a frequency distribution

With the midpoints of the classes substituting for the exact values of
the data, one proceeds to calculate the mean and standard deviation of
these midpoints, where each midpoint is weighted by the frequency of
that class. In Table 5–3, the third column contains the midpoints for the
classes. The midpoint of each class is multiplied by the frequency of that
class, to give them proper weights. These products are entered in the
fourth column of the table. Multiplying the entries of the fourth column,
$f \cdot x$, by the entries of the third column, x, the resulting products, $f \cdot x^2$,
are the squares of the midpoint values properly weighted by their respective frequencies. The mean and standard deviation for these weighted
values are then calculated by the formulas:

$$\bar{x} = \frac{\Sigma f \cdot x}{n},$$

$$s = \sqrt{\frac{\Sigma f \cdot x^2}{n - 1} - \frac{(\Sigma f \cdot x)^2}{n(n - 1)}}.$$

The calculations appear in Table 5–3, where the mean is found to be
185.00 and the standard deviation is approximately 19.09. These values,
of course, represent dollar amounts, since the data were in dollars.

Looking at the calculations of Table 5–3, the student may have been
impressed at the amount of labor involved, even if a desk calculator were
available. The effort required to perform the calculations can be reduced
substantially, if the class widths of the distribution are all equal, through
an additional computational strategem. This procedure consists in transforming the midpoints of the distribution in much the same fashion as a
normal distribution is standardized. Specifically, the midpoints are expressed as deviations from an arbitrarily selected value, in terms of class
widths. Although the arbitrary value can be any value whatsoever, it is
convenient to select one of the midpoints themselves. Further convenience
is gained by selecting a midpoint near the heaviest concentration of frequencies in the distribution. Letting x' denote this value and w denote
the class width, we transform the values of the midpoints to a set of
"coded" values, $x_c = \dfrac{x - x'}{w}$. The mean and standard deviation of the

coded values are calculated, using the same formulas as in Table 5–3. These values, $\bar{x}_c$ and s_c, are converted to original units by reversing the earlier transformation. Thus,

$$\bar{x} = x' + w \cdot \bar{x}_c$$
$$s = w \cdot s_c .$$

Table 5–4 indicates how this procedure can be applied to the frequency distribution of Table 5–3. The class width for this distribution

Table 5–4

Class	f	Midpoint (x)	$x_c = \dfrac{x - 189.50}{10}$	$f \cdot x_c$	$f \cdot x_c{}^2$
145–154	3	149.50	−4	−12	48
155–164	8	159.50	−3	−24	72
165–174	19	169.50	−2	−38	76
175–184	28	179.50	−1	−28	28
185–194	15	189.50	0	0	0
195–204	11	199.50	1	11	11
205–214	7	209.50	2	14	28
215–224	5	219.50	3	15	45
225–234	3	229.50	4	12	48
235–244	1	239.50	5	5	25
	100			−45	381

$$\bar{x}_c = \frac{\Sigma f \cdot x_c}{n} = \frac{-45}{100} = -.450$$

$$\bar{x} = x' + w \cdot \bar{x}_c = 189.50 + 10(-.450) = 189.50 - 4.50 = 185.00$$

$$s_c = \sqrt{\frac{\Sigma f \cdot x_c{}^2}{n-1} - \frac{(\Sigma f \cdot x_c)^2}{n(n-1)}} = \sqrt{\frac{381}{99} - \frac{(-45)^2}{(100)(99)}} \simeq \sqrt{3.644380} = 1.909$$

$$s = w \cdot s_c = 10(1.909) = 19.09$$

is $w = 10$, and the arbitrary value chosen is $x' = 189.50$, the midpoint of the fifth class. The transformation is therefore $x_c = \dfrac{x - 189.50}{10}$. The fourth column of Table 5–4 contains these coded values. Notice that all one must do is place a zero in place of 189.50 and count successively in either direction through the remaining classes, placing a negative sign on the numbers for classes smaller than the zero-class. The products $f \cdot x_c$ and $f \cdot x_c{}^2$ are generated as before and the results are used in similar formulas (x_c being used now, where x was used before). Finally, the coded mean and standard deviation are reconverted to uncoded units, to arrive at the same values as in Table 5–3. The computational effort has been reduced considerably, however.

Other characteristics of a frequency distribution

In the earlier discussion of the characteristics of probability distributions, measures for the median, mode, and coefficients of skewness and kurtosis were developed. Similar measures exist for a frequency distribution. To complete the parallel in treatment of the two types of distribution, methods of arriving at these measures are explained in this section.

Recalling that the median of a probability distribution was defined as the value that halved the distribution, the median of a frequency distribution is defined similarly. The median of a frequency distribution is a value such that half the values in the distribution are below it and half

Table 5–5

Class	f	$\Sigma_c f$	
145–154	3	3	
155–164	8	11	$\text{med}(x) = B_\ell + w \left(\dfrac{\dfrac{n}{2} - \Sigma_c f}{f_m} \right)$
165–174	19	30	
175–184	28	58	
185–194	15		$= 174.50 + 10 \left(\dfrac{\dfrac{100}{2} - 30}{28} \right)$
195–204	11		
205–214	7		$\simeq 174.50 + 7.14 = 181.64$
215–224	5		$\text{mod}(x) = B_\ell + w \left[\dfrac{f_m - f_b}{(f_m - f_b) + (f_m - f_a)} \right]$
225–234	3		
235–244	1		$= 174.50 + 10 \left[\dfrac{28 - 19}{(28 - 19) + (28 - 15)} \right]$
	100		
			$= 174.50 + 10 \left(\dfrac{9}{9 + 13} \right)$
			$\simeq 174.50 + 4.09 = 178.59$

are above it. The point has already been made that the exact values of the set of data are no longer known when we deal with a frequency distribution. This means that the median must be approximated by interpolation. The procedure is to locate the class of the distribution in which the median must lie and to interpolate to a value within that class to represent the median. The class which contains the median is the one at which the cumulated sum of frequencies (cumulated from the lowest class[6]) first becomes larger than one half of the number of values in the distribution.

The procedure is illustrated in Table 5–5. The values in the third column of the table, $\Sigma_c f$, are the cumulated frequencies up to and includ-

---

[6] One can cumulate from the highest class with consequent change in the remainder of the procedure. We adopt the procedure above for convenience.

ing the frequency of the class for the row on which each entry appears. The cumulated frequency first exceeds $\frac{n}{2} = \frac{100}{2} = 50$ in the fourth row. Consequently, the class which contains the median is the fourth class. Letting B_ℓ denote the lower bound of this class, and f_m the frequency, the median is located by interpolation using the formula below, where the value for $\Sigma_c f$ to be inserted is the cumulated frequency up to but not including the median class.

$$\text{med}(x) = B_\ell + w \left(\frac{\frac{n}{2} - \Sigma_c f}{f_m} \right).$$

Paralleling the definition of the mode for a probability distribution (the value most likely to occur), the mode of a frequency distribution can be defined as the value with the largest frequency. Once again, because of the lack of exact values, the mode is approximated through a process of interpolation. In this case, however, the interpolation is accomplished so as to give proportionate weight to the frequencies of the classes on either side of the class containing the mode. The class with the largest frequency is, of course, chosen as the modal class. Letting B_ℓ denote the lower bound of the modal class, f_m its frequency, f_b the frequency of the class below it, and f_a the frequency of the class above it, the formula is:

$$\text{mod}(x) = B_\ell + w \left[\frac{f_m - f_b}{(f_m - f_b) + (f_m - f_a)} \right].$$

The mode of the frequency distribution we have been considering is calculated by this formula in Table 5–5. Since the largest frequency, 28, is associated with the fourth class, this is the modal class. Consequently,

$$B_\ell = 174.50, f_m = 28, f_b = 19, f_a = 15, \text{ and } w \text{ is, of course, } 10 \ .$$

The bracketed term of the formula performs the interpolation. It should be noted that it places the mode at a point within the modal class proportionally to the relative size of the frequencies on either side of the modal class. Thus, if these two frequencies were equal, the mode would be placed at the midpoint of the class. In the present case, the frequency of the class below the modal class is larger, and the mode is consequently located below the midpoint.

Finally, formulas for calculating the coefficient of skewness and the coefficient of kurtosis are presented below. These formulas may be used with either the original or the coded values for the midpoints. To perform the calculations, one needs only to add seventh and eighth columns to Table 5–4, corresponding to $f \cdot x_c^3$ and $f \cdot x_c^4$, respectively. The symbol s that appears in the denominator of each formula is, of course, the sample standard deviation.[7]

$$\text{sk}(x) = \text{sk}(x_c) = \frac{\dfrac{\Sigma f \cdot x_c^3}{n-1} - 3\dfrac{\Sigma f \cdot x_c \cdot \Sigma f \cdot x_c^2}{n(n-1)} + 2\dfrac{(\Sigma f \cdot x_c)^3}{n^2(n-1)}}{s_c^3} \cdot$$

$$\text{kur}(x) = \text{kur}(x_c) = \frac{\dfrac{\Sigma f \cdot x_c^4}{n-1} - 4\dfrac{\Sigma f \cdot x_c \cdot \Sigma f \cdot x_c^3}{n(n-1)} + 6\dfrac{(\Sigma f \cdot x_c)^2 \cdot \Sigma f \cdot x_c^2}{n^2(n-1)} - 3\dfrac{(\Sigma f \cdot x_c)^4}{n^3(n-1)}}{s_c^4}$$

Before leaving the subject of frequency distributions, it is appropriate to make an observation concerning the nature of the data which one will summarize in such a distribution. The example which has been used to illustrate the methods of computation was in dollar amounts. This is a discrete variable, since the lowest divisible unit in such amounts is the penny. The question is, Would the procedures need to be modified if the variable were a continuous one, such as lengths or weights? The answer is no. It is important to note that although the variable we are concerned with may be continuous, the data which we record for it will be discrete. The recorded values for any continuous variable will be a set of measurements. These measurements are not continuous. We must always express them as rounded to some arbitrarily defined unit. Thus, if we record the diameter of a ball bearing as 1.003 inches, we are saying that the diameter is closer to 1.003 inches than to either 1.004 inches or 1.002 inches. The measurements for all the ball bearings in a sample, measured to the same degree of tolerance, will be discrete. It will not be possible for a value such as 1.0025 to appear in the data.

Having cataloged all of the computational procedures that we may require for frequency distributions, it is time to turn to a consideration of sampling distributions. It was noted earlier that there are a number of sampling distributions associated with a particular population, corresponding to different sample statistics. Thus, there is a sampling distribution of the sample means, another distribution for the sample variances, and so forth. We will be concerned in the remainder of this chapter with the distribution of sample means only.

---

[7] If the values used in the numerators of the formulas of skewness and kurtosis are for x_c, as shown above, the values of s which appear in the denominators must be in units of x_c, also.

Problem Set 5–4

1. A pharmaceutical firm recently developed a tablet to be taken by over-weight persons as an aid in dieting. In order to test the effectiveness of the tablet, the firm conducted an experiment in which 100 overweight persons were given the pill as prescribed for a period of one year. At the end of this period, their weight losses were noted and recorded. These data are sum-marized in the frequency distribution set out below.

Weight Loss (Pounds)	Number of Persons
10–19.9	14
20–29.9	29
30–39.9	22
40–49.9	14
50–59.9	10
60–69.9	6
70–79.9	3
80–89.9	2

   a) Calculate the mean weight loss of the 100 persons participating in the experiment.
   b) Calculate the median weight loss for the persons in the experiment.
   c) Estimate the modal value of weight loss for persons participating in the experiment.
2. Using the appropriate ones of the values which were calculated in problem 1, answer the following questions:
   a) What was the approximate typical weight loss of the 100 persons involved in the experiment?
   b) Approximately one half of the persons involved in the experiment lost fewer than how many pounds?
3. If you were an overweight person and had heard of the experiment described in problem 1, which of the "averages" which were calculated there would you be most interested in and why?
4. Suppose that the sample of 100 persons who took part in the dieting experiment of problem 1 were very representative of the population of persons who are overweight. If this were the case, we might be able to use the mean weight loss in the sample and the standard deviation of weight losses in the sample and invoke the Tchebycheff Inequality in order to say something about the probability that a person undertaking the dieting program would enjoy a weight loss which would fall within certain ranges. Make those assumptions and do the following:
   a) Calculate the sample standard deviation for the data presented in problem 1.
   b) Indicate the range for the weight loss which an overweight person might enjoy if he were to undertake the dieting program, such that the probability that his weight loss would fall in this range would be at least 0.75.

   c) What is the range of weight loss associated with a probability of at least
   0.89?

5. It is indicated in the chapter that when one groups a set of data into a
   frequency distribution, a certain amount of information is lost in the process. In the usual case, this loss of information is not very serious, however,
   since there is a tendency for the differences between the actual values represented in any one class and the midpoint of the class to be compensated
   throughout the whole distribution. The result is that, usually, the mean and
   the standard deviation as calculated from the frequency distribution will
   not vary too much from the mean and the standard deviation which one
   would get as a result of calculating these from the original set of values.
   This point can be illustrated by reference to the data on the weekly wages
   if white-collar workers which were set out in problem 3 of Problem Set
   5–1. You will recall that in problem 4 of Problem Set 5–2 you were asked
   to calculate the mean and standard deviation from the original list of values.
   Now, using the frequency distribution for this same set of data which you
   constructed in problem 1 of Problem Set 5–3, calculate the mean and standard deviation by use of the shortcut formulas using coded values. Compare
   the results of these calculations with the results of the calculations in the
   earlier problem.

6. In Problem Set 5–3, it was noted that one must make arbitrary decisions as
   to class width and class limits in setting up a frequency distribution. It was
   also noted that the form of the frequency distribution might vary somewhat
   depending on these decisions. Naturally, the calculated values for the mean
   and the standard deviation will also vary as the particular distribution varies
   with these decisions. In most cases, this variation will not be substantial,
   however. To illustrate this point, use the distribution for wages paid unskilled workers which was constructed in problem 2 of Problem Set 5–3
   and the distribution for the same data which was constructed in problem 4
   of Problem Set 5–3 (use the bimodal distribution of problem 4).

   a) Using coded values, calculate the mean and standard deviation of the
   distribution in problem 2 of Problem Set 5–3.

   b) In the same manner, calculate the mean for the bimodal distribution of
   problem 4. Compare to the mean in (*a*).

   c) Find, also, the standard deviation of the distribution of problem 4. Compare to the value in (*a*).

7. For the frequency distributions specified below, find the coefficient of skewness.

   a) The frequency distribution which you set down in problem 2 of Problem Set 5–3.

   b) The frequency distribution of problem 1 above.

   c) The first of the three frequency distributions which you constructed
   for the wages of skilled workers in problem 5 of Problem Set 3.

In working through the problems above, the student should have become aware of two points. One point is that one of the major uses of the
frequency distribution is to group the data in a fashion so that the

computations involved in finding the mean, standard deviation, coefficient of skewness, and similar measures of the characteristics of the data, can be accomplished more easily. A second point is that through the use of the frequency distribution some detail concerning the values of the data is sacrificed and the result of this is that values of these characteristics which are calculated from the grouped data necessarily beome only approximate values. It has been pointed out that the degree of approximation involved is usually relatively close to the actual values required. This being the case, the statistician often will proceed with the calculations from grouped data rather than from the ungrouped data because the degree of accuracy sacrificed is not considered worth the additional effort involved in the calculations.

If one has a digital computer available, however, this situation is changed. With the computer, calculations based upon the ungrouped data can be performed nearly as easily as on the grouped data. Consequently, the calculations should be performed using formulas such as those presented in the section, "Sample statistics," page 152. It may happen, of course, that the data of interest have already been grouped into a frequency distribution for some other purpose. Consequently, one would like a program which will calculate the desired characteristics on the basis of the formulas presented in the section immediately preceding this problem set. Two programs designed to perform these calculations are presented in Appendix B, at the end of this chapter.

The sampling distribution of the mean: Finite populations

The method of selecting a completely random sample was illustrated in an earlier section by selecting a sample of 2 values from a population of 12 values. The result was a sample consisting of the values 14 and 12. The corresponding sample mean is $\frac{14 + 12}{2} = 13$. This is only one of a number of sample means that might have resulted from the selection process. If we were to set down in a table all the possible sample means that we might have gotten in this selection, along with the frequency with which each could occur, the table would represent the sampling distribution of sample means for this particular situation. We wish to compare the characteristics of the sampling distribution with the characteristics of the population from which the samples would have been selected.

Table 5–6 depicts two frequency distributions. The distribution on the left is the distribution for the population values which appeared earlier in Table 5–1. The distribution appearing on the right is the sampling distribution of the mean for samples of size 2 drawn from the population. To see the relationship between the two distributions, consider how one

Table 5–6

X	f	X_c	$f \cdot X_c$	$f \cdot X_c^2$	$\bar{x}$	f	$\bar{x}_c$	$f \cdot \bar{x}_c$	$f \cdot \bar{x}_c^2$
10	2	-2	-4	8	10.0	1	-3	-3	9
11	4	-1	-4	4	10.5	8	-2	-16	32
12	3	0	0	0	11.0	12	-1	-12	12
13	2	1	2	2	11.5	16	0	0	0
14	1	2	2	4	12.0	13	1	13	13
	12		-4	18	12.5	10	2	20	40
					13.0	4	3	12	36
					13.5	2	4	8	32
						66		22	174

For Computations

$$X_c = \frac{X - X'}{w} = \frac{X - 12}{1}$$

Number of items $= \Sigma f = 12$

$$m(X) = 12 + 1(-4/12) \simeq 11.67$$

$$\sigma_X = 1 \cdot \sqrt{\frac{18}{12} - \frac{(-4)^2}{(12)^2}}$$

$$\simeq \sqrt{1.500000 - 0.111111}$$

$$= \sqrt{1.388889}$$

$$\simeq 1.179$$

For Computations

$$\bar{x}_c = \frac{\bar{x} - \bar{x}'}{w} = \frac{\bar{x} - 11.5}{0.5}$$

Number of items $= \Sigma f = 66$

$$m(\bar{x}) = 11.5 + \frac{(0.5)(22/66)}{} \simeq 11.67$$

$$\sigma_{\bar{x}} = (0.5)\sqrt{\frac{174}{66} - \frac{(22)^2}{(66)^2}}$$

$$\simeq (0.5)\sqrt{2.6363 - 0.1111}$$

$$\simeq 0.795$$

might get a sample mean of $\bar{x} = 10.0$ through a selection of two values from the population. This can happen in only one way: The first value selected must be one of the two values of 10, and the second value must then be the remaining 10. Thus, the frequency associated with $\bar{x} = 10$ is $f = 1$. The frequency associated with $\bar{x} = 10.5$ is $f = 8$. The sample mean will be 10.5 for any sample containing the values 10 and 11. Since there are two values of 10 in the population and four values of 11, such a sample could be selected in $(2)(4) = 8$ ways. There are, in all, $C_{12,2} = 66$ possible samples of size 2 that could have been selected from the population of size 12.

There are two important relationships between a finite population and a sampling distribution of means from that population which we wish to illustrate by a comparison of the distributions in Table 5–6. Since there are two distributions involved, there will be two sets of symbols representing analogous characteristics in the two distributions. The size of the population will be denoted by N, the size of the sample by n. To distinguish the values of the two distributions, the values of the population are given the symbol X and the sample means are denoted by $\bar{x}$. The standard deviation of the population is denoted σ_X, while the standard deviation of the sampling distribution is referred to as $\sigma_{\bar{x}}$. The mean of the population values is written $m(X)$, and the mean of the sampling distribution is $m(\bar{x})$. The mean and standard deviation of each distribution are calculated below it.

The calculations are performed in the manner illustrated in earlier sections, with one slight modification. In the computation of the standard deviations of these distributions, there is no problem of degrees of freedom. This is so because we do not intend to use these standard deviations as estimates, as was the case with the sample standard deviation. We wish to know the exact standard deviation of the distributions appearing in Table 5–6. Thus, the appropriate figure to use is the number of items in the distributions, not that number minus one. This accounts for the fact that the denominators appearing in the calculation of σ_X are 12 and 12^2, rather than 11 and $(12)(11)$ as one would expect from the formulas used in computing a sample standard deviation. The same observation applies to the computation of $\sigma_{\bar{x}}$.

The size of the population is $N = 12$. The samples represented by the sampling distribution are of size $n = 2$. The calculations appearing below the distributions indicate that $m(X) \simeq 11.67$, $\sigma_X \simeq 1.179$, $m(\bar{x}) \simeq 11.67$, $\sigma_{\bar{x}} = 0.795$.

The relationship existing between $m(X)$ and $m(\bar{x})$ is obvious. They are equal. The relationship existing between σ_X and $\sigma_{\bar{x}}$ is not so obvious, but it is as definite as the relationship between the means. It can be verified from the figures of Table 5–6 that

$$\sigma_{\bar{x}} = \frac{\sigma_X}{\sqrt{n}} \sqrt{\frac{N - n}{N - 1}}.$$

In the present case, $N = 12$, $n = 2$, $\sigma_X \simeq 1.179$, so that

$$\sigma_{\bar{x}} \simeq \frac{1.179}{\sqrt{2}} \sqrt{\frac{12 - 2}{12 - 1}} = (0.834)(0.953) \simeq 0.795 \,,$$

which corresponds to the value of $\sigma_{\bar{x}}$ calculated in Table 5–6.

The two relationships demonstrated for the two distributions of Table 5–6 hold for any finite population, and a sampling distribution of sample means drawn from it, for any size sample. The mean of the sampling distribution will always be equal to the mean of the population. Also, the dispersion of the sample means about the population mean will be smaller for larger size samples.

These points can be illustrated further by considering two extreme possibilities. First, suppose that the sample size considered is $n = 1$. In that case, of course, the sampling distribution would just be a duplication of the population itself. The means of the two distributions would be equal, and so would their dispersion, since

$$\sigma_{\bar{x}} = \frac{\sigma_X}{\sqrt{1}} \sqrt{\frac{N - 1}{N - 1}} = \sigma_X \,.$$

At the other extreme, consider a sample whose size was equal to that of the population, $n = N$. In this case, obviously, there is only one sample possible. The size of the sampling distribution is one. The mean of the sampling distribution is the mean of the population, and the standard deviation of the sampling distribution is

$$\sigma_x = \frac{\sigma_X}{\sqrt{N}} \sqrt{\frac{N - N}{N - 1}} = 0 \,.$$

The dispersion in this sampling distribution is zero, since there is only one value in the distribution.

The sampling distribution of the mean: Infinite populations

Before proceeding to a discussion of the practical importance of relationships developed above, the form of these relationships for samples drawn from an infinite population will be demonstrated. On first thought, an infinite population may seem like an impossibility. It is easy to think of populations that are very large—the population consisting of the incomes of all residents of the United States, for example—but they still fall short of infinite. If one were to consider a process in which ball bearings were machined to a certain diameter, however, it is clear that this represents an infinite population. There are an infinite number of diameters any one ball bearing might possibly take.

In a sense, however, the term "infinite" is perhaps a misnomer. What we wish to consider is situations where the sample is selected so that the probability of a particular value being selected for the sample is independent of the result on any prior selection for the same sample. This condition was not met in the previous illustration. We assumed that having selected one of the 12 values to include in the sample, there remained only 11 from which to choose the second. If we have a truly infinite population, such as the ball bearing diameters, it is evident that the population of possible diameters is not reduced in size by the fact that each ball bearing included in the sample has one particular diameter.

A finite population can be transformed to an infinite population in this latter sense, if the sample is selected *with replacement*. What this means is that once we have noted the value of an item selected for the sample, we make it available to be selected again.[8] If we consider sampling with replacement from the population of Table 5–6, this population takes on the characteristics of an infinite population. The difference between sampling with replacement and without replacement is easy to show. Consider the value of 14 appearing in the population. In sampling without replacement, it would not be possible to select a sample of two items, both of which had the value 14. In sampling with replacement, however, a sample of two can be selected in which both values are 14. The proba-

---

[8] This is a pedagogic device to provide us with an "infinite" population that is easy to use. In actual sampling practice, once a particular item of a population has been selected for inclusion in the sample, it usually is not replaced in the population.

bility of selecting a 14 on the second draw is independent of the result of the first draw. Notice, however, that we can no longer consider the population as a *frequency* distribution if we wish to treat it as an infinite population. Rather, we must treat it as a *probability* distribution. Consequently, Table 5–7 shows the population we have been considering as a probability distribution.

The sampling distribution for samples of size two drawn with replacement from this population also appears in Table 5–7. It is easily derived

Table 5–7

X	$P(X)$	$XP(X)$	$X^2P(X)$	$\bar{x}$	$P(\bar{x})$	$\bar{x}P(\bar{x})$	$\bar{x}^2P(\bar{x})$
10	2/12	20/12	200/12	10.0	4/144	40/144	400/144
11	4/12	44/12	484/12	10.5	16/144	168/144	1,764/144
12	3/12	36/12	432/12	11.0	28/144	308/144	3,388/144
13	2/12	26/12	338/12	11.5	32/144	368/144	4,232/144
14	1/12	14/12	196/12	12.0	29/144	348/144	4,176/144
	12/12	140/12	1,650/12	12.5	20/144	250/144	3,125/144
				13.0	10/144	130/144	1,690/144
				13.5	4/144	54/144	729/144
				14.0	1/144	14/144	196/144
					144/144	1,680/144	19,700/144

$$m(X) = \Sigma XP(X) = 140/12 \simeq 11.67$$

$$\sigma_X = \sqrt{\Sigma X^2P(X) - [m(X)]^2}$$

$$= \sqrt{\frac{1650}{12} - \left(\frac{140}{12}\right)^2}$$

$$\simeq \sqrt{137.500000 - 136.111111}$$

$$= \sqrt{1.388889} \simeq 1.179$$

$$m(\bar{x}) = \Sigma \bar{x}P(\bar{x}) = 1,680/144 \simeq 11.67$$

$$\sigma_{\bar{x}} = \sqrt{\Sigma \bar{x}^2P(\bar{x}) - [m(\bar{x})]^2}$$

$$= \sqrt{\frac{19,700}{144} - \left(\frac{1,680}{144}\right)^2}$$

$$= 1/12\sqrt{19,700 - \frac{(1,680)^2}{144}}$$

$$= 1/12\sqrt{19,700 - 19,600}$$

$$= 1/12\sqrt{100}$$

$$\simeq 0.833$$

from the elementary rules of probability discussed in Chapter 1, as a couple of examples will indicate. A value of $\bar{x} = 10.0$ is possible as a result of the sampling procedure. Since the sample must consist of two values of 10 for the mean to equal 10.0, the probability of this result is equal to the probability of drawing 10 on two successive selections. The distribution for the population shows that the probability of drawing a 10 on any selection is 2/12. Consequently, $P(\bar{x} = 10.0) = (2/12)(2/12) = 4/144$. As another example, the sample mean will be $\bar{x} = 10.5$ if the sample contains values of 10 and 11. This can happen by drawing a 10 first and an 11 second, or an 11 first and then a 10. Thus, the probability for a mean of 10.5 is $P(\bar{x} = 10.5) = (2/12)(4/12) + (4/12)(2/12) = 16/144$.

Since the distributions of Table 5–7 are probability distributions, their means and standard deviations are calculated by the formulas presented in Chapter 3. The mean and standard deviation of the population have the same values, of course, as they were found to have in the frequency distribution of Table 5–6. The mean of the sampling distribution is equal to the mean of the population, as before. Comparing the standard deviations of the two sampling distributions of Table 5–6 and Table 5–7, it will be noted that the latter is somewhat larger (0.833, as compared to 0.795). This is the natural result of the fact that sampling with replacement allows extreme values (such as $\bar{x} = 14$, which appears in the distribution of Table 5–7 but not in the distribution of Table 5–6) a greater probability of occurrence.

Once again, however, there is a definite relationship between the standard deviation of the sampling distribution and the standard deviation of the population. This relationship can be guessed by examining the relationship for finite populations,

$$\sigma_{\bar{x}} = \frac{\sigma_X}{\sqrt{n}} \sqrt{\frac{N - n}{N - 1}},$$

and inquiring what would be the effect of increasing the value of N indefinitely. Evidently, the term $\sqrt{\frac{N - n}{N - 1}}$ would come closer and closer to unity, since the relative size of $N - n$ (for n fixed) would increase when compared to the size of $N - 1$. Replacing this term with a value of one in the relationship for finite populations leads to the relationship as it exists for infinite populations: $\sigma_{\bar{x}} = \frac{\sigma_X}{\sqrt{n}}$. This relationship can be verified in the present case. In Table 5–7, it is shown that $\sigma_X = 1.179$. The relationship indicates that

$$\sigma_{\bar{x}} = \frac{1.179}{\sqrt{2}} \simeq 0.834,$$

which agrees with the value calculated in Table 5–7, except for differences of rounding.

It has been indicated that for either a finite or an infinite population, the mean of the sampling distribution of sample means equals the mean of the population. Moreover, there is a definite relationship between the standard deviation of the population and the standard deviation of the sampling distribution. The form of this relationship differs, depending on whether the population is finite or infinite. In the case of a large finite population, however, if the sample size is small relative to the population size, there is little advantage to using the finite relationship. This is true because the term $\sqrt{\frac{N - n}{N - 1}}$ becomes close to one. To use some rather odd figures that fit the formula well, suppose that $N = 1,001$, $n = 51$. Then

$$\sqrt{\frac{N-n}{N-1}} = \sqrt{\frac{950}{1,000}} \simeq 0.975 \text{ and } \sigma_{\bar{x}} = \frac{\sigma_x}{\sqrt{n}}(0.975) \text{ which is nearly } \sigma_{\bar{x}} = \frac{\sigma_x}{\sqrt{n}}.$$

As a matter of fact, using the relationship for infinite populations actually lends an element of conservatism which may be desirable in certain problems of inference, since it will lead to a larger value for the standard deviation of the sampling distribution. This point will become clear as we discuss inference procedures based on these relationships.

One final comparison between the population and the sampling distribution of the mean is helpful. This is the fact that the sampling distribution will be less skewed than the population, if in fact the latter is skewed. If the population is itself symmetrical, the sampling distribution will be also. The reduction in skewness could be demonstrated in the same manner as before by calculating the coefficients of skewness for the respective distributions. It is easier to make a visual appeal by presenting graphs of

Figure 5–3

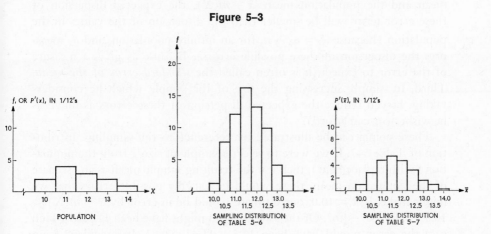

the distributions, as in Figure 5–3. It is easy to see that the sampling distributions are less skewed than the population.

The sampling distribution of the mean and the normal distribution

We have discusssed the sampling distribution of the mean as if all possible samples were selected. This was merely a device to point up the differences between a population and the sampling distribution and to illustrate the relationships between them. In actual practice, of course, the statistician who is investigating a population will not endeavor to select all possible samples of a given size from that population. His problem is due to the fact that the population is too large for him to have ready access to all its values. He must therefore settle for a small part of the total population, and this small part will usually consist of one sample.

The importance of the sampling distribution is that for the one sample which the statistician does select, it must be true that the mean of that sample is from the sampling distribution associated with the population for samples of that size. Suppose that the statistician decided that he would estimate the mean of the population to be equal to the mean of the sample which he selected. Following such a procedure, it is highly likely that his estimate would be either too high or too low. There also might be a fairly large probability that his estimate would be correct.

Of course, the statistician could never know which was the case for any given sample—it might be too high, too low, or correct. But based on our knowledge of the sampling distribution, he would be entitled to believe the following: First, the *expected value* of his estimate is equal to the true value of the population mean [because $m(\bar{x}) = m(X)$]. Second, denoting the error in his estimate as the difference between the sample mean and the population mean, $\bar{x} - m(X)$, the expected dispersion of these error terms will be smaller than the dispersion of the values in the population (because $\sigma_{\bar{x}} = \sigma_X/\sqrt{n}$, for an infinite population, and $\sigma_{\bar{x}}$ measures the dispersion of these possible errors). Because $\sigma_{\bar{x}}$ gives a measure of the error to expect, it is often called the *standard error of the mean*. Third, by simply increasing the size of the sample which he considers taking, he can reduce the expected dispersion of these errors as much as he wishes (or can afford).

These points can be illustrated by reference to the sampling distribution of Table 5-7. If we were to select a sample of size 2 from the population (with replacement), then use the resulting sample mean as an estimate of the population mean, there would be varying possible errors that we might make. If $\bar{x} = 10.0$, our estimate would be in error by $\bar{x} - m(X) = 10.0 - 11.67 = -1.67$. Or the sample mean might have been 12.5, in which case the error would have been $12.5 - 11.67 = 0.83$. It is evident from the sampling distribution, however, that it is more likely that the error would be small than it would be large. As a matter of fact, the probability is nearly one half that the error will not be greater than 0.5. This can be seen by noting that if the sample mean took either of the values 11.5 or 12.0, the estimate would be in error by less than 0.5. The probability that the sample mean would be either of these values is $32/144 + 29/144 = 61/144$. If a larger sample were taken, large errors would become even less likely. Finally, for whatever size sample he chose, the *expected* error of his estimate would be zero, since the expected deviation of a random variable from its mean is zero.

This is all very well and good, but in order to know the probability of making a certain size error, the statistician would have to know the form taken by the sampling distribution. And since he does not know the form of the population, how is he to know the form of the sampling distribution associated with that population? The answer to that question, for a wide class of practical applications, depends on a theorem of mathematical statistics known as the Central Limit Theorem. This theorem has several alternative forms, but for our purposes its substance is:

For samples of size n selected from a population with a mean equal to m and a standard deviation of σ, the sampling distribution of the sample means approaches a normal distribution with mean m and standard deviation of $\sigma_{\bar{z}} = \sigma/\sqrt{n}$, as n increases indefinitely.

Notice that the theorem makes no provision concerning the form of the population distribution, except that it have a mean and standard deviation. It is obvious that an infinite population is assumed, since the sample size is considered to increase indefinitely. If the population is finite but large, the practical effect of the theorem is much the same. Notice also that there is no point in the size of n beyond which it can be said that the sampling distribution *is* normal. The theorem assures us only that the sampling distribution *approaches* normality.

For situations in which the population can be expected to diverge widely from a normal distribution, the size of the sample may have to be very large in order for the statistician to assume that the normal curve will give a good approximation to the sampling distribution. There are, consequently, many areas of statistical analysis where the normal approximation cannot be validly used. On the other hand, much useful analysis of business and economic statistics has utilized the normal approximation with good results. It is worthwhile, therefore, to consider these traditional techniques based on the assumption of normality in the sampling distribution of the mean. We turn our attention to these techniques in the next chapter.

Problem Set 5–5

1. Assume that you wish to draw a sample of two values from a population of five values: 10, 11, 12, 13, and 14.
   a) Graph the frequency distribution of the population, letting X represent the population values.
   b) Set up a table of the frequency distribution (or probability distribution, as the case may require) of the possible sample means for samples of size 2 ($n = 2$), and graph this distribution on the same scale as the graph of (*a*). (Do this on the basis of drawing without replacement.)
   c) Calculate $m(X)$, $m(x)$, σ_x, and $\sigma_{\bar{z}}$, using coded values.
   d) Using the values of (*c*), verify the relationships between the population and the sampling distribution of the mean, as they are indicated in the text.
   e) Repeat steps (*a*) through (*d*) for samples of size 2 which are drawn with replacement.

    f) Repeat steps (*a*) through (*e*) for samples of size 3 (*n* = 3), with replacement only.

    g) Comment on the relative merits of estimates based on samples of size *n* = 2, compared to estimates based on samples of size *n* = 3 (consider only the case of drawing with replacement).

2. Suppose that we are considering drawing a sample of *n* = 100 values from a very large population which is only moderately skewed. Assume, further, that the mean of the population is $m(X) = 1,250$ and that the standard deviation is $\sigma_x = 30$.

    a) Assuming that the Central Limit Theorem is applicable in this case, what would be the probabilities attached to the following possible values of $\bar{x}$?

        i) $\bar{x}$ between 1,247 and 1,253.

        ii) $\bar{x}$ between 1,244 and 1,256.

        iii) $\bar{x}$ between 1,241 and 1,259.

    b) Based on the results of (i), (ii), and (iii) above, set up a table of probabilities for the possible errors corresponding to these ranges.

    c) Repeat (*a*) and (*b*) for the case where we are considering drawing a sample of size *n* = 225.

    d) Consider the probability distributions of errors resulting from the procedures carried out above. If we had not known that the mean of the population was $m(X) = 1,250$, would that have changed the sizes of error included in these distributions, or their probabilities?

    e) On the basis of your answer to (*d*), what appears to be the important factors that affect the precision (that is, the relative dispersion of the errors possible) of an estimate of a population mean based on the mean of a sample?

3. In problem 1 of Problem Set 5–1, you were asked to select a random sample of 10 values from the 100 values which appear on page 153 of the text. For these 10 values which you selected, find the arithmetic mean, $\bar{x}$. Compare this value of $\bar{x}$ for your sample with the mean of the 100 values from which your sample was taken. (This value is approximately 185, as shown in the calculations of Table 5–3.) How does the difference between your sample mean and 185 compare with the differences between the minimum and maximum values appearing in the set of 100 values and the mean of the 100 values, 185?

    In class, all students can pool their individual sample means, and a frequency distribution for these sample means can be constructed. This frequency distribution will *not* be the sampling distribution of the mean for samples of size 10 taken from this population. It will represent, however, some of the possible sample means and should give a reasonably good indication of what the full sampling distribution would look like. Note how the frequency distribution of sample means relates to the frequency distribution of the population as given in Table 5–3 and Figure 5–2 of the text.

4. Suppose that we wish to estimate the breaking strength of ¼-inch sisal rope. In order to get such an estimate, we decide to take a random sample of 36 lengths of the rope and subject them to a breaking test. Although we are not certain of the exact figure, we know that the standard deviation of the

breaking strength of this rope is approximately 24 pounds. If we were to use the mean breaking strength of the 36 ropes in our sample as an estimate of the mean breaking strength of the ¼-inch sisal rope, what are the probabilities for the size errors listed below (assume the population is only moderately skewed so that the central limit theorem may be invoked)?

a) The size of the error is greater than 8 pounds.

b) The error is no greater than 4 pounds.

c) The estimate will be greater than the true mean of the population by at least 6 pounds.

5. For the statements listed below, indicate whether or not they are true, and if they are false, write a modified statement which would be true.

a) The variation inherent in the sampling distribution of sample means is usually assumed to be due to careless sampling methods.

b) For large-size random samples one may assume that the sampling distribution of the mean is normal or nearly so.

c) If a sample is randomly selected from a population, one can expect the sample to be normally distributed.

d) The standard error of the mean measures the amount of variation we would expect to find among the means of all possible random samples of a given size drawn from a population.

e) The larger the number of items in a sample, the larger one would expect the standard error of the mean to be.

f) The standard error of the mean is the difference between the mean of a sample selected from a population and the mean of the population.

g) If a sample of size $n = 10$ is taken from a population, the standard error of the mean for the relevant sampling distribution of the mean will be equal to one third of the standard error of the mean of a sampling distribution for samples of size 90 taken from the same population (assume an infinite population).

h) Because it is probably true that few sets of economic and business data are normally distributed, this fact makes our study of the normal distribution useless.

i) The Central Limit Theorem assures us that the sampling distribution of the mean for given size samples selected from the population will be normally distributed, even though the population itself is not normally distributed.

Appendix A

Several points of some importance which were made in the text can be expanded with the use of rules for expected values (see Appendix B of Chapter 3). We consider these points to give the student added insight into the bases of statistical methods.

First, in the Central Limit Theorem, it is stated that the sampling distribution of the mean has parameters $m(\bar{x}) = m(X)$ and $\sigma_{\bar{x}} = \sigma/\sqrt{n}$. We show these on page 176:

$$m(\bar{x}) = E(\bar{x}) = E\left(\frac{\Sigma x}{n}\right) \text{ by definition}$$

$$= E\left(\frac{\Sigma X}{n}\right),$$

since $x = X$ (the lowercase x was introduced to indicate that the value was one of the population, X, which happened to be selected for the sample)

$$= \frac{1}{n} E(\Sigma X) \text{ by Rule } E\text{-}1$$

$$= \frac{1}{n} (n \cdot E(X)) \text{ by Rule } E\text{-}7,$$

and noting that the summation occurs over n terms,

$$= E(X) = m(X) \text{ by definition} .$$

Thus, $m(\bar{x}) = m(X)$.

Secondly,

$$\text{var}(\bar{x}) = \text{var}\left(\frac{\Sigma x}{n}\right) = \text{var}\left(\frac{\Sigma X}{n}\right)$$

$$= \frac{1}{n^2} \text{var}(\Sigma X) \text{ by Rule } E\text{-}2,$$

$$= \frac{1}{n^2} [n \cdot \text{var}(X)]$$

by Rule E-7, and noting that the summation occurs over n terms,

$$= \frac{1}{n} \cdot \text{var}(X) .$$

But since $\sigma_{\bar{x}} = \sqrt{\text{var}(\bar{x})}$ and $\sigma = \sqrt{\text{var}(X)}$, we have

$$\sigma_{\bar{x}} = \sqrt{\text{var}(\bar{x})} = \sqrt{\frac{1}{n} \cdot \text{var}(X)}$$

$$= \sigma \cdot \sqrt{\frac{1}{n}}$$

$$\sigma_{\bar{x}} = \sigma/\sqrt{n} .$$

The third point we wish to consider is the reason why we divide by $n - 1$ rather than n in $s = \sqrt{\Sigma(x - \bar{x})^2/n - 1}$. We noted in the text that one degree of freedom was lost in taking deviations of the sample values about their own mean. We can show, more precisely, why the adjustment is required if we consider the expected value for $\Sigma(x - \bar{x})^2/n$.

It is shown below that

$$E\left(\frac{\Sigma(x - \bar{x})^2}{n}\right) = \frac{n - 1}{n} \text{var}(X) .$$

What this means is that, on the average over the long run, we would expect estimates of var(X) based on $\Sigma(x - \bar{x})^2/n$ to be somewhat small.

As a matter of fact, the expected value of this statistic is a fraction equal to $(n - 1)/n$ of the parameter value. It should be obvious, then, that division by $(n - 1)$ rather than n would lead to precisely the correct expected value. That is

$$E\left(\frac{\Sigma(x - \bar{x})^2}{n - 1}\right) = \text{var}(X) .$$

An estimate of the population variance based on $\Sigma(x - \bar{x})^2/n - 1$, then, would be correct "on the average." When this is the case, we say that such an estimate is *unbiased*.

We show, here, what has been indicated above: $E(\Sigma(x - \bar{x})^2/n) = \dfrac{n - 1}{n} \text{var}(X)$.

$$E(\Sigma(x - \bar{x})^2/n) = \frac{1}{n} E(\Sigma(x - \bar{x})^2)$$

$$= \frac{1}{n} E(\Sigma(x^2 - 2\bar{x}x + \bar{x}^2))$$

$$= \frac{1}{n} [E(\Sigma x^2) - E(2\bar{x}\Sigma x) + E(\Sigma \bar{x}^2)]$$

$$= \frac{1}{n} \left[E(\Sigma x^2) - n \cdot E\left(2\bar{x} \cdot \frac{\Sigma x}{n}\right) + E(\Sigma \bar{x}^2)\right]$$

$$= \frac{1}{n} [E(\Sigma x^2) - 2n \cdot E(\bar{x}^2) + n \cdot E(\bar{x}^2)]$$

$$= \frac{1}{n} [E(\Sigma x^2) - nE(\bar{x}^2)]$$

$$= \frac{1}{n} \left\{ E(\Sigma X^2) - nE\left[\left(\frac{\Sigma X}{n}\right)^2\right]\right\} .$$

Since $x = X$ and $\bar{x} = \Sigma x/n = \Sigma X/n$,

$$= \frac{1}{n} \left\{ nE(X^2) - \frac{n}{n^2} E[(\Sigma X)^2]\right\} .$$

Note that

$$\left(\sum_{i=1}^{n} X_i\right)^2 = X_1^2 + X_2^2 + \cdots + X_n^2 + 2X_1X_2 + 2X_1X_3 + \cdots + 2X_{n-1}X_n$$

and that the number of cross-product terms $- X_1X_2$, etc.—will be the number of ways we can choose two objects from n:

$$O_{n,2} = \frac{n!}{(n-2) \, !2!} = n(n - 1)/2 .$$

Note, also, that $E(X_1X_2) = E(X_1) \cdot E(X_2)$, since the values of X selected for the sample are independently selected (see Rule E–5). Since $E(X_1) = E(X_2) = \ldots = E(X_n) = E(X)$ and $E(X_1^2) = E(X_2^2) = \ldots = E(X_n^2) = E(X^2)$, we have for the last term in brackets:

$$E[(\Sigma X)^2] = E(X_1^2 + X_2^2 + \cdots + X_n^2 + 2X_1X_2 + \cdots + 2X_{n-1}X_n)$$
$$= nE(X^2) + \frac{2(n)(n-1)}{2}[E(X)]^2$$

and

$$E\left[\frac{\Sigma(x-\bar{x})^2}{n}\right] = \frac{1}{n}\left\{nE(X^2) - \frac{1}{n}[nE(X^2) + (n)(n-1)(E(X))^2]\right\}$$
$$= \frac{1}{n}\left\{nE(X^2) - E(X^2) - (n-1)(E(X))^2\right\}$$
$$= \frac{1}{n}\left\{(n-1)E(X^2) - (n-1)(E(X))^2\right\}$$
$$= \frac{n-1}{n}[E(X^2) - (E(X))^2].$$

But $E(X^2) - (E(X))^2 = \text{var}(X)$ (see Rule E-6).

Thus,

$$E\left(\frac{\Sigma(x-\bar{x})^2}{n}\right) = \frac{n-1}{n}\cdot\text{var}(X),$$

which was to be shown.

On the basis of the results above, we can make a stronger intuitive appeal through Figure 5-1 of the text. Notice that we can modify the expression above to show

$$E\left(\frac{\Sigma(x-\bar{x})^2}{n}\right) = \frac{n-1}{n}\cdot\text{var}(X) = \text{var}(X) - \frac{1}{n}\text{var}(X)$$
$$= \text{var}(X) - \text{var}(\bar{x}).$$

This last mode of writing the expression shows that an estimate based on division by n will have an expected value equal to the true variance, $\text{var}(X)$, minus the variance of the sample means, $\text{var}(\bar{x})$. In terms of the sample indicated in Figure 5-1, the variation attributable to this sample is too small because the reference point is $\bar{x}$ which, itself, varies from $m(X)$. Thus, for example, the deviation $x_3 - \bar{x}$ can be written:

$$x_3 - \bar{x} = x_3 - m(X) + m(X) - \bar{x}$$
$$= (x_3 - m(X)) - (\bar{x} - m(X)).$$

And this shows that the true variance component, $x_3 - m(X)$, includes the component of variation of the sample mean about the population mean, $\bar{x} - m(X)$.

Appendix B

This appendix contains listings of four computer programs. There are two programs to be used in computing the characteristics of ungrouped data. One is written in FORTRAN, and appears in Figure

5–B–1. The second is written in BASIC. It is listed in Figure 5–B–2. There are also two programs, one in each language, to compute the characteristics of grouped (i.e., set out in a frequency distribution) data. The FORTRAN program is listed in Figure 5–B–4. The BASIC program appears in Figure 5–B–5. For a detailed description of the FORTRAN programs, see the appendix, "Statistical Analysis and the Computer" at the end of this book. For a description of the method of input of the FORTRAN programs and BASIC programs, see also Appendix C, following Chapter 3.

The program of Figure 5–B–1: Data input is by punched cards, one card for each item of data. The first seven columns of the card are

Figure 5–B–1

```
C        A PROGRAM TO COMPUTE VALUES FOR THE MEAN, STANDARD DEVIATION,
C        COEFFICIENT OF SKEWNESS FOR UNGROUPED DATA
      1  FORMAT (F7.2)
         EN = 0.0
         SUMX = 0.0
         SUMX2 = 0.0
         SUMX3 = 0.0
     10  READ 1, X
         IF (X-99999.99) 2, 3, 2
      2  SUMX = SUMX + X
         SUMX2 = SUMX2 + X**2
         SUMX3 = SUMX3 + X**3
         EN = EN + 1.0
         GO TO 10
      3  XMEAN = SUMX/EN
         VARX = SUMX2/(EN-1.0) - SUMX**2/(EN*(EN-1.0))
         STDVX = SQRTF(VARX)
         SKW1 = SUMX3/(EN-1.0)
         SKW2 = (SUMX*SUMX2)/(EN*(EN-1.0))
         SKW3 = SUMX**3/(EN**2*(EN-1.0))
         SKWX = (SKW1 - 3.0*SKW2 + 2.0*SKW3)/STDVX**3
         PRINT 4, XMEAN, STDVX, SKWX, EN
      4  FORMAT(2XF9.2, 2XF9.2, 2XF6.3, 2XF6.0)
         STOP
         END
```

punched with the value of each data item. The sixth and seventh columns are reserved for the first two decimal places in a fractional number. There is no column punch required for a decimal point. Thus, the value 12345.67 would be punched in the first seven columns as 1234567. Following the last data card, there must be inserted a signal card consisting of all nines punched in the first seven columns. This card signals the computer that all data have been processed prior to it. Output of the program is printed in one line in the following order: mean, standard deviation, coefficient of skewness, and number of values in the set of data.

The program of Figure 5–B–2: Data appear as an integral part of the program. The first DATA line, 400 DATA 100, indicates that there are 100 values in the set of data. The following DATA lines contain the actual values, separated by commas. If the set of data to be analyzed

Figure 5–B–2

```
100   REM PROGRAM TO ANALYZE UNGROUPED DATA
110   DIM X(100)
120   READ N
130   LET T1 = 0
140   LET T2 = 0
150   LET T3 = 0
160   LET T4 = 0
170   FOR I = 1 TO N
180   READ X(I)
190   LET X1 = X(I)
200   LET X2 = X(I)*X1
210   LET X3 = X(I)*X2
220   LET X4 = X(I)*X3
230   LET T1 = T1 + X1
240   LET T2 = T2 + X2
250   LET T3 = T3 + X3
260   LET T4 = T4 + X4
270   PRINT X1;X2;X3;X4
280   NEXT I
290   PRINT
300   PRINT T1;T2;T3;T4
310   PRINT
320   PRINT
330   LET M = T1/N
340   LET V = T2/(N − 1) − T1↑2/N/(N − 1)
350   LET S = SQR(V)
360   LET W = (T3/(N − 1) − 3*T1*T2/N/(N − 1) + 2*T1↑3/N↑2/(N − 1))/S↑3
370   LET K = (T4/(N − 1) − 4*T1*T3/N/(N − 1) + 6*T1↑2*T2/N↑2/(N − 1))
380   LET K = (K − 3*T1↑4/N↑3/(N − 1))/S↑4
390   PRINT "MEAN = "M; "S = "S; "VAR = "V; "SK = "W; "KUR = "K
400   DATA 100
410   DATA 171,164,161,193,183,197,194,224,188,173,175,158,186,220
420   DATA 202,180,199,187,178,188,156,179,185,208,206,177,186,180
430   DATA 173,176,181,174,177,165,168,184,200,234,162,243,166,216
440   DATA 175,172,183,155,150,175,165,182,181,173,187,180,181,173
450   DATA 174,169,190,205,178,181,184,201,196,171,203,197,147,230
460   DATA 153,171,179,182,185,203,216,168,213,210,227,177,162,166,200
470   DATA 221,166,183,206,189,167,163,181,191,179,185,198,190,179,206
480   END
```

contains other than 100 values, line 400 must be changed accordingly. (See Appendix C, Chapter 3.) If the set of data contains more than 100 values the statement, 110 DIM X(100) must be changed accordingly (see Appendix C, Chapter 3).

The output of the program is shown in Figure 5–B–3. There appears, first, a table with columns for the values of X, X^2, X^3 and X^4. This is followed by a row that shows the sums of these columns. Finally, a last row indicates values of selected characteristics of the data, as indicated. The data presented in Figures 5–B–2 and 5–B–3 are the an-

Figure 5–B–3

171	29241	5000211	855036081
164	26896	4410944	723394816
161	25921	4173281	671898241
193	37249	7189057	1.38749 E 9
190	36100	6859000	1.30321 E 9
179	32041	5735339	1026625681
206	42436	8741816	1.80081 E 9
18491	3455381	652802879	1.24733 E 11

MEAN = 184.91   S = 19.1248   VAR = 365.76   SK = .688972   KUR = 3.30701

nual insurance premiums used in the text to illustrate the discussion of frequency distributions.

The program of Figure 5–B–4: The input for this program requires one card for each class of the frequency distribution. The first seven columns of each card are to contain the value of the midpoint of the class. The sixth and seventh columns are reserved for two decimal places in the midpoint value. Columns 8–11 are to contain the frequency for the class. For example, the first class of the frequency distribution in Table 5–4 of the text has a midpoint of 149.5 and a frequency of 3. This information will be recorded in the first data card as 00149500003 (actually, it is not necessary to punch the zeros). Once again, a card is

Figure 5–B–4

```
C           A PROGRAM TO CALCULATE THE MEAN, VARIANCE, STANDARD DEVIATION,
C           AND COEFFICIENT OF SKEWNESS FOR GROUPED DATA
     1  FORMAT (F7.2, F4.0)
     6  EN = 0.0
        SUMX = 0.0
        SUMXSQ = 0.0
        SUMXCU = 0.0
     2  READ 1, X, FX
        IF (X − 99999.99) 3, 4, 3
     3  SUMX = SUMX + X*FX
        SUMXSQ = SUMXSQ + X**2*FX
        SUMXCU = SUMXCU + X**3*FX
        EN = EN + FX
        GO TO 2
     4  XMEAN = SUMX/EN
        VARX = SUMXSQ/(EN − 1.0) − SUMX**2/EN/(EN − 1.0)
        STDVX = SQRTF(VARX)
        SKWX = (SUMXCU/(EN − 1.0) − 3.0*XMEAN*(SUMXSQ/(EN − 1.0)) + 2.0*XM
       1EAN**2*(SUMX/(EN − 1.0)))/STDVX**3
        PRINT 5, XMEAN, VARX, STDVX, SKWX, EN
     5  FORMAT (2XF9.2, 2XF9.2, 1XF10.3, F6.2, F8.0)
        PAUSE
        GO TO 6
        END
```

required to signal the end of the data. This card requires all nines in the first seven columns. The output of the program appears on one printer line: mean, variance, standard deviation, coefficient of skewness, and the sum of the frequencies.

More than one set of data can be analyzed in sequence. Each set of data must be followed by its own signal card with all nine punches in the first seven columns. After the output for each set of data is printed, the next set is processed by depressing the START key of the computer console.

The program of Figure 5–B–5: The first DATA line, 410 DATA 10 specifies the number of classes in the frequency distribution. The following DATA lines record the values of each class: midpoint and frequency. If there are more than 10 classes, insert a statement, 105 DIM X(n), F(n), where n is the number of classes.

Figure 5–B–5

```
100   REM PROGRAM TO ANALYZE GROUPED DATA
110   READ N
120   LET T1 = 0
130   LET T2 = 0
140   LET T3 = 0
150   LET T4 = 0
160   LET F = 0
170   FOR I = 1 TO N
180   READ X(I), F(I)
190   LET X1 = X(I)*F(I)
200   LET X2 = X(I)*X1
210   LET X3 = X(I)*X2
220   LET X4 = X(I)*X3
230   LET T1 = T1 + X1
240   LET T2 = T2 + X2
250   LET T3 = T3 + X3
260   LET T4 = T4 + X4
270   LET F = F + F(I)
280   PRINT X(I);F(I);X1;X2;X3;X4
290   NEXT I
300   PRINT
310   PRINT "              ";T1;T2;T3;T4
320   PRINT
330   PRINT
340   LET M = T1/F
350   LET V = T2/(F − 1) − T1 ↑ 2/F/(F − 1)
360   LET X = SQR(V)
370   LET W = (T3/(F − 1) − 3*T1*T2/F/(F − 1) + 2*T1 ↑ 3/F ↑ 2/(F − 1))/S ↑ 3
380   LET K = (T4/(F − 1) − 4*T1*T3/F/(F − 1) + 6*T1 ↑ 2*T2/F ↑ 2/(F − 1))
390   LET K = (K − 3*T1 ↑ 4/F ↑ 3/(F − 1))/S ↑ 4
400   PRINT "MEAN = ";M; "S = ";S; "VAR = ";V; "SK = ";W; "KUR = ";K
410   DATA 10
420   DATA 149.5,3,159.5,8,169.5,19,179.5,28,189.5,15
430   DATA 199.5,11,209.5,7,219.5,5,229.5,3,239.5,1
440   END
```

Figure 5–B–6 presents the output of the program for the data included in the program of Figure 5–B–5. The columns of the table record the values of X, F, FX, FX^2, FX^3 and FX^4. Note, once again, the use of the "E" notation. The value of FX^4 in the first row is $1.49860 \text{ E } 9 = 1.49860(10^9) = 1,498,600,000$. The data of Figure 5–B–5 and Figure 5–B–6 are from Table 5–4 of the text.

Figure 5–B–6

149.5	3	448.5	67050.8	1.00241 E 7	1.49860 E 9
159.5	8	1276	203522	32461759	5.17765 E 9
169.5	19	3220.5	545875.	9.25258 E 7	1.56831 E 10
179.5	28	5026	902167	1.61939 E 8	2.90680 E 10
189.5	15	2842.5	538654.	1.02075 E 8	1.93432 E 10
199.5	11	2194.5	437803.	8.73416 E 7	1.74247 E 10
209.5	7	1466.5	307232.	6.43651 E 7	1.34845 E 10
219.5	5	1097.5	240901.	5.28778 E 7	1.16067 E 10
229.5	3	688.5	158011.	3.62635 E 7	8.32247 E 9
239.5	1	239.5	57360.3	1.37378 E 7	3.29020 E 9
		18500	3458575	653611248	1.24899 E 11

MEAN = 185   S = 19.0891   VAR = 364.394   SK = .620247   KUR = 3.03955

chapter 6

Tests of hypotheses, part two

Introduction

In this chapter, we turn our attention once again to tests of hypotheses. The formal structure of the tests to be discussed here does not differ from that of the tests discussed earlier. The difference lies in the fact that the tests to be explained in this chapter all involve the assumption that a normal distribution is applicable to the problem. It was noted in the preceding chapter that this assumption will often lead to useful results because of the properties of sampling distributions of the mean which are summarized in the Central Limit Theorem. The justification for the procedures of this chapter lies in this theorem, unless it can be demonstrated, for a particular problem, that the population of concern can, itself, reasonably be viewed as a normal distribution. There are methods available by which this last possibility can be tested.

Before we go on to an explanation of the particular techniques of this chapter, it is worth pausing to offer a strong contrast between these methods and the methods discussed in Chapter 2. It was not explicitly noted there; but the student will recall, upon a little reflection, that the tests developed in Chapter 2 did not depend upon the assumption that a particular kind of distribution was applicable, or that a certain value attached to a parameter of the population. In the test of the two training methods, to determine if one was superior, for example, no assumption was made that the scores of the workers were normally distributed or that the mean score of all workers taking method A would be a certain value. This contrasts directly with the methods of this chapter, as the student will soon notice. The methods of this chapter require such assumptions, whereas the methods of Chapter 2 do not. For this reason, methods of the type discussed in the earlier chapter are referred to as *nonparametric* methods, or *distribution-free* methods. There is a growing use of such methods in business and economics applications of statistics, in those situations where the normality assumption is open to serious doubt. Meanwhile, however, a large portion of statistical work still rests on the type of analysis which is presented below.

Statistical quality control, a second example

The exact form of the test that should be made will depend on the amount of knowledge one has of the population, either actually or by hypothesis, and on the size of the sample which one is able to collect. We begin the discussion with a case where much information concerning the population is given (by hypothesis), and this example will be used to introduce some facets of tests of hypotheses not already introduced in the discussion of Chapter 2. The points discussed in the context of this particular example are relevant to the other tests to be explained later.

Suppose that a large machine shop has set up a production line to produce on a continuing basis a particular type of ball bearing. The shop has a contract with a purchaser to fill the latter's entire requirements for this type of ball bearing. A number of qualities of the ball bearings have been specified in the contract—qualities relating to hardness, alloy composition, dimensions, and so forth. We shall concern ourselves with the problem of meeting contract specifications with respect to dimension. Two aspects of the dimensions of the ball bearings are of primary importance to the purchaser: the mean diameter of the bearings and the variation in the diameters. Consequently, the contract reads that the mean diameter of the ball bearings delivered to the purchaser must be 1.2 inches, and their standard deviation is to be 0.001 inch. Failure to meet the specifications of the contract carries rather severe penalties which the machine shop wishes to avoid, so they are concerned with the problem of controlling these two aspects of the dimension of the bearings.

The first element of control enters in the design of the production process by which the ball bearings will be manufactured. This is largely an engineering problem, and we shall assume that the engineers are able to design a process capable of meeting the specifications. It is a notorious fact, however, that even the best designed production processes are subject to change through continued use. Because of this fact, the machine shop must introduce a second element of control—statistical quality control. The shop must institute a procedure which will allow them to test the diameters of the ball bearings in such a way that they will be reasonably assured of "catching" the process when it begins to deviate from the specifications. One possibility is to subject each ball bearing produced to a careful measurement, but the inspection costs entailed would be prohibitive. The obvious alternative is to institute a sampling procedure in which a certain number of ball bearings are periodically selected from the production stream (in some random manner). On the basis of the result for these samples, the decision is made as to whether the process remains "in control."

The situation described is one involving a test of a hypothesis each time a new sample is taken. Letting H_0 represent the *null* hypothesis and H_1 represent the alternative these hypotheses are, in a practical context:

H_0: the process is "in control,"
H_1: the process is not "in control."

In terms more suited to the specifications of the contract, the hypotheses are:

H_0: $m(X) = 1.2$ and $\sigma_X = 0.001$,
H_1: either $m(X) \neq 1.2$, or $\sigma X \neq 0.001$, or both.

Let us suppose that the null hypothesis is to be tested by selecting a sample of 25 ball bearings.

We need, now, to consider what we can expect to be true *if the null hypothesis is true*. To dispose of it at the outset, can we assume that the diameters of the ball bearings are from a population which is *normally* distributed? The answer will have to be no. It is possible, of course, that these diameters are indeed normally distributed, but we have no a priori basis for assuming this to be the case. What can be said, then? Well, first it might be noted that the population is one of the type which we termed an infinite population in the preceding chapter. Second, although this population cannot be assumed to be normal, past experience with this sort of situation indicates that the distribution of the diameters probably does not diverge greatly from a normal distribution. The significance of this last observation is that good results are likely if we assume that the *sampling distribution of the mean* for samples of size 25 is approximately normal (because of the Central Limit Theorem).

We shall assume, then, that the sampling distribution is normal. What else can be said of the sampling distribution, if the null hypothesis stated above is true? We learned that the mean of the sampling distribution will equal the mean of the population. Also, if the population is infinite, the standard deviation of the sample means—the standard error of the mean —will be $\sigma_{\bar{x}} = \sigma_X/\sqrt{n}$. Thus we can assume the sampling distribution to be normal, and if the null hypothesis is true, it will have the following characteristics:

$$m(\bar{x}) = m(X) = 1.2,$$
$$\sigma_{\bar{x}} = \sigma_X/\sqrt{n} = 0.001/\sqrt{25} = 0.0002.$$

Figure 6–1 is an attempt to demonstrate graphically the statements presented in the preceding two paragraphs. The graph for the sampling distribution is superimposed on the graph of the population. Both graphs are for density functions because of the continuous nature of the variable being measured—diameters. A comparison of the relative heights of the two curves is meant merely to be suggestive and not precise. The im-

Figure 6–1

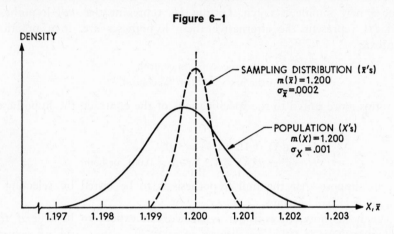

portant things to notice are the equality of the means of the population and the sampling distribution and the comparative closeness of the latter distribution about the mean. Please remember that the figure represents the position and the dispersions of the two distributions *on the assumption that the null hypothesis is correct.*

As before, we must ask, What should one expect of the sample result if the null hypothesis is in fact true? This expectation must be couched in terms of probability statements. Evidently, if the null hypothesis is true, we should expect the mean of the sample which we selected to be relatively close to 1.200 inches. To be more precise, since the sampling distribution would be approximately normal with a mean of 1.200 inches and a standard deviation of 0.0002 inch, the probability would be about 0.68 that the sample mean would fall in the interval 1.200 ± 0.0002. This is so because the interval stated extends one standard deviation on either side of the mean, and a glance at Table C in the section of tables indicates that $P(-1 \leq z \leq 1) \cong 0.68$. In the same manner, it can be determined that the probability would be approximately 0.95 that the sample mean would fall in the interval $1.200 \pm 2(0.0002)$: $P(-2 \leq z \leq 2) = 0.95$. Similar probability statements could be associated with other intervals.

The considerations above make it clear how one can test the null hypothesis. The procedure to follow is to reject the null hypothesis (and accept its alternative) if the mean of the sample is *enough different* from the value assumed in the hypothesis. It must be agreed that a large enough difference is one such that the probability of a difference this large or larger is a specified value, a, or smaller. Since the probability to be associated with a given sample result is to be learned by reference to the distribution of the standardized normal variate, z, it is customary to restate the criterion for rejection in terms of the values that z must take. The procedure will become clear as we continue our example.

Even if the null hypothesis is in fact true, there is a range of values that the mean of a sample of 25 bearings might *possibly* take. Wide deviations of the sample mean from the assumed mean are very unlikely, however, if the hypothesis is true. Suppose that it is agreed that a deviation large enough to occur with probability of 0.01 or less will be a basis for rejecting the null hypothesis (i.e., the significance level is $a = 0.01$). Looking at Table C, we note that a value of z which would *exclude* 0.01 of the area in the tails (or *include* 0.99 of the area in the central portion of the distribution) is about 2.58. The test procedure will therefore be:

1. For the given sample mean, $\bar{x}$, calculate $z = \dfrac{\bar{x} - 1.200}{0.0002}$.

2. If $|z| > 2.58$,[1] reject the null hypothesis; otherwise, accept it.

To illustrate the test, suppose that on one day a sample of 25 bearings yielded a mean of 1.20025 inches. Then,

$$z = \frac{1.20025 - 1.200}{0.0002} = 1.25, \text{ and } |z| < 2.58 .$$

On the basis of this sample result, we would accept the null hypothesis— we would conclude that the process is "in control." Suppose, now, that on the following day the sample mean for 25 bearings is 1.1994. This yields:

$$z = \frac{1.1994 - 1.200}{0.0002} = -3.0, \text{ and } |z| > 2.58 .$$

On the basis of the second sample, we would reject the null hypothesis —conclude the process is no longer in control. In that circumstance, the process would be halted, and the production engineers would begin a search for the trouble with the view of readjusting the process. In an actual quality control setup, it is almost certain that records kept on the

---

[1] The absolute value of z is used because, from the symmetry of the situation, we would be just as concerned with negative values of z as with positive values. More will be said about this shortly.

successive sample results would be most useful to these engineers in pinpointing the trouble.

The generalized test procedure can be summarized in a flow diagram of the type used earlier. Letting $z_{a/2}$ denote the *critical* value of z such that $P(|z| > z_{a/2}) = a$, the diagram is as shown.

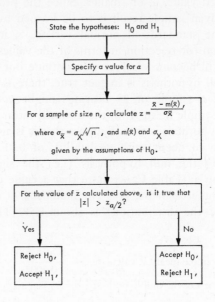

It should perhaps be stated explicitly that the test given here is of the type often referred to as a "two-tail" test. The reason for this is that the null hypothesis will be rejected for both large and small values of the test statistic, z. Extreme values in either tail of the distribution lead to rejection. This, in turn, is based on the fact that divergence of the process in either direction from the desired mean of 1.2 inches was considered undesirable. Situations are quite common in which two-tail tests are required. There are also many situations in which one-tail tests are needed. A manufacturer of elevator cables, for example, might be little concerned if the mean breaking strength were too high; but if the cables exhibited a breaking strength below a certain value, he would be most concerned.

If the test to be performed is a one-tail test, the difference in procedure is that the value of z calculated for the sample is compared to the (positive or negative) value of z_a. If low values of the mean are to be guarded against, rejection of the null hypothesis is made only if the calculated z is less than the relevant value, $-z_a$. If high values of the mean are to be avoided, rejection will occur only for cases where the calculated z is more than z_a. Figure 6–2 illustrates the three situations for

Figure 6–2

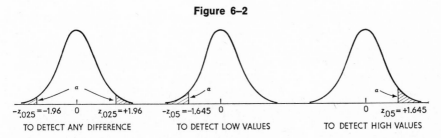

the same significance level, $a = 0.05$. The values of $z_a = z_{0.05}$ and $z_{a/2} = z_{0.025}$ come from Table C. Notice that the one-tail tests put the full value of a in one tail, whereas the two-tail test divides the value of a equally between the two tails. The result is that the critical value of z differs between the two types of tests in numerical value as well as sign, for the same significance level.

It is worth asking: If the sample result leads us to a rejection of the null hypothesis, what should we suspect has happened to the process? Rejection of the hypothesis means that we are doubtful concerning the statements associated with that hypothesis. In the present case, there are two statements associated with H_0: the mean of the process is 1.2 inches, and the standard deviation is 0.001 inch. Strictly, the rejection of the entire hypothesis does not indicate whether one or the other, or both, of these statements is more in doubt. It could be, for example, that the process is "in control" as regards the mean but that the dispersion of the diameters about the mean has widened. In that case, an extreme value for $\bar{x}$ would be more likely than before the change.

The effect of an increase in the standard deviation is indicated by a comparison of Figure 6–3(a) with Figure 6–3(b). The two sets of graphs are drawn so as to have the same mean, but the graphs of 6–3(b) have about twice the dispersion (and therefore about half the relative height) of the graphs in 6–3(a). For each graph, the shaded portion represents the area under the sampling distribution which would fall below 1.1994 inches, which is the value of $\bar{x}$ used as an example above of a case where the null hypothesis would be rejected. The contrast is evident. The shaded area in 6–3(a) is small, corresponding to a small probability that the sample mean would be this low if the null hypothesis were true. Figure 6–3(b) represents the situation where the hypothesis is not true but, in fact, the standard deviation is much larger. In this case, there is a high probability that the sample mean would have a value as low as 1.1994 inches.

Another possibility for lack of control is that the mean of the process has shifted, with the dispersion remaining constant. This situation is illustrated through a comparison of Figures 6–3(a) and 6–3(c). If a

Figure 6–3

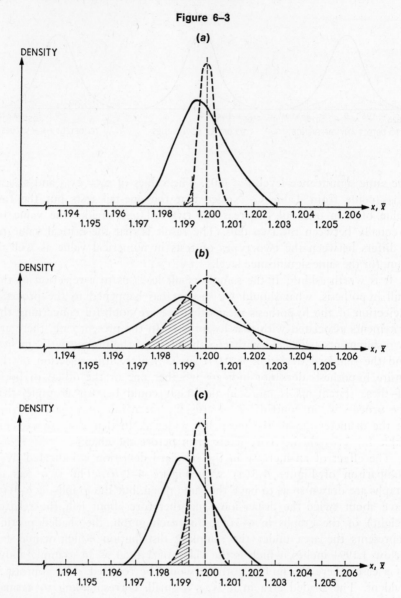

(a)

(b)

(c)

sample mean of 1.1994 inches leads us to reject the null hypothesis because it is too far below the assumed mean of 1.2 inches, we would suspect that any shift in the mean would have been downward, as illustrated. It is easy to see by a comparison of the shaded areas of the two figures that such a shift would make the sample result more likely.

A third possibility for lack of control is that both the mean and the standard deviation have changed, with consequent changes in the probabilities of possible sample results.

It is important to be aware that a cause of rejection of the null hypothesis may be changes in the dispersion of the population. There are statistical techniques for testing this possibility, which we shall not discuss here. Our present concern is with methods of testing hypotheses concerning the mean of a population. In order to isolate that problem, we shall therefore assume that the dispersion of the population is stable —that the standard deviation has an unchanging value. In most practical situations, the value of the standard deviation will not be known, however, and this fact requires that a test somewhat different from the one already illustrated be made. Before we consider that situation, it is convenient for us to continue with the present example in which the standard deviation is known to have a particular value. This will allow us to develop, in the simplest manner, the concepts of error arising from the test of a hypothesis.

Problem Set 6–1

1. In performing a test of a null hypothesis, we calculate the absolute value of z and compare that value to a critical value of z. Indicate the critical values of z which correspond to the various levels of significance listed below (assume a two-tail test):

    a) $a = 0.01$.

    b) $a = 0.05$.

    c) $a = 0.10$.

2. List the critical values of z corresponding to the significance levels given in problem 1 above, in the case of a one-tail test of the null hypothesis.

3. In the preceding section, an example of statistical quality control was discussed which involved the production of ball bearings. In that example, the null hypothesis was H_0: $m(X) = 1.2$ and $\sigma_X = 0.001$. A control plan involving samples of size $n = 25$ and a significance level of $a = 0.01$ was established. With this plan it was indicated that the null hypothesis would be rejected in those cases where the value of $z = \dfrac{\bar{x} - 1.200}{0.0002} < -2.58$ or $> +2.58$. Given these facts, do the following:

    a) Determine the values for $\bar{x}$ corresponding to the values of $z = -2.58$ and $z = +2.58$. (The first value of $\bar{x}$ so determined indicates the lower limit which a sample mean might take and not lead to rejection of the null hypothesis. The second value of $\bar{x}$ is the maximum value which a sample mean may take and still lead us to accept the hypothesis.)

    b) Suppose, now, that unknown to us the mean and/or the standard deviation of the process which makes ball bearings had changed to the values indicated below. For these different possible values of $m(X)$ and σ_X, calculate the probability that we would be led to reject the null hypothesis stated above on the basis of a randomly selected sample of $n = 25$.

    i. $m(X) = 1.20002$ and $\sigma_X = 0.001$.

    ii. $m(X) = 1.2$ and $\sigma_X = 0.002$.

    iii. $m(X) = 1.1999$ and $\sigma_X = 0.0015$.

4. Repeat the steps of problem 3, only in this case assume a level of significance of $a = 0.05$.

5. Comparing the results of problem 3 and problem 4, what do you learn concerning the role of the significance level, a, in the test of a null hypothesis?

6. Repeat the steps of problem 3, but assume that the sample size is $n = 100$.

7. Comparing the results of problem 3 and problem 6, what do you conclude concerning the role of sample size in the test of a null hypothesis?

8. For the situations described below indicate whether the primary interest would be in the one-tail test or a two-tail test of the null hypothesis, and why.

   a) A food processor wishes to maintain the mean net weight of cans of peas at 16 ounces.

   b) A steel manufacturer wishes to maintain the tensile strength of steel girders at 50,000 pounds per square inch.

   c) A gasoline engine to be used on a lawn mower is guaranteed to deliver 2½ horsepower.

   d) A manufacturer of ammunition supplies a rifle shell to the Army which is to contain 0.1 ounces of powder.

   e) The manufacturer of a "long-life" light bulb guarantees that his bulb will not burn out in less than 3,000 hours of use.

   f) A drug manufacturer has determined that an aspirin tablet should dissolve completely in little more than 10 minutes in order for the tablet to be optimally effective.

9. In the situation described in Problem 8(*a*), test the null hypothesis H_0: $m(X) = 16$ ounces, versus the appropriate alternative hypothesis (be sure to state this alternative hypothesis). Assume that $\sigma_X = 0.5$ ounce and set the level of significance at $a = 0.05$. Suppose that a randomly selected sample of 25 cans of peas yielded a sample mean of $\bar{x} = 16.5$ ounces. Should the null hypothesis be rejected?

10. In the situation described in problem 8(*f*), test the null hypothesis H_0: $m(X) = 10$ minutes versus the appropriate alternative hypothesis, on the basis of the sample means indicated below for samples of size $n = 25$. Assume that $\sigma_X = 1$ and set the significance level at $a = 0.05$.

   a) $\bar{x} = 10.2$ minutes.

   b) $\bar{x} = 10.5$ minutes.

   c) $\bar{x} = 9.5$ minutes.

11. In the situation described in 8(*e*), suppose that the standard deviation of the life of light bulbs has been determined to be 10 hours. Suppose, also, that a random sample of 100 bulbs is periodically selected from the production line and tested in such a fashion that their lifetime is accelerated. Suppose that three such tests lead to the values of $\bar{x}$ given below in terms of the life of the bulbs under normal usage. Test for each sample result the null hypothesis H_0: $m(X) = 3,003$ versus the appropriate alternative hypothesis (be sure to state the alternative hypothesis). Set the significance level at $a = 0.1$.

a) $\bar{x} = 3,003$
b) $\bar{x} = 3,001$
c) $\bar{x} = 3,007$

12. In the situation described in problem 8(d), set up the appropriate null hypothesis and alternative hypothesis. Assume that the standard deviation is 0.01 ounce and use a significance level of $\alpha = 0.01$ to test the null hypothesis on the basis of the sample results given below:
    a) $n = 25, \bar{x} = 0.105$ ounce.
    b) $n = 100, \bar{x} = 0.105$ ounce.
    c) $n = 100, \bar{x} = 0.102$ ounce.
    d) $n = 25, \bar{x} = 0.097$ ounce.
    e) $n = 25, \bar{x} = 0.094$ ounce.

Decision errors in the test of a hypothesis

Toward the end of the preceding section, the possibilities were discussed in which the ball bearing process might have gone out of control. The rejection of the null hypothesis leads us to suspect that control is lacking, and by agreement we have decided to consider only the possibility of change in the mean. It should be recognized, however, that rejection of the hypothesis does not lead inescapably to the fact that the process is out of control. It leads us to *decide* that the process must be out of control. But it is possible that this decision would be in error.

To see this, look again at Figure 6–3(a), which represents the situation when the process is in control. Is it not possible that we might get a sample mean, such as the value of 1.1994 inches discussed earlier, which would lead to rejection of the hypothesis *even though the hypothesis was in fact correct?* Of course it is! There is some small probability that a sample mean would be as low as 1.1994 inches. There is, therefore, that same small probability that the sample result $\bar{x} = 1.1994$ would have led us to reject the hypothesis even though it was true. A decision to reject the hypothesis would be an error. An error of this type is called a Type I error. To summarize, a Type I error is committed if the null hypothesis is rejected when it is, in fact, correct.

Unfortunately, the statistician can never be certain when he rejects a hypothesis whether or not the decision was a correct one. The situation is not altogether hopeless, however. He can state the probability of making a Type I error if the null hypothesis is indeed correct. In terms of the quality control example, the hypothesis was rejected if the absolute value of $z = \dfrac{\bar{x} - 1.200}{0.0002}$ was greater than 2.58. Thus, rejection of the hypothesis would occur only in those cases where the sample mean was more than 2.58 standard errors $(2.58\,\sigma_{\bar{x}})$ above or below the assumed mean of 1.200 inches. If the mean truly is 1.200 inches, the probability of this occurring is equal to the probability that $|z| > 2.58$. This probability is easily determined to be 0.01, which is just the value for a in this particular case.

It should be evident that the reasoning above would apply to any test of a null hypothesis. If the null hypothesis is true, the probability of Type I error is just the value specified for a in the test. If the null hypothesis is *not* true, of course, it is not possible to commit a Type I error, by definition of this type of error.

Although one cannot commit a Type I error when the null hypothesis is not true, it is possible to commit a second type of error. Even though the null hypothesis is not true, the sample result may be one which will lead the statistician to accept the hypothesis. An error of

Figure 6–4

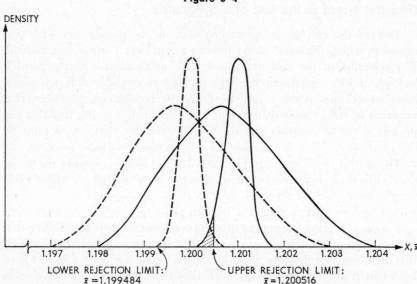

DENSITY

1.197   1.198   1.199   1.200   1.201   1.202   1.203   1.204 $X, \bar{x}$

LOWER REJECTION LIMIT:
$\bar{x} = 1.199484$

UPPER REJECTION LIMIT:
$\bar{x} = 1.200516$

this type is called a Type II error. A case where Type II error might be committed is illustrated in Figure 6–4. The graphs in broken lines represent the positions of the population and the sampling distribution on the assumption that the null hypothesis is correct. The graphs in unbroken lines represent the true positions of the population and sampling distribution, following a shift in the mean of the process.

It bears repeating that the null hypothesis will be accepted, according to the proposed test, if the sample mean is found to be within 2.58 standard errors of the assumed value of the population mean. For our example, with the assumed value of 1.200 inches and a standard error of $\sigma_{\bar{x}} = 0.0002$, this means that if the sample mean falls within the interval $1.200 \pm 2.58(0.0002)$, the null hypothesis will be accepted. We shall refer to the upper and lower points in this interval as the upper rejection limit and the lower rejection limit. The upper rejection limit is $1.200 + 2.58(0.0002) = 1.200516$. If the sample mean should be larger than this value, the null hypothesis will be rejected. The lower rejection limit is $1.200 - 2.58(0.0002) = 1.199484$, and a sample mean below this value will also lead to rejection of the null hypothesis. For any value of the sample mean between these rejection limits, however, the null hypothesis is accepted.

The positions of the upper and lower rejection limits are indicated by arrows in Figure 6–4. It is easy to see that a portion of the true sampling distribution (the shaded area) falls within this interval. This area represents graphically the probability that a sample mean selected from the true sampling distribution would lead us to accept, erroneously, the null hypothesis that the distribution actually had its mean at 1.200 inches. If it were known where the true mean of the population (and sampling distribution) is located, this probability could be determined simply by expressing the upper rejection level as the standardized normal variate, relative to the true mean. Unfortunately, it is because we do not know the true value of the population mean that we have been forced to test the hypothesis in the first place. This illustrates a point made at the end of Chapter 2. We state the hypothesis to be tested as a null hypothesis because at least in that formulation we know what to expect if the hypothesis is correct. Specifically, we know that the probability of Type I error is equal to the significance level of the test, a. If we were to test the hypothesis that the mean of the process is *not* equal to 1.200 inches, however, we could not specify the probability of Type I error unless we knew by precisely how much it was unequal. If we knew that, of course, there would be no point in making the test.

A discussion of Type I and Type II errors leads to an opportunity for another illustration of the value of additional information. It should be evident at this point that if we do not have full knowledge concerning the population, we always run a risk of making an error in the test. It is always possible to reduce the probability of Type I error. All one must do is to set a lower value for a. An examination of Figure 6–4 makes it clear, however, that if a is reduced (which would correspond to moving the upper and lower rejection limits farther out on either side of the assumed mean), the effect will be to *increase* the probability of Type II error if it happens to be the case that the null hypothesis is not true.

This problem of robbing Peter to pay Paul can be avoided if one is willing or able to increase the sample size. Since it is true that $\sigma_{\bar{x}} = \sigma_X/\sqrt{n}$, an increase in n reduces the dispersion of the sampling distribution.[2] The effect of this on Type II error can be seen by visualizing

---

[2] Suppose, for example, that $\sigma_x = 10$. For samples of size $n = 4$, $\sigma_{\bar{x}} = \sigma_x/\sqrt{n} = 10 / \sqrt{4} = 5$. Increase the sample size to $n = 16$, however, and $\sigma_{\bar{x}} = 10 / \sqrt{16} = 2.5$, only half as large as in the first case.

Figure 6–4 with the two sampling distributions shown there drawn in more closely around their respective means. The shaded area representing the probability of Type II error would obviously decrease. Additional information in the form of a larger sample gives more precision to the test and reduces the probability of Type II error associated with any given position of the true mean of the population.

Test of a hypothesis: A generalization

The preceding illustration of the test of a hypothesis served well to point up the main features of such tests. Since there are many different tests, which depend on the exact nature of the hypothesis to be tested as well as the amount of information available prior to the test, it seems advisable to note some of the general characteristics of such tests and to relate these characteristics to the example just completed.

The first point is that the hypothesis relates to some characteristic(s) of a population(s). While the example given was a hypothesis relating to the mean of a population, there are other possibilities. It has already been noted that tests can be made concerning the value of the standard deviation of a population. Another possibility is to test the hypothesis that two or more different sample means have come from the same population, versus the alternative hypothesis that they have come from different populations. There are others.

The second point to note is that the test proceeds by calculating the value of a sample statistic and determining the probability that the statistic would have the calculated value if the hypothesis were true. The statistic of the example was the sample mean. By agreeing that the standard deviation of the population was known and constant, we could transform the sample mean to the standardized normal variate, which led to an easy test of the hypothesis. If we had not known the standard deviation of the population, we should have had to estimate it from the sample; and, as we shall see, the normal distribution would no longer be appropriate. We shall see that an easy test is available in this case, on the basis of a slightly different statistic.

A third point is that in order to apply the test on the basis of the value of some sample statistic, it is necessary that we know the relationship between the population distribution and the sampling distribution for the statistic in question. Thus, our test of the mean of the population carried out above depended on a knowledge of the relation between the sampling distribution of the mean and the population distribution. The Central Limit Theorem was the source of assurance for us that treating the sampling distribution of the mean as normal will usually be adequate in cases where the population is not expected to deviate too greatly from normal. Many of the tests employed in business and economics applications depend in some way on the assumption that a normal distribution is appropriate.

Finally, the hypothesis to be tested is usually a null hypothesis. This assures us of knowing what to expect if the hypothesis is true. The hope is that the decision made on the basis of the test will be correct, but it is possible to commit errors of either Type I or Type II. In order to minimize the probability of both types of error, and to lend precision to the test, the size of the sample should be as large as feasible. The question as to which type of error is the more to be avoided cannot be answered without an appeal to the consequences of each type of error. In the quality control example, commission of a Type I error means that the process will be halted while it is "checked out" to learn what adjustments will be required. Since this decision will have been in error, unnecessary costs of delay and intensive search will have accrued. On the other hand, a Type II error will mean that the process will not be halted when it actually is out of control. The costs in this case depend on the extent of loss of control and any penalties—direct or indirect—arising from the reaction of the purchaser to variation in the quality of the ball bearing.

Problem Set 6–2

1. Consider once again the test of a hypothesis which you developed in problem 9 of Problem Set 6–1, above. For this situation do the following things:

   a) Indicate the probability of committing Type I error.

   b) Draw a graph representing the sampling distribution of the mean for the situation where the null hypothesis is true. On this graph shade in the area(s) which represent values of a sample mean which would lead to Type I error.

   c) Suppose that on one particular day the canning process had deviated to the point where the mean weight of peas in a can was 16.3 ounces (assume that the standard deviation is unaffected). Given this fact, what is the probability that a sample result would lead us to commit Type II error?

   d) Construct a graph showing the location of the sampling distribution of the mean under the assumptions of the null hypothesis (draw this graph in broken lines). Also, draw on the same figure a graph for the sampling distribution which would correspond to the fact that the mean is now 16.3 ounces (draw this graph in solid line). Shade in the area on the figure which corresponds to the probability of Type II error.

2. For the test of a hypothesis which you constructed in problem 12 of Problem Set 6–1, do the following things (assume throughout that $n = 25$).

   a) Construct a graph of the sampling distribution involved and indicate, by shading, the area(s) which would lead to a Type I error.

   b) Suppose that unknown to us the process by which the shells are filled with powder deviates to the extent that the mean powder charge is $m(X) = 0.102$ (assume that the standard deviation remains the same). On the basis of this fact, what is the probability that we should commit a Type II error on the basis of a sample of 25 shells drawn from the production line?

  c) Construct a figure in which a broken-line graph indicates the sampling distribution of the mean as assumed under the null hypothesis and a solid-line graph represents the sampling distribution of the mean as it would exist if the mean powder charge were actually 0.102 ounces. Shade in the area on this figure which would correspond to the probability of Type II error.

3. Work through problem 1, above, again on the assumption that the sample size considered is to be doubled.

4. Work through problem 2 again, on the assumption that the sample size is to be doubled.

5. Comparing the results of problems 1 and 3 and/or problems 2 and 4, what are your conclusions concerning the role of sample size in the test of the hypothesis?

   In a situation calling for a one-tail test of the null hypothesis, the major concern is to guard against the process mean shifting in one particular direction. In such a situation, Type I error will occur only if the mean, in fact, has not shifted in the direction to be guarded against, but the sample result indicates that it has, thereby leading us incorrectly to reject the null hypothesis. On the other hand, Type II error will have occurred only if the mean of the process has indeed shifted in the direction that is undesirable, but our sample result leads us incorrectly to accept the null hypothesis. With these points in mind, work the following problems:

6. For the testing procedure which you outlined in problem 11 of Problem Set 6–1, do the following things:

  a) Construct a graph representing the sampling distribution under the assumption of the null hypothesis. On that graph shade in the area(s) which corresponds to the probability of Type I error.

  b) Suppose that the mean life of light bulbs currently being produced is actually 3,000 hours. Construct a figure with a broken-line graph to indicate the sampling distribution of the mean under the assumption of the null hypothesis and a solid-line graph showing the sampling distribution as conditions actually exist.

  c) Shade in the area in the figure which would correspond to the probability of Type II error.

7. Repeat the steps of problem 6, this time for the null hypothesis developed in problem 10 of Problem Set 6–1. For the case of Type II error, assume that the mean dissolving time of the tablets actually is 10.6 minutes.

8. Discuss the practical consequences of Type I error and Type II error in problems 1, 2, 6, and 7.

9. A large food-processing company distributes its own brand of coffee in a bag which is sold as containing 16 ounces. Long experience with the sacking

process indicates that the actual net weights of these bags have a dispersion measurable by a standard deviation of $\sigma = 0.2$ ounces. This dispersion is virtually stable, but it has been found that the mean net weight of bags filled by the process is subject to some variability. Over a period of continued operation, the process mean may drift upward or downward. It is also known that the distribution of net weights is very close to a normal distribution.

a) If the company were to maintain the process in control at a mean weight per bag as advertised, about what proportion of the bags sold would contain less than the claimed quantity of coffee?

b) Suppose that the company decides that it will attempt to maintain the actual mean weight of the process at 16.5 ounces per bag. If they were successful in doing this, about what proportion of customers would receive bags with less than 16 ounces of coffee?

c) In order to assure the "target level" of 16.5 ounces for the process mean, the company requires a random sample of 25 bags to be selected from the process stream occasionally. The null hypothesis H_0: $m(X) = 16.5$ is tested, on the basis of these samples, with a significance level of $a = 0.01$. A two-tail test is specified.

   i. Why should the company require that a two-tail test be performed?

   ii. Describe the conditions that would lead to a Type I error in the situation outlined above. Whose interests (the customers', or the company's) would be affected by commission of a Type I error? What is the probability that the sampling plan described will result in a Type I error?

   iii. Describe the conditions that would lead to commission of a Type II error. Whose interests would be affected by such an error (the customer's, the company's, or both)? Will the interests of customers and the company be affected differently, depending on the position of the true process mean, relative to the value of the mean assumed in the null hypothesis? If so, why and how?

   iv. Suppose that in the sampling plan described above, the sample mean was as indicated below. What action should the company take in each case?

     a) $\bar{x} = 16.62$ ounces.

     b) $\bar{x} = 16.42$ ounces.

   v. Suppose that, at the time the sample of [iv(*b*)] was taken, the process mean actually was 16.3 ounces per bag.

     a) Is it possible, if the mean of the process were 16.3 ounces, that a random sample of 25 bags of coffee might have a mean of 16.42 ounces or larger?

     b) In these circumstances, would the decision the company made on the basis of the sample mean $\bar{x} = 16.42$ be good or bad? Why?

     c) With the mean of the process at 16.3 ounces, and given the decision reached in [iv (*b*)], what is the probability that an individual bag will be filled with less than the required weight of coffee (16 ounces)?

    d) With the process mean equal to 16.3 ounces, what is the probability that the sampling plan used by the company will result in Type II error? What is the probability of a Type I error?

    vi. Assume that the company decides to increase the sample size from $n = 25$ to $n = 100$ (this is the only change in the sampling plan). How does this change affect your answers in [v (*d*)]? Would such a change in the sampling plan be desirable?

10. A test of the population mean based on the null hypothesis is designed so that as the population mean varies further from the value assumed in the hypothesis, the probability increases that this difference will be noted and the hypothesis will be rejected. Explain.

11. Discuss exactly what the statistician is saying if he rejects a null hypothesis on the basis of a sample result, with the significance level set at 0.05.

12. Discuss the part played by each of the distributions listed below in the process of testing a hypothesis (that is, How are the three related in the test procedure?):
    a) The population.
    b) The sample.
    c) The sampling distribution.

Student's *t* distribution

A quality control example was used as an introduction to this chapter because in some applications of this type it may not be unusual to know (or assume known) the value of the standard deviation of the population. Also, the test arising in such a situation is the most convenient one to use in illustrating points generalized in the preceding section. It is unfortunately more often the case that the standard deviation of the population will not be known. In this circumstance, one can no longer use the standardized normal distribution to perform the test, since the value of z depends on a known value of σ_X. If σ_X is unknown, then we are forced to estimate it from the sample results. Specifically, the standard deviation of the sample, s, is used in the place of σ_X. To show exactly the relation between the two methods, both the standardized normal variate, z, and the new ratio, t, are given below with σ_X and s appearing explicitly:

$$z = \frac{\bar{x} - m(\bar{x})}{\sigma_{\bar{x}}} = \frac{\bar{x} - m(\bar{x})}{\sigma_X / \sqrt{n}} ; \quad t = \frac{\bar{x} - m(\bar{x})}{\sigma'_{\bar{x}}} = \frac{\bar{x} - m(\bar{x})}{s / \sqrt{n}} .$$

The difference in the two ratios is that, whereas the exact value of $\sigma_{\bar{x}}$ is given in the ratio for z by $\sigma_X / \sqrt{n}$, in the t ratio an estimate, $\sigma'_{\bar{x}}$, is required and is based on $s / \sqrt{n}$.

It is evident that the ratio, t, is a statistic, since its value depends on two characteristics of the sample, its mean and standard deviation. Consequently, the distribution of t is a sampling distribution also, with its characteristics determined by the characteristics of the distributions of sample means and sample standard deviations. The *t* ratio does *not* have a normal distribution, except in a very special limiting case.

The characteristics of the *t* distribution were studied by W. S. Gosset, *on the assumption that samples were selected from a normal distribution*.[3] He published the results of his study under the *nom de plume*, "Student," wherefore the commonly used designation of the distribution as "Student's *t*." His studies indicated that the *t* distribution is a family of symmetrical distributions with a mean of zero (which follows from the fact that the mean of the numerator, $\bar{x} - m(\bar{x})$, is zero) and a dispersion which varies with the number of degrees of freedom associated with the sample (which is $n - 1$, the student will recall).

It is easy to explain (superficially, at least) why the dispersion of *t* depends on the number of degrees of freedom. For a sample with a few degrees of freedom, the possible values taken by the sample standard deviation, *s,* will have a relatively wide dispersion, as will the possible values taken by the sample mean. With increasing sample size (and, therefore, increasing degrees of freedom), dispersion in both of these statistics is reduced, but it reduces faster for *s* than it does for $\bar{x}$. Consequently, the dispersion exhibited by *t* is reduced as the number of degrees of freedom is increased.

A bit more insight into the characteristics of the *t* distribution can be gained by comparing the two ratios for *z* and *t* given above. Notice again that the only difference in the two ratios is that σ_x in *z* is replaced by *s* in *t*. As the sample size considered increases, the sampling distribution of *s* becomes more closely dispersed about the value of σ_x. As a matter of fact, as the sample size (and the degrees of freedom) increases indefinitely, the sample standard deviation approaches the population standard deviation. So, also, the *t* distribution approaches the normal distribution as the degrees of freedom associated with the sample increase indefinitely.

This last fact is responsible for the distinction that is often made by practicing statisticians between "large sample methods" and "small sample methods." In some instances, where the standard deviation of the population is not known but the sample is large, the *t* ratio is calculated using the sample standard deviation, but the test of the hypothesis is made by treating this ratio as if it were *z*. It is often convenient to do this, because the statistician may not have a table available for the *t* distribution associated with the number of degrees of freedom in his sample. A sample of size 30 is often cited as large enough that this substitution will yield satisfactory results.

The test of a hypothesis concerning the mean of a population proceeds in the same manner as in earlier tests. The value of *t* is calculated on the

---

[3] Because of this assumption, the general considerations of caution expressed earlier are in order.

basis of the sample mean and standard deviation. This value of t is compared to $t_{a/2}$ or t_a, depending on whether one desires a two-tail or a one-tail test, respectively. If the absolute value of t is larger than the critical value, the hypothesis is rejected. To find the critical value of $t_{a/2}$ (or t_a), one makes use of a table such as the brief one appearing as Table E in the section of tables. The explanation above the table indicates that the critical t values appear in the body of the table. If one wished to test the null hypothesis on the basis of a sample with 10 degrees of freedom, and a significance level of $a = 0.05$, the critical value of t would be 1.812 for a one-tail test and 2.228 for a two-tail test. Note that the table gives areas included in the central portion of the graph, whereas a is the area to be excluded in the tail(s). Thus, for $a = 0.05$ in a one-tail test, we read the critical value of t from the column headed by the value 0.45.

Testing a hypothesis concerning the mean, σ unknown

To illustrate the use of Student's t distribution in the test of a hypothesis, let us consider a marketing problem. Specifically, suppose that a firm which manufactures a certain product is considering introducing that product to a new marketing area. This product is a luxury article, and the firm's past experience indicates that successful promotion of the product requires that the resident households of the area have a mean annual income in excess of $7,500. One question to be resolved before promotion plans are given a go-ahead is, Can it be assumed that the residents of the prospective area have a mean income in excess of that amount? The area contemplated contains well over a million households, making it impossible to reach an exact evaluation of their mean income. The decision is made to gather a sample of 30 income figures from the population of the area,[4] and to test the null hypothesis that mean income is $7,500, versus the alternative that mean income is in excess of this figure.

The hypotheses against which the test is to be made are:

$$H_0: m(X) = m(\bar{x}) = \$7,500, \text{ versus,}$$
$$H_1: m(X) = m(\bar{x}) > \$7,500 .$$

Let us stop for a moment to consider why the hypotheses are stated in this fashion. Remember that the question to be answered is: Is mean income in excess of $7,500? The primary hypothesis cannot be stated in this fashion, however, since there is no specification of *how much* in excess. The primary hypothesis is, therefore, the null hypothesis that mean income is $7,500, and the question of real concern to us becomes the alternative hypothesis.

---

[4] In an actual situation such as the one described, the sample would almost certainly be much larger, and a multistage area sampling technique would probably be used. The illustration is simplified in order to concentrate attention on the nature of the test.

We wish the test to lead us to accept H_1 if we reject H_0. It is clear that only a sample mean larger than \$7,500 should lead to this choice; a sample mean smaller than \$7,500 runs counter to our question, not in support of it. We therefore should reject the null hypothesis only if the value of the test statistic, t, is enough larger than one would expect on the basis of the null hypothesis. Since, as has already been indicated, the mean of the t distribution is zero, we should reject H_0 and accept H_1 if t is significantly greater than zero. The critical value of t will be t_a, such that $P(t > t_a) = a$.

Suppose, then, that the significance level is set at $a = 0.05$, and that a sample of $n = 30$ yields a mean of $\bar{x} = \$7,766$ and a standard deviation of $s = \$801$. First, we estimate the standard error of the mean on the basis of the sample standard deviation:

$$\sigma_{\bar{x}}^! = s/\sqrt{n} = \$801/\sqrt{30} \simeq \$801/5.48 = \$146 .$$

We now calculate the t ratio:

$$t = \frac{\bar{x} - \$7,500}{\$146} = \frac{\$7,766 - \$7,500}{\$146} \simeq 1.82 .$$

Finally, the calculated value of t is compared to the critical value, t_a. In this example, there are $n - 1 = 29$ degrees of freedom and $a = 0.05$, all of which is to be located in one tail. From Table E, we find that the critical value of $t_{0.05}$ for 29 degrees of freedom is 1.699. A comparison of the calculated and critical values of t indicates that

$$t = 1.82 > t_{0.05} = 1.699 .$$

We conclude that the difference is a significant one, and we reject the null hypothesis. The sample result leads us to believe that mean income in the new area is large enough to justify introduction of the product in the area.[5]

A number of observations should be made concerning this example. First, it should be pointed out that the population of interest was large but it was not infinite. The method used to test the hypothesis depends, however, on an assumption of an infinite population. For a population as large as the one suggested in this case, any discrepancy due to finiteness would be too small to have a practical effect on the result.

A second point is that the t distribution applies strictly only where the values comprising the sample are drawn from a normal distribution. It is a well-known fact, however, that most distributions of income among persons are skewed to the larger values (there is no effective upper bound on incomes, but they cannot fall below zero). The presence of this skew-

---

[5] There appears in Appendix A at the end of this chapter a computer program, written in BASIC language, which will perform the calculations indicated above for a set of sample observations.

ness will introduce a discrepancy in the result. Once again, however, the degree of skewness involved is likely to be small enough that, for a sample of the size illustrated, the effect will be minor. Larger samples would give greater assurance.

A third point to note is that while the values for t carried in Table E run out to four digits, the calculated value of t above is carried to only three digits. The reason for this is that given the assumed accuracy of the reported incomes, the t ratio calculated above consists of the division of one number with three significant[6] digits by another number with three significant digits. A rule to follow is that the result of a process of division or multiplication cannot have more significant digits than the least significant of the numbers used in performing the operation. Both numbers used in the division process have three significant digits, and the result thus has three significant digits.

In a case where the calculated t ratio agrees with the critical value of t, out to the last significant digit, a conservative rule would be to round the critical value of the table *up* to the same number of digits. To illustrate, if in our example the calculated value of t had been 1.69, this would have agreed with the critical value of $t_{0.05} = 1.699$ out to the third digit. Rounding this critical value up to the third digit, however, makes its value 1.70. Now, the result of the comparison will be to accept the null hypothesis, which would be the conservative decision to make in this case.

A final point can be made by comparing the critical value of t associated with the test above, $t_{0.05} = 1.699$, with the critical value of z, the standardized normal variate, which would have been applicable. One need not turn to the table for the normal curve to learn this, since the t distribution for infinite degrees of freedom will give the same values. The last line of Table E, therefore, shows selected critical values of z for the levels of significance included. The value of $t_{0.05}$ for infinite degrees of freedom is seen to be 1.645. Thus, the comparison shows that the calculated value of t which will lead to rejection of the null hypothesis must be somewhat larger in the case where there are 29 degrees of freedom than where the sample size is indefinitely large. Notice, however, that the practical effect of this difference is small. For larger, but finite, sample sizes the difference would become very slight. This illustrates, once again, the basis for using the normal distribution in "large sample methods" even though the standard deviation of the population is not known.

---

[6] The last significant digit in a measurement or estimate indicates that the actual value is within one half a *unit* of the stated value, where a *unit* is the size of the measurement interval in which the value is stated. In the above example, the figures are stated in dollar amounts, with no cents appended. The *unit* is, therefore, dollars and the sample mean of $7,766 has four significant digits. If the sample mean had been rounded to tens-of-dollars, it would have been stated as $7,770, which has only three significant digits.

Problem Set 6–3

1. A food canner wishes to maintain a mean "fill" of 16 ounces per can of peas. As a control of the process, he has a random sample of 64 cans selected periodically. Suppose one such sample yielded $\bar{x} = 16.2$ ounces, $s = 0.88$ ounces. Test the null hypothesis, against the appropriate alternative hypothesis, at a significance level of $a = 0.05$. What is your conclusion?

2. Suppose that the standard deviation of the coffee sacking process described in problem 9 of Problem Set 6–2 is unknown. On the basis of the sample results below, test the hypothesis H_0: $m(X) = 16.5$, versus H_1: $m(X) < 16.5$, using a significance level of $a = 0.05$:

$$n = 25, s = 0.22, \bar{x} = 16.1 .$$

What is your conclusion?

3. Suppose that it is desirable that the time required for an aspirin tablet to dissolve be in the neighborhood of 10 minutes. The time required should not be very much greater than 10 minutes, however, if the tablet is to be fully effective. A pharmaceutical company that makes aspirin tablets attempts to maintain a mean dissolution time of 9.5 minutes. On the basis of the sample results below, test the null hypothesis against the appropriate alternative, using $a = 0.005$:

$$n = 16, \bar{x} = 9.7745 \text{ mins.}, s = 0.366 \text{ min.}$$

4. Suppose that the pharmaceutical company of problem 3 desires to maintain the mean and standard deviation of the dissolution time of aspirin at levels so that, at most, only 4 percent of the aspirin produced would have a dissolution time greater than 10 minutes. Assume that the value of the sample standard deviation in problem 3, $s = 0.366$ minutes, is a good estimate of the standard deviation of dissolution times for all aspirin produced by the process: that is, $\sigma_x = s = 0.366$ minutes. With these facts in mind, evaluate the company's policy of attempting to maintain control of the process at a mean of 9.5 minutes, under the assumption of parts (a) and (b) below:

   a) Assume that nothing is known concerning the distribution of dissolution times of the aspirin beyond the fact that the standard deviation is approximately 0.366 minutes.

   b) Assume that it is known that the distribution of dissolution times is approximately normal, in addition to the fact that the standard deviation is approximately 0.366 minutes.

   c) If it appears, in either (a) or (b) above or both, that the company is not achieving its goal with present policy, indicate the alternative possible actions it might take to achieve that goal relative to the values of a mean and standard deviation of the process.

5. An electronics firm that manufactures transistors wishes to maintain a defective rate of 5 percent or less in its output of these transistors. As one feature of its quality control program, random samples of $n = 200$ transistors are selected, and the number of defective transistors is noted. By use of the

approximate approximation, test H_0: $p = 0.05$ versus H_1: $p > 0.05$, on the basis of a sample of 200 transistors in which 17 are defective (use a significance level in the test of $a = 0.01$).

6. The manufacturer of light bulbs described in problem 11 of Problem Set 6–1 guarantees his light bulbs to last at least 3,000 hours. He recognizes the possibility that, due to variation in the process by which the bulbs are made, there will be some cases in which a bulb will not last 3,000 hours. Consequently, he actually attempts to maintain a mean life for the light bulbs produced by his process of 3,010 hours. If a randomly selected sample leads him to believe the process mean has shifted to a value lower than 3,010 hours, he will stop the process and have his engineers check it out. As statistician for the firm, you are asked to set up a test based upon a sample of size $n = 30$, such that the probability the process will be incorrectly halted when the mean actually is 3,010 will not be greater than 0.05.

   a) Describe the testing procedure which you would recommend, including the null hypothesis, the alternative hypothesis, the appropriate test statistic, and the critical value thereof.

   b) Suppose that a sample under this plan yields a mean of $\bar{x} = 3,008.25$ hours and a standard deviation of $s = 6.26$ hours. Should the process be stopped, or allowed to continue?

7. The light bulb manufacturer of problem 6 above will be satisfied if no more than 25 percent of the bulbs manufactured have a lifetime less than 3,000 hours. Since it adds to his costs to try to maintain the mean life of these bulbs at a higher value than necessary, however, he would like his control system to be set up so as to maintain the minimum mean lifetime for the bulbs which is consistent with no more than 25 percent of the bulbs lasting less than 3,000 hours. Assuming that the sample standard deviation, $s = 6.26$ hours, is a good approximation to the standard deviation of the process, advise the manufacturer of what target level he should set for the mean of the process under the assumptions of parts (a) and (b) below:

   a) Assume that the distribution of lifetimes for light bulbs is approximately normal.

   b) Assume nothing concerning the form of the distributions of lifetimes on light bulbs.

8. The ammunition manufacturer described in problem 12 of Problem Set 6–1 wishes to maintain the mean powder charge in the shells he is producing at approximately 0.1 ounce of powder. He has instructed you, as the statistician for the firm, to design a testing procedure based on random samples of size $n = 225$ which will guard against the possibility that the mean powder charge will shift away from the value of 0.1 ounce. He does not wish to assume a risk greater than 0.10 that the process will be stopped when actually it is in control.

   a) Specify the characteristics of the testing plan which you would recommend, including the null hypothesis, the alternative hypothesis, the appropriate test statistic to be used, and the critical value thereof.

   b) Suppose that in the pursuance of the sampling control plan which you described in (*a*), a sample yielded a mean of $\bar{x} = 0.1015$ ounce and a standard deviation of $s = 0.009$ ounce. On the basis of this sample result should the process be stopped or should it be allowed to continue?

Testing for a difference between two sample means

One of the more important areas of application for tests of hypotheses in business involve problems of deciding whether two or more methods of achieving a certain goal differ significantly in their ability to achieve that goal. Where such a decision is required, sample means of the output of each method often are compared. We shall restrict our attention here to the case where two methods are to be compared. As a vehicle for illustrating the test procedure to be employed, we shall use the example of two training methods which was introduced in Chapter 2. The problem, it will be recalled, was to determine if training method A was superior to training method B. In the procedure to be illustrated, the decision will be made by comparing the mean scores of the two groups of men who were given the different training programs.

We wish to test the null hypothesis that the two training methods do not differ in effectiveness. In terms of the scores for trainees of each training method, this amounts to saying that the distributions of scores in both methods are the same. In particular, the null hypothesis is that the mean score which trainees can expect to receive in the two methods are the same (as before, we ignore the question of a possible difference in dispersions). The test will be made by calculating the difference between two sample means, however, so we must utilize the characteristics of the sampling distribution for differences between sample means. These characteristics, and the manner in which they are utilized to arrive at a suitable test procedure, require explanation before we proceed to the test itself.

It can be shown that the differences of the means of two samples independently drawn from two populations with equal means will have a distribution with a mean equal to zero. It is also true that the variance of the distribution of these differences will be equal to the sum of the variances of the two samples' respective sampling distributions. The variance of either one of these sampling distributions is, of course,

$$\text{var}(\bar{x}) = \frac{\text{var}(X)}{n}.$$

Since we assume that the two populations of concern have the same dispersion, the value of $\text{var}(X)$ in the above expression will be the same for both sampling distributions. We do not know this value, however, so we must estimate it. This estimate is found by pooling the information contained in the two samples. Specifically, the deviations of the sample values in each sample from their respective sample means are squared.

These squared deviations are added over both samples, and the sum is divided by the total number of degrees of freedom in the two samples. The result is our estimate of the (common) variance of the two populations. Letting var$'(X)$ be the estimate, this procedure is summarized as:

$$\text{var}'(X) = \frac{\Sigma(x_a - \bar{x}_a)^2 + \Sigma(x_b - \bar{x}_b)^2}{(n_a - 1) + (n_b - 1)},$$

where the subscripts a and b indicate values for the two different samples.

Using this estimate of the population variance, we estimate the variances of the sampling distributions for the two sample means:

$$\text{var}'(\bar{x}_a) = \frac{\text{var}'(X)}{n_a}, \text{ and var}'(\bar{x}_b) = \frac{\text{var}'(X)}{n_b}.$$

Finally, we use these estimates to arrive at an estimate of the variance of the distribution of differences between sample means:

$$\text{var}'(\bar{x}_a - \bar{x}_b) = \text{var}'(\bar{x}_a) + \text{var}'(\bar{x}_b) \cdot$$

The square root of this last value gives us an estimate of the standard deviation of the distribution:

$$\sigma'_{(\bar{x}_a - \bar{x}_b)} = \sqrt{\text{var}'(\bar{x}_a) + \text{var}'(\bar{x}_b)} \cdot$$

With an estimate of the standard deviation of the distribution in hand, we test for a significant difference between the means of the two samples which we have selected by calculating:

$$t = \frac{\bar{x}_a - \bar{x}_b}{\sigma'_{(\bar{x}_a - \bar{x}_b)}} \cdot$$

We could expect this ratio to be close to zero if the two populations have the same mean value. The test of the null hypothesis, therefore, consists of comparing this calculated value to t_a, for a number of degrees of freedom equal to $(n_a - 1) + (n_b - 1)$.

The steps outlined above will be illustrated with the data for the two groups of workers in training programs A and B. The scores for these two groups were: for A—70, 74, 80, 83, 88, 91; and for B—55, 63, 65, 68, 71, 77. These scores constitute two independent samples of sizes $n_a = 6$ and $n_b = 6$. We wish to test for a significant difference between the mean scores, showing method A superior to method B.

We shall test at a significance level of $a = 0.05$ the hypotheses:

$$H_0: m(\bar{x}_a - \bar{x}_b) = 0, \text{ versus,}$$
$$H_1: m(\bar{x}_a - \bar{x}_b) > 0 \cdot$$

The first step is to estimate the common variance of the two populations. This requires the values of $\Sigma(x_a - \bar{x}_a)^2$ and $\Sigma(x_b - \bar{x}_b)^2$, which are calculated in Table 6–1. Using these values, the estimate of population variance is:

$$\text{var}'(X) = \frac{\Sigma(x_a - \bar{x}_a)^2 + \Sigma(x_b - \bar{x}_b)^2}{(n_a - 1) + (n_b - 1)} = \frac{324 + 279.5}{5 + 5} = 60.35 \cdot$$

With this estimate of var(X), we get estimates of the variances of the respective sampling distributions:

$$\text{var}'(\bar{x}_a) = \frac{\text{var}'(X)}{n_a} = \frac{60.35}{6} = 10.06 \, ;$$

$$\text{var}'(\bar{x}_b) = \frac{\text{var}'(X)}{n_b} = \frac{60.35}{6} = 10.06 \, .$$

These values are added to give an estimate of the variance of the distribution of differences in sample means:

$$\text{var}'(\bar{x}_a - \bar{x}_b) = \text{var}'(\bar{x}_a) + \text{var}'(\bar{x}_b) = 10.06 + 10.06 = 20.12 \, .$$

The square root of this value is our estimate of the standard deviation,

$$\sigma'_{(\bar{x}_a - \bar{x}_b)} = \sqrt{\text{var}'(\bar{x}_a - \bar{x}_b)} = \sqrt{20.12} \simeq 4.5 \, .$$

Finally, a value for t is calculated for the two sample means:

$$t = \frac{\bar{x}_a - \bar{x}_b}{\sigma'_{(\bar{x}_a - \bar{x}_b)}} = \frac{81 - 66.5}{4.5} = 3.2 \, .$$

Table 6–1

x_a	x^2_a	x_b	x^2_b
70	4,900	55	3,025
74	5,476	63	3,969
80	6,400	65	4,225
83	6,889	68	4,624
88	7,744	71	5,041
91	8,281	77	5,929
486	39,690	399	26,813

$\bar{x}_a = 486/6 = 81$
$\Sigma(x_a - \bar{x}_a)^2 = \Sigma x_a^2 - n_a(\bar{x}_a)^{2*}$
$\qquad = 39,690 - (6)(81)^2$
$\qquad = 324$

$\bar{x}_b = 399/6 = 66.5$
$\Sigma(x_b - \bar{x}_b)^2 = \Sigma x_b^2 - n_b(\bar{x}_b)^{2*}$
$\qquad = 26,813 - (6)(66.5)^2$
$\qquad = 279.5$

* This is a shortcut computational formula of the same type used in Chapter 5 with frequency distributions. It is easy to show: $\Sigma(x - \bar{x})^2 = \Sigma(x^2 - 2\bar{x}x + \bar{x}^2) = \Sigma x^2 - 2\bar{x}\Sigma x + n\bar{x}^2 = \Sigma x^2 - 2n\bar{x}\frac{\Sigma x}{n} + n\bar{x}^2 = \Sigma x^2 - 2n\bar{x}^2 + n\bar{x}^2 = \Sigma x^2 - n\bar{x}^2$.

The critical value of t against which this is to be compared is $t_{0.05}$ for $(n_a - 1) + (n_b - 1) = 10$ degrees of freedom. Table E indicates that the value is $t_{0.05} = 1.812$. Since the calculated value of $t = 3.2$ is much larger than the critical value, we reject the null hypothesis. The conclusion is that training method A is superior to training method B.[7]

[7] A computer program in BASIC language is included in Appendix A at the end of this chapter which performs the analysis demonstrated above for two sets of sample observations.

Problem Set 6–4

1. With the data of problem 1 in Problem Set 2–4, test for a significant difference in the bricks produced by firm A and firm B using the t distribution (test at $a = 0.05$). What assumption is required for this test procedure to be strictly valid?

2. An identical achievement test was given to two groups of students randomly selected from the student bodies of two different schools. Based on the following sample results, test at a significance level of 0.01 whether there appears to be a difference in the level of student attainment in the two schools; $n_a = 50$, $\bar{x}_a = 89$, $s_a = 4$, $n_b = 50$, $\bar{x}_b = 92$, $s_b = 3$. (Notice that since a sample standard deviation is $s = \sqrt{\Sigma(x - \bar{x})^2/(n - 1)}$ we can find the sum of the squares of the deviations as $\Sigma(x - \bar{x})^2 = (n - 1)(s)^2$. We need the sum of squares for each of the samples described in order to estimate the variance of the population from which, by hypothesis, the two samples come.)

3. In problem 7 of Problem Set 2–4, two sets of data were given on the muzzle velocity of two types of shell produced by an ammunition manufacturer. These data are summarized in the table appearing below, where x_a represents the muzzle velocities for the new shells tested and x_b is the muzzle velocities of the old-type shells which were tested. On the basis of these data, perform a one-tail test at a significance level of $a = 0.05$ of the null hypothesis, versus the alternative hypothesis that the new shells have a higher muzzle velocity. (For your convenience, some of the characteristic values which are required are summarized here: $\bar{x}_a = 3{,}022.8$, $\Sigma(x_a - \bar{x}_a)^2 = 1{,}153$.)

x_a	x_b
3,040	3,025
3,033	3,018
3,029	3,012
3,024	3,008
3,020	3,002
3,017	2,995
2,997	2,990
	2,982

4. The purchaser of 9-volt batteries for his transistorized radio now has a choice of the usual carbon-zinc battery or the new mercury battery. The mercury battery is reputed to have a longer life than the carbon-zinc battery. Suppose that two random samples are selected, one for each type of battery, and these batteries are then played in identical transistorized radios until they are dead. The results of the two samples appear below. Test at a significance level of $a = 0.05$ the hypothesis that the mercury batteries have a longer life. (Before attempting to work this problem note the statement which appears in parentheses following problem 2 above.)

Sample A (carbon-zinc): $n_a = 13$, $\bar{x}_a = 300$ hrs., $s_a = 20$ hrs.;
Sample B (mercury): $n_b = 14$, $\bar{x}_b = 500$ hrs., $s_b = 18$ hrs.

5. The distributor of a major brand of gasoline has discovered a new additive which he believes will lead to increased mileage for cars which use it. In order to test this assumption, he performs an experiment involving 26 new automobiles of the same type. These automobiles are all tuned up and put in their best working order. All of the cars are run on a track for a distance of 5,000 miles at the same uniform speed. The quantity of gasoline used by each car is carefully measured. Thirteen of the 26 cars used the distributor's present gasoline, which we shall denote as Brand A. The other 13 cars used the gasoline with the new additive, which we shall denote as Brand B. The table below indicates the number of miles per gallon over the 5,000 mile distance driven by each car. The values x_a are the mileages for the gasoline without the additive; the values for x_b are the mileage figures for the cars which used the gasoline additive. Test the null hypothesis versus the appropriate alternative hypothesis on the basis of the data given below.

x_a	x_b
14.8	15.7
15.0	15.9
15.1	15.9
15.2	16.0
15.2	16.1
15.5	16.2
15.6	16.4
15.8	16.4
15.8	16.4
16.1	16.7
16.2	16.8
16.3	16.8
16.3	17.0

The effect of additional information, a second look

It is appropriate once again to pause and consider the role of additional information in statistical analysis. In Chapter 2, a comparison of the results of the Fisher-Irwin and the Wilcoxon tests was used to point to the importance of additional information. A comparison of the test just completed to the Wilcoxon test can add to our insight.

In the Wilcoxon test of Chapter 2, the ranks of the test scores in the two groups of workers were used to advantage. The resulting test was an improvement over the Fisher-Irwin test, which did not take that information into account. The Wilcoxon test did not attempt to take advantage of other information available, however. This additional information comprises the exact values of the scores, and it was lost when the scores were restated as ranks only. The question we raise here is: Is this loss of information good or bad? This question is not easily answered. Rather than attempt a decisive answer, we shall consider some of the points that are cogent in arriving at such an answer.

The first point to consider is: Just how good is the information which is lost when the results are stated as ranks only? In our present example, are the actual score values assigned to the workers valid? To phrase the question more exactly, would a difference of 10 points between the scores of John Smith and Albert Jones reflect the same difference in effectiveness as a difference of 10 points between the scores of Albert Jones and Fred Martin? The answer to this is, probably not. The essence of the scores assigned to the workers is probably that of a ranking device at the outset. That is, we might feel reasonably assured that a score of 80 reflects a greater effectiveness than a score of 40, but not so certain that it indicates twice the effectiveness. In such a case, it is rather doubtful that we would have lost any valid information by converting the scores to ranks, as we did with the Wilcoxon test.

By way of contrast, suppose that we wished to test the effectiveness of two methods of making rope. Our measure of effectiveness is to be the breaking strength of the rope. With samples of rope produced by both methods, we could test for a significant difference in breaking strength either by the Wilcoxon test or by the test using the t distribution. In using the Wilcoxon test, we would be required to throw away the information concerning the exact breaking strengths of the various ropes tested. In this case, such information seems certain to be valuable. If the two tests were equally valid from other standpoints, we should use the t distribution and avail ourselves of the additional information.

The effect of such additional information can be pointed up by a comparison of the results for the two types of test in our training example. We have already made the point that for this type of data the Wilcoxon test is probably better. If we consider the test to be for data which constitutes "harder" information, however, we can profit by the comparison. Looking back to Chapter 2, we find that when the result of the training experiment was stated in terms of ranks, the probability of the particular outcome observed was calculated to be approximately 0.008 (see page 60). This led to rejection of the null hypothesis. In a test of the same outcome with the t distribution, the value of t was 3.2, which also led to rejection of the hypothesis.

The practical result of the tests was the same, but let us look at the probabilities arising in each test. It has already been noted that the probability associated with the outcome under the Wilcoxon test was 0.008. Looking at Table E, we find that the probability associated with a value of $t = 3.2$ (for 10 degrees of freedom) is somewhat below 0.005. If the information contained in the scores were valid, and if the t distribution were applicable, the probability associated with the outcome is on the order of only one half that indicated by the Wilcoxon test. Even though the practical result is the same in this case, the t test would force us to place less credence in the null hypothesis than would the Wilcoxon test! Therein lies the value of the additional information.

A second point to consider in the question of which test procedure to use has, hopefully, already occurred to the student. That is the question of applicability. The test based on the t distribution is strictly valid only where the two populations of concern have normal distributions. This leads to the same observations that have already been made elsewhere. It is almost certain that a population of concern to the statistician will not be normal, so that use of the t distribution must be considered to give only an approximate result. For large sample size, however, this approximation will probably be good enough for many practical situations. This is subject to the condition that the population of concern does not appear to be widely divergent, in skewness or kurtosis, from a normal distribution.

The Wilcoxon test, by contrast, is not based on any assumption concerning the distribution of the population. It is valid for any distribution, no matter what its form. It is, however, less precise in its result, as indicated above. A conservative approach to the problem of choice would be to use the Wilcoxon test in cases where the samples are not larger than eight items each, unless there is strong reason to believe that the normal distribution is a good approximation of the populations of concern. For situations where the samples are larger than eight, the t distribution should give fairly reliable results. If the t distribution is to be used, all effort should be made to collect relatively large samples (say, 30 or more) in order to assure good results.[8]

A test of a hypothesis concerning a proportion

There is a class of problems in which the question is what proportion of values in a given population has some characteristic. We discussed earlier, for example, the problem of what proportion of the parts produced by a machine is defective. In another context, the problem might be to make an inference concerning the proportion of persons in a specified area or social group who have some economic characteristic, such as high incomes, low savings balances, and so forth. In such problems, the binomial distribution is often applied, even though the assumptions of the Bernoulli model which were explained in an earlier chapter may not be strictly met. There are two approaches to tests based on the binomial distribution. In one approach, the binomial distribution is applied directly. In a second approach, the test is made using the normal distribution as an approximation for the binomial distribution. In the

---

[8] For samples of intermediate size, say 9 through 29, it has been shown that a test can be based on an approximation by a normal distribution (see Mann and Whitney, "On a Test whether One of Two Random Variables Is Stochastically Larger than the Other," *Annals of Mathematical Statistics*, Vol. XVIII (1947), p. 50. We shall not consider this test procedure here.

following discussion, both approaches will be illustrated. Moreover, the discussion will be utilized as a vehicle for consideration of the point made earlier concerning the relationship between sample size and effectiveness of a test based on the sample. Hopefully, a comparison of this type will be helpful for the student in realizing the importance of sample size.

As an illustration of an instance where the test of a proportion might be appropriate, suppose that an executive of a large insurance company has learned that, according to the report of a national survey agency, less than one half of persons holding insurance policies have an effective understanding of the terms of their policies. The validity of this report strikes the executive as dubious, especially if the same proportion were to be attributed to persons holding policies issued by his company. It is his belief that "not less than one half of the policyholders in his company understand the terms of their policies." He decides to test the null hypothesis that one half of his policyholders do understand their policies against the alternative hypothesis that less than one half of them do so. The test is to be at a significance level of $a = 0.05$ and is to be made on the basis of interviews of 20 policyholders selected at random from the files of the firm.

The sample is duly selected, and the results of the interviews indicate that only 6 of the 20 interviewees are judged to understand their policies adequately. An "exact" test is made by finding, from a table or by calculation, the probability that six or fewer of the interviewees in a randomly selected sample would understand their policies if, in fact, these interviewees were drawn from a population in which one half of all policyholders did understand their policies.[9] If this probability is determined to be equal to or less than 0.05, the null hypothesis will be rejected. Otherwise, the null hypothesis will be accepted. In this case the required probability is:

$$P(r \leq 6 | n = 20, p = 0.5) = 0.0577 ,$$

which can be found in Table B in the section of tables. Since this probability is larger than $a = 0.05$, the null hypothesis is accepted. The conclusion is that the report of the national survey agency does not apply to this company's policyholders.

The student's reaction to this conclusion may be one of dismay. A sample result in which only three tenths of the interviewees had adequate understanding of their policies was the basis for rejecting the conclusion that less than half of the company's policyholders understand their

---

[9] The word "exact" appears in quotation marks above because one cannot strictly suppose that the Bernoulli assumptions hold and the binomial distribution is therefore not strictly correct. It would be a useful exercise for the student to consider in what ways the assumptions are not correct and to assess the effect of these discrepancies on the validity of the test.

policies! There are two reasons for this seeming anomaly. One reason is the manner in which the hypotheses were stated. The statement was such that the burden of the proof lay in showing that the proportion was definitely (significantly) less than one half. The second factor is the small size of the sample. For a sample as small as $n = 20$, quite wide divergences of the sample result are consistent with the null hypothesis, if the value of a is not large.[10] The combined effect of these two considerations is that a rather small sample proportion is required before the null hypothesis can be rejected.

The burden of proof for the sample result could have been reversed if, at the outset, the alternative to the null hypothesis had been that "more than half of the policyholders of the company understand their policies." In this case, the proportion of interviewees who had adequate understanding of their policies would have to be significantly *larger* than one half in order for the conclusion to be that the national finding did not apply to the company.

The problem of wide divergences being required to bring rejection of the null hypothesis is avoided, to whatever degree is wished, simply by increasing the sample size. The point can be underscored by considering the outcome of the test if in a random sample of 100 interviewees only three tenths of the interviewees were judged to understand their policies. This proportion is the same as for the results specified for the sample of size 20, but the outcome is quite different. In this case the probability of this wide a divergence in the sample result is

$$P(r \leq 30 | n = 100, p = 0.5) < 0.0001 \ ,$$

which is much below the significance level of 0.05. Thus, the null hypothesis would be rejected. The conclusion would be that less than one half of the company's policyholders understand their policies. This conclusion would hold, it turns out, if a sample of 100 had 41 or fewer interviewees who understood their policies. A binomial table for $n = 100$ and $p = 0.5$ indicates that:

$$P(r \leq 41 | n = 100, p = 0.5) = 0.0443 \ , \text{and}$$
$$P(r \leq 42 | n = 100, p = 0.5) = 0.0666 \ ,$$

which makes $r = 41$ the critical value for $a = 0.05$.

Test of a proportion, the normal approximation

If a test of the type above is to be made on the basis of a large sample (large in absolute terms, but still small as a proportion of the population to be sampled), the test is often performed by using a normal approximation to the binomial distribution. In that case, the normal distribution

---

[10] In most cases, relatively small values of a are considered desirable. Typically, the significance level seems to be set at 0.05 or smaller.

which is used is one with a mean and standard deviation equal to the binomial distribution which would be applicable if the null hypothesis were in fact true.

To illustrate, we consider a test of the hypotheses stated above at the same significance level of $a = 0.05$. We shall determine the outcome of the test on the assumption that a sample of size $n = 100$ yields 41 interviewees who understand their policies. We have seen already that this sample result would lead to rejection of the null hypothesis under the "exact" test.

In order to test a hypothesis on the basis of the normal distribution, we must express the divergence of the sample result from the appropriately specified mean value in standard units. That is, we need the value of z for the sample result, where

$$z = \frac{\text{Sample result} - \text{assumed mean}}{\text{Standard error}} .$$

The sample result in our problem is the number of interviewees with adequate knowledge of their policies, denoted by r. The appropriate value for the assumed mean is the mean of the binomial distribution for $n = 100$ and $p = 0.5$, since these are the parameter values associated with the null hypothesis and the test procedure. Thus, letting μ denote the value of the mean, the assumed mean is $\mu = np = (100)(0.5) = 50$. The value of the standard error will be the standard deviation for a binomial distribution with $n = 100$ and $p = 0.5$, or $\sigma = \sqrt{(np(1 - p)} = \sqrt{(100)(0.5)(0.5)} = 5$.

Recall, now, that when we wish to approximate a discrete distribution such as the binomial distribution with a continuous distribution such as the normal distribution, we must correct for the difference in the nature of the variables (see Chapter 4). We wish to approximate the probability that r would be less than or equal to 41, so that the value we enter for the sample result in calculating z is 41.5.

Substituting the appropriate values of the sample result, assumed mean, and standard error, we arrive at a value for z of:

$$z = \frac{41.5 - 50}{5} = -1.7 .$$

Table C in the section of tables indicates that $P(z < -1.7) = 0.0446$, which leads us to reject the null hypothesis. The outcome of the test is the same as in the "exact" method. Notice, also, that the probabilities associated with the sample results stated in the two ways are substantially the same (0.0443 in the "exact" case, as compared to 0.0446 in the approximation). Usually one can expect the approximation to yield good enough results for most practical business applications if the points made in Chapter 4 are observed.

Problem Set 6–5

1. Suppose that in 10 tosses of a coin only one "head" occurs. On the basis of this information, test the hypothesis that the coin is a fair one, versus the appropriate alternative hypothesis, at a significance level of $a = 0.05$.

2. A manufacturer of a certain type of paper bag is content if he can maintain a defective rate among these bags of 10 percent. He has instituted a program of statistical quality control which requires that a random sample of 20 bags be selected from the production stream periodically. On the basis of the results in each of these samples, a test is made of the null hypothesis, H_0: $p = 0.10$, versus the alternative hypothesis, H_1: $p > 0.10$. Under an exact testing procedure, what will be the critical value of r if the manufacturer wishes the probability of Type I error not to exceed 0.10?

3. It is sometimes possible with the procedures of the preceeding section to test whether or not people have a distinct preference for one product over another. This is done by making the assumption of "no preference" correspond to the null hypothesis H_0: $p = 0.5$. For example, suppose that 20 persons are selected at random to act as subjects in a test for preference between two brands of coffee, Coffee A and Coffee B. These 20 persons each receive two cups of coffee. One cup contains Coffee A and the other cup contains Coffee B, but the person is unaware of which cup contains which brand of coffee. Each person is asked to taste the two cups of coffee until he decides which one he prefers, and his preference is noted, although he is not informed of which brand coffee he chose. Suppose that the results of the experiment were that 17 of the 20 persons preferred Coffee A to Coffee B. On the basis of these results, test the null hypothesis versus the alternative that Coffee A is preferred to Coffee B at a level of significance of $a = 0.01$. Use both an exact test and an approximate test.

4. An electronics firm that manufactures transistors wishes to maintain a defective rate of 5 percent or less in its output of these transistors. As one feature of its quality control program, random samples of $n = 200$ transistors are selected, and the number of defective transistors is noted. By use of the appropriate approximation, test H_0: $p = 0.05$, versus H_1: $p > 0.05$, on the basis of a sample of 200 transistors in which 17 were defective (use $a = 0.01$).

5. A student is given an examination consisting of 20 multiple-choice questions with four alternative answers to each question. Only one of the four alternatives listed with each question is correct. Suppose that the student answers half of the 20 questions correctly. On the basis of this result, test the null hypothesis corresponding to the assumption that the student knows nothing about the material on which he is being examined, versus the alternative hypothesis which would be appropriate. Do this with an exact test.

6. The public relations staff of a television network has as its goal to attract 40 percent of television viewers in a large metropolitan area to their network during a particular time on Monday evening. In order to test the effectiveness of their public relations program, they periodically select a random

sample of 1,000 television viewers from the metropolitan area. These 1,000 persons are asked what television program they are watching at that time Monday evening. Suppose that, on one particular Monday evening, 365 of the 1,000 persons asked said that they were watching the network's program. On the basis of this result, test the null hypothesis against the appropriate alternative hypothesis, using a level of significance of $a = 0.10$.

A test of a hypothesis concerning two or more proportions

One is sometimes interested in testing a hypothesis that two or more proportions are significantly different from one another. An approximate test for such a hypothesis is based on a statistic which we have not mentioned heretofore, the chi-square (χ^2) statistic. We shall depart from previous practice, in that we shall not discuss an exact interpretation of the chi-square statistic and situations in which it is strictly appropriate. Suffice it to say that the chi-square distribution is developed on the assumption that the population from which the sample statistic is drawn has a normal distribution. Consequently, all the caveats issued earlier apply here also, and the test should be used only for large samples. An example and ensuing remarks will be sufficient to indicate the nature of situations in which the test might be applied and the procedure for making the test.

To illustrate the test, suppose that an advertising agency wishes to determine whether an ad it has been running in a certain magazine has different appeal for men than for women. It is decided to sample readers of the magazine and find what numbers of men and women readers in the sample are able to remember the ad. Suppose that a sample of 225 readers is randomly selected and questioned, with results as indicated in the table below. From the table we learn that, of the men, a proportion of $70/120 \simeq 0.583$ remembered the ad.

	Remember	Do Not Remember	Total
Men	70	50	120
Women	55	50	105
Total	125	100	225

Of the women, only a proportion of $55/105 \simeq 0.524$ remembered the ad. The question is: Is the difference in these sample proportions large enough to support the hypothesis that men and women readers of the magazine display different receptiveness to the ad?

The null hypothesis is, as usual, that there is no difference in receptiveness. If the null hypothesis were true, what might one expect to be the result of the sample? Evidently, the proportion of women (and men) readers who remembered the ad should be the same as the proportion of all readers in the sample who remembered the ad. That is, if the null hypothesis were supported exactly by the sample results, the proportion of women (and men) readers who remembered the ad would be $125/225 \simeq 0.556$. Also, the proportion of women (and men) readers who did not remember the ad would be $100/225 \simeq 0.444$. Thus, on the basis of the null hypothesis, we could *expect* the breakdown of the sample results to be as follows:

Number of men who remembered: $(0.556)(120) = 66.72$;
Number of women who remembered: $(0.556)(105) = 58.38$;
Number of men who did not remember: $(0.444)(120) = 53.28$;
Number of women who did not remember: $(0.444)(105) = 46.62$.

Letting f denote the numbers who actually did or did not remember the ad, and f_e denote the *expected* numbers under the null hypothesis, the two sets of numbers can be compared in a table as below:

	Remember	Do Not Remember	Total
Men	$f = 70$ $f_e = 66.72$	$f = 50$ $f_e = 53.28$	120 120
Women	$f = 55$ $f_e = 58.38$	$f = 50$ $f_e = 46.62$	105 105
Total	125 125.1*	100 99.9*	225 225

* These totals are "off" by 0.1 because of rounding errors.

The chi-square statistic is calculated from this table by summing over the four cells of the table (those not in a "total" row or column) the values of $(f - f_e)^2/f_e$. Thus, for the table above,

$$x^2 = \Sigma \frac{(f - f_e)^2}{f_e} = \frac{(70 - 66.72)^2}{66.72} + \frac{(50 - 53.28)^2}{53.28} + \frac{(55 - 58.38)^2}{58.38}$$
$$+ \frac{(50 - 46.62)^2}{46.62} \simeq 0.8039 .$$

This calculated value must be compared to a critical value of chi-square. Evidently, if the null hypothesis were exactly supported by the sample, all differences, $f - f_e$, would equal zero, and so would the value of chi-square. Conversely, the further the differences, and the value of chi-square, depart from zero, the more doubt is placed on the null hypothesis. Because of the squaring operation applied to the differences in the calculation of chi-square, only positive values of the statistic are possible, and we will reject the null hypothesis only if the value is sufficiently large.

The chi-square statistic, like the t statistic, has a distribution which varies according to the number of degrees of freedom present in the computation of the statistic. In the present case, with the numbers of men and women readers in the sample, and the numbers of readers who remembered and who did not, fixed at the totals shown in the "total" row and column, there is only one degree of freedom. The student can verify this by placing a value in any one of the four "nontotal" cells. He will find that the values for the other three cells are automatically determined, since the values in these four cells must sum up to equal the values appearing in the "total" row and column. Thus, only one entry is "free" to take any value.

Supposing that the test is to be made at a significance level of $a = 0.05$, we require the critical value of $\chi^2_{0.05}$ with one degree of freedom. The value can be found from a table of the type appearing as Table F in the section of tables. In Table F, it is indicated that, for one degree of freedom, the critical value is $\chi^2_{0.05} = 3.841$. Since the calculated value of $\chi^2 = 0.8039$ is much below this, we accept the null hypothesis. The conclusion is that the sex of the reader does not make a difference in receptiveness to the ad.

The table summarizing the results of the sample above is called a 2×2 table, since two classes of readers (men and women) were categorized in two groups (those who remembered and those who did not). Larger tables can be constructed where the number of categories considered meaningful is larger. The test procedure does not vary, except in determining the number of degrees of freedom. Generally, if there are at least two rows and two columns in the table, the number of degrees of freedom are determined by $(r - 1)(c - 1)$, where r is the number of rows and c is the number of columns.

Problem Set 6–6

1. Two young men of your acquaintance recently joined the sales staff of the same insurance company. You have the following information concerning the number of interviews of sales prospects made by each man and the number of policies sold by each man:

> Mike: 120 interviews, 30 sales.
> Pat: 130 interviews, 45 sales.

Test at the significance level $a = 0.05$ for a significant difference in the persuasiveness of the two men.

2. The sample results below indicate the reading habits of 300 persons interviewed. Test at a significance level of $\alpha = 0.05$ the hypothesis that there is no difference in the reading habits of persons which can be attributed to their having obtained or not obtained a college education.

Of the 300 persons interviewed, 50 had a college education. Twenty-five of these college-educated persons asserted that they read 10 or more books annually, while 25 said they do not. Of the 250 persons without a college education, 100 said that they read 10 or more books annually and 150 do not.

3. In order to determine if taking supplemental vitamins in tablet form tends to reduce the number of colds a person contracts during the winter, a major pharmaceutical company performed a test involving 1,000 subjects. The group of 1,000 persons was divided into two groups which were similar in composition with respect to all factors considered relevant to their general level of health. One group of 500 persons was instructed to maintain their regular diet throughout the winter but not to use any supplemental vitamin capsules. The second group was asked to continue their regular diet throughout the winter but also to take daily a vitamin supplement supplied by the company. Records were kept of the number of colds contracted by each individual throughout the winter. The table below summarizes these data with group A representing those individuals who used a vitamin supplement throughout the winter and group B representing the individuals who used no vitamin supplement. On the basis of the results indicated in the table, test for a significant difference in the experience of each of the two groups (use a significance level of $\alpha = 0.01$).

	No. of Colds <1	No. of Colds >1
Group A............200		300
Group B............150		350

4. As an executive in a large public relations firm which has many clients in the television entertainment industry, you are interested in determining whether there is a difference in preference for documentary programs between urban members of the population and rural members of the population. In order to test this assumption, you cause a random sample to be selected of individuals living in urban areas and rural areas. The persons so selected are asked whether they prefer documentary television programs to other types of television programming. The results of this survey are as set out in the table below. On the basis of these data, test for a significant difference between urban and rural areas of preferences for documentary television programming (use a significance level of $\alpha = 0.05$).

	Prefer Documentaries	Do Not Prefer Documentaries
Urban...............600		900
Rural...............600		600

5. A large company has developed a new training procedure which it is anticipating using in place of its present procedure for giving in-house training to young executives. Before initiating the new program, however, management would like some assurance that it is indeed better than the present training program. In order to get a preliminary judgment on this matter, the management divides a group of 100 new trainees randomly into two groups of 50 each. One of these groups is trained according to the new program and the other according to the present program. At the end of the training programs, each group of 50 is subjected to an oral examination by head executives in the company, who are asked to rate them as either falling in a superior group or a satisfactory group. The results of the rating procedure appear in the table below. On the basis of those results, test at a significance level of $a = 0.05$ that the new training procedure is superior to the old.

	Superior	*Satisfactory*
New training................40		10
Present training...............35		15

Appendix A

This appendix contains listings of two computer programs, written in BASIC language. The first of these, listed in Figure 6–A–1, performs the necessary calculations on a set of sample observations to allow a test of the null hypothesis, $m(X) = H$. The second program, shown in Figure 6–A–3, performs the required calculations on two sets of sample observations to allow a test of the null hypothesis, $(m(\bar{x}_a) - m(\bar{x}_b)) = 0$.

The program of Figure 6–A–1: Required input for this program be-

Figure 6–A–1

```
100   REM A PROGRAM TO TEST THE HYPOTHESIS M(X) = H
110   READ N
120   READ H
130   LET T1 = 0
140   LET T2 = 0
150   FOR I = 1 TO N
160   READ X(I)
170   LET X1 = X(I)
180   LET X2 = X(I)*X1
190   LET T1 = T1 + X1
200   LET T2 = T2 + X2
210   PRINT X1;X2
220   NEXT I
230   PRINT
240   PRINT T1;T2
250   LET M = T1/N
260   LET S = SQR(T2/(N − 1) − T1↑2/N/(N − 1))
270   LET T = (M − H)/(S/SQR(N))
280   PRINT
290   PRINT "MEAN = "M; "S = "S; "T = "T
300   DATA 6
310   DATA 90
320   DATA 70,74,80,83,88,91
330   END
```

gins with DATA line 300. The numerical entry on this line is the number of values included in the sample. In the case illustrated, 300 DATA 6, there are $n = 6$ sample observations. If the number of sample observations should be greater than 10, a new line must be added to the program: 105 DIM X(N), where N is the number of observations.

The second DATA line, 310 DATA 90, indicates the hypothetical value of $m(X)$ to be tested. Generally, if the null hypothesis is $m(X) = H$, this DATA line will be 310 DATA H.

Beginning on DATA line 320 and successive DATA lines, the values of the sample observations are entered, separated by commas. Successive DATA lines may be numbered 321, 322, and so forth, or 330, 340, and so forth. If a DATA line numbered 330 or larger is required, a new END line also must be inserted. The number on this line must be larger than the largest number assigned to a DATA line.

The output of the program is shown in Figure 6–A–2. The data used

Figure 6–A–2

70	4900
74	5476
80	6400
83	6889
88	7744
91	8281
486	39690

MEAN = 81   S = 8.04984   T = −2.73861

are for the first of the two samples described in Table 6–1. In the output, a table is printed with columns for X and X^2. This is followed by a line indicating the values of ΣX and ΣX^2. The last line of output records the values of the mean of the sample observations, their standard deviation, and the value of Student's t related to the hypothesis $m(X) = 90$.

The program of Figure 6–A–3: This program performs the calculations required to test the hypothesis $[m(\bar{x}_a) - m(\bar{x}_b)] = 0$. The data used in the program as illustrated are for the two samples of Table 6–1. Data related to the first sample, sample "a," appear in DATA lines 500 and 510. The DATA line, 500 DATA 6, records the number of observations, n_a. DATA line 510 and successively higher numbered lines record the values of the observations. Following the last DATA line required to record the values of the first sample, the data related to sample "b" are recorded in the same manner. Once again, if the last DATA line requires a number equal to or larger than 540 (the END line in the program as shown) a new END line must be provided with a number larger than that of the last DATA line. Also, if either sample contains more than ten

Figure 6–A–3

```
110   REM A PROGRAM TO TEST THE DIFFERENCE IN TWO MEANS
120   FOR J = 1 TO 2
130   READ N
140   LET T1 = 0
150   LET T2 = 0
160   PRINT
170   PRINT
180   FOR I = 1 TO N
190   READ X(I)
200   LET X1 = X(I)
210   LET X2 = X(I)*X1
220   LET T1 = T1 + X1
230   LET T2 = T2 + X2
240   PRINT X1;X2
250   NEXT I
260   PRINT
270   PRINT T1;T2
280   LET M = T1/N
290   LET S = SQR(T2/(N − 1) − T1↑2/N/(N − 1))
300   PRINT
310   PRINT "FOR SAMPLE NUMBER" J
320   PRINT "          MEAN =" M; "S =" S
330   LET M(J) = M
340   LET S(J) = S
350   LET N(J) = N
360   NEXT J
370   LET V = ((N(1) − 1)*S(1)↑2 + (N(2) − 1)*S(2)↑2)/(N(1) + N(2) − 2)
380   LET V1 = V/N(1)
390   LET V2 = V/N(2)
400   LET T = (M(1) − M(2))/SQR(V1 + V2)
410   LET M = M(1) − M(2)
420   LET N = N(1) + N(2) − 2
430   LET S = SQR(V1 + V2)
440   PRINT
450   PRINT "FOR THE TWO SAMPLES"
460   PRINT "       DIFFERENCE IN MEANS IS" M
470   PRINT "       STANDARD ERROR IS" S
480   PRINT "       VALUE OF T IS" T
490   PRINT "       DEGREES OF FREEDOM ARE" N
500   DATA 6
510   DATA 70,74,80,83,88,91
520   DATA 6
530   DATA 55,63,65,68,71,77
540   END
```

observations, an additional line is required: 115 DIM $X(N)$, where N is the number of observations in the largest sample.

The output of the program is shown in Figure 6–A–4. A table for the values of X and X^2 in the first sample is recorded, followed by a row with ΣX and ΣX^2. This is followed by a listing of the mean and standard deviation. This format is repeated for the second sample. There then follows a listing of the relevant values for the test: the difference in sample means, the value of $\sigma'_{(\bar{x}_a - \bar{x}_b)}$, the value of Student's t, and the number of degrees of freedom. These may be compared to the values shown in Table 6–1 and the accompanying text.

Figure 6–A–4

70	4900
74	5476
80	6400
83	6889
88	7744
91	8281
486	39690

FOR SAMPLE NUMBER 1
     MEAN = 81   S = 8.04984

55	3025
63	3969
65	4225
68	4624
71	5041
77	5929
399	26813

FOR SAMPLE NUMBER 2
     MEAN = 66.5   S = 7.47663

FOR THE TWO SAMPLES
     DIFFERENCE IN MEANS IS 14.5
     STANDARD ERROR IS 4.48516
     VALUE OF T IS 3.23288
     DEGREES OF FREEDOM ARE 10

chapter 7

Estimation procedures

Introduction

Our concern thus far in inferential statistics has been with testing a hypothesis concerning the mean of a population on the basis of a sample selected from the population. The inference in this case is the hypothesis, and we allow the sample result to persuade us to accept or reject the validity of the inference that we made prior to taking the sample. The technique is a powerful one and is widely used in many areas other than business and economics. The examples used in the discussion of the technique have been simplified illustrations of situations in which a test of a hypothesis would be useful in a business context.

Generally, such tests are useful where there is a basis, prior to the selection of the sample, for assuming a particular value for the population mean. This prior basis may spring from knowledge of conditions that pertained in the past, as in the case of quality control where the mean of the process may have been known at the time the process was set up. Or the prior basis for assuming a particular value for the population mean may arise because of some desired "target" or "threshold" level for the mean in question. Such a case was illustrated by the marketing example in which a mean income level of at least $7,500 was required before entry into the marketing area could be considered a good risk. Finally, the prior basis for the test may consist of the assumption that one form of treatment, or one set of conditions, differ in their effectiveness (suitably defined) from another treatment or set of conditions. Examples of this type were the alternative tests developed for the two methods of training workers and the test for a difference in receptiveness to a magazine ad as between men and women readers.

It must have occurred to the student that there are many situations in which no prior basis exists, or is desired, for stating a hypothesis about the unknown population mean. Indeed, it is often the case that the statistician must estimate the unknown mean of a population with no prior judgment as to what its value might be. Our task in this chapter is to introduce procedures by which such estimates can be made, and to indicate the characteristics of such estimates. Following that discussion, the topic of regression analysis—another estimation procedure of great usefulness—will be developed.

Estimating the population mean, σ known

As in our discussion of the test of a hypothesis in Chapter 6, it is pedagogically useful to begin the discussion of estimation procedures with the case where the standard deviation of the population is known. It is not likely, in a real situation, that one would know the standard deviation of a population if he did not also know its mean, but the assumption is useful as a teaching device. If the principles of estimation are learned in this less realistic but simpler situation, they can be applied with (hopefully) no confusion in a more realistic situation.

As a further aid in explaining the principles of estimation, we shall stage a small, not too exciting, drama. The characters in the drama will consist of us, the observers, and the statistician, whom we observe. The major difference in the two sets of characters is that we, the observers, will have perfect knowledge concerning the population, whereas the statistician will not. Specifically, he will not know the value of the mean of the population, although he will know its standard deviation.

Let us suppose that the population of concern has a normal[1] distribution, and that its mean is $m(X) = 100$ and its standard deviation is $\sigma_X = 10$. Of this information, the statistician knows only the last fact, but he is willing to assume that the population is at least close to normal. It is his task to estimate the mean of the population on the basis of a sample of, say, size $n = 25$.

It seems intuitively apparent that the statistician should make use of the mean of the sample which he selects in order to estimate the population mean. One possibility is to note the value of the sample mean and to make the statement that the mean of the population is equal to the

---

[1] This assumption allows us to develop the discussion without constant comment on the differences between normality and near-normality, about which many observations have already been made in earlier chapters. Those observations apply here equally, however.

value of the sample mean. Thus, if a sample of 25 items drawn from the population were to have a mean of $\bar{x} = 102$, the statistician would estimate the population mean to be $m'(X) = 102$. Such an estimate is called a *point* estimate, because the statistician has singled out one point on the axis of the population values as his estimate of the population mean. Knowing all that we do about the situation, we could draw a picture of what has happened in this case—as in Figure 7-1.

In Figure 7-1 the point estimate $m'(X) = 102$ appears as a point to the right of the true mean, $m(X) = 100$. The two graphs appearing in the figure represent approximately the relative characteristics of the population and the sampling distribution of sample means for samples of size $n = 25$. Since we have full knowledge of the population—and, therefore, also of the sampling distribution—we know that the statistician's

Figure 7-1

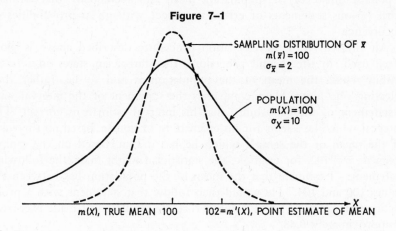

SAMPLING DISTRIBUTION OF $\bar{x}$
$m(\bar{x}) = 100$
$\sigma_{\bar{x}} = 2$

POPULATION
$m(X) = 100$
$\sigma_X = 10$

$m(X)$, TRUE MEAN 100 $102 = m'(X)$, POINT ESTIMATE OF MEAN

estimate of the population mean is in error by the amount $+2$. The statistician, of course, does not know this. He is aware of the fact that is evident to us from an examination of Figure 7-1, that his estimate is almost certainly in error by some amount. But he is not able to say what the magnitude or the sign of the error is. In making a point estimate, it behooves the statistician to say as much as he can about the error associated with his estimate. But, what can he say?

To answer that question, we need to examine what the statistician knows. First, he knows that the standard deviation of the population is $\sigma_X = 10$ and that the size of the sample he has selected is $n = 25$. From these two facts, he knows that the standard deviation of the sampling distribution with which he is dealing is $\sigma_{\bar{x}} = \sigma_X/\sqrt{n} = 2$. He also is reasonably sure, we have assumed, that the sampling distribution is nearly normal. In other words, on the basis of his knowledge, the statistician could draw a picture of the situation much like the one we presented as

Figure 7–1. The only difference between his picture and ours would be that he could not say that the distributions shown centered on a mean of 100 and that his estimate was therefore in error by +2.

If we asked the statistician what he *could* say about the error in his estimate, however, he could make a number of statements. For one thing, he could tell us that the probability that his estimate is in error by as much as ±2 (that is, two units in either direction) is only about 0.32. This is so because $\sigma_{\bar{x}} = 2$ and the probability that a sample mean drawn from a normal sampling distribution will be one standard error or more from the mean of the distribution is 0.32. In like manner, the probability associated with an error of ±4 or more is only about 0.05, since the probability of drawing a sample mean this far away from the population mean ($\pm 4 = \pm 2\sigma_{\bar{x}}$) is about 0.05. The statistician could, therefore, make a point estimate of the population mean and accompany that estimate with various statements of errors to expect with given probabilities of occurrence.

An alternative to the estimation procedure described above is more often used. In the second procedure, the statistician states an *interval* within which the mean of the population is said to lie, rather than selecting one *point*. He accompanies the statement of the interval with a statement of the probability that his interval estimate is correct. The interval which he selects for his estimate is, of course, based on the value of the mean of the sample which he has drawn. Based on the sample mean of $\bar{x} = 102$, for example, the statistician might make the following statement: "I estimate that the mean of the population lies between the values 100 and 104." He would then follow that statement with a probability statement: "The probability that the estimate just made is correct is approximately 0.68."

Let us examine the reasoning underlying our statistician's statements. In the first statement an interval is given for the population mean. The limits on the interval are 100 and 104. They were arrived at by subtracting and adding, respectively, the value of the standard error of the mean ($\sigma_{\bar{x}} = 2$) from the value of the sample mean ($\bar{x} = 102$). Symbolically, the interval estimate in the statistician's first statement is $102 - 2 \leq m'(X) \leq 102 + 2$. The probability of 0.68 assigned to the correctness of this estimate arises from the fact that the interval is formed by adding and subtracting *one* standard error of the mean from the sample mean. Since the probability is 0.68 that a sample mean selected from a normal sampling distribution will lie within one standard error of the true mean of the population, it follows that the probability is also 0.68 that an interval ranging one standard error on either side of the sample mean will contain the true population mean. Since it is also true that the estimate will be correct if the interval does, in fact, contain the true population mean, the probability that the estimate is correct is 0.68.

These points can be made clearer by illustration in Figure 7–2. This figure duplicates the sampling distribution of Figure 7–1. It has been "blown up" for easier viewing, and the graph of the population has been discarded for the same reason. The two vertical lines appearing on either side of the mean of the distribution are placed at distances of plus and minus one standard error for purposes of reference. Figure 7–2 depicts the true situation as we, the observers, know it. Once again, however, our statistician would have to draw his picture without actual values for the mean and the two vertical lines.

Figure 7–2

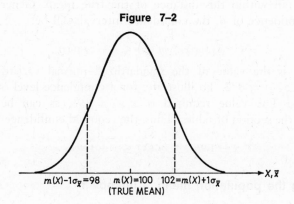

$m(X)-1\sigma_{\bar{x}}=98 \quad m(X)=100 \quad 102=m(X)+1\sigma_{\bar{x}}$
(TRUE MEAN)

Now, let us see what kind of results the statistician might have if he made an interval estimate of the type described above. First, notice that the estimate he made in the preceding paragraph is correct. The true mean does lie in the interval from 100 to 104. It should be evident, however, that if the sample mean had been just slightly larger than 102, then an interval one standard error on either side of this larger value would not have led to a correct estimate. As a matter of fact, for any value of the sample mean above 102, an estimate so constructed could not be correct. Looking at the other tail of the sampling distribution, moreover, it is also evident that any sample mean below 98 would also lead to an incorrect estimate. For all other possible sample means, the values between 98 and 102, the estimate would be correct. Since the probability is 0.68 that the mean of the sample selected will be within this interval, the probability is 0.68 that the estimate will be correct.

Does the fact that the statistician is not able to insert the numbers such as 98 and 102 change the reasoning for him? The answer is: not a bit. Even though he does not know the location of the true population mean, he does know that the probability is 0.68 that the sample he draws will have a mean within one standard error of the population mean. He can, therefore, be confident that the probability is 0.68 that his estimate is correct.

The probability associated with the correctness of the estimate reflects the statistician's confidence in his estimate. For this reason, an interval estimate is often referred to as a *confidence interval.* Evidently, greater confidence can be placed in a larger interval than in a smaller interval. The *level of confidence* we can have in a confidence interval is just the probability that the confidence interval will be correct. If we wished to construct a confidence interval with a level of confidence of 0.95, we should have to construct an interval ranging 1.96 standard errors on either side of the sample mean, since the probability is 0.95 that a sample mean will fall within this distance of the true mean. Generally, for a level of confidence of β, the confidence interval will be:

$$\bar{x} - z_{\beta/2}(\sigma_{\bar{x}}) \leq m'(X) \leq \bar{x} + z_{\beta/2}(\sigma_{\bar{x}}) ,$$

where $z_{\beta/2}$ is the value of the standardized normal variate such that $P(0 \leq z \leq z_{\beta/2}) = \beta/2$. To illustrate, for a confidence level of $\beta = 0.95$, $z_{\beta/2} = z_{0.475}$. The value required is $z_{0.475} = 1.96$, as can be found in Table C in the section of tables. Thus, the required confidence interval is:

$$\bar{x} - 1.96\sigma_{\bar{x}} \leq m'(X) \leq \bar{x} + 1.96\sigma_{\bar{x}} .$$

Estimating the population mean, σ unknown

The procedure for estimating the mean when the standard deviation of the population is known has been used to develop a general procedure for arriving at a confidence interval. In the larger number of cases, the statistician will be required to state a confidence interval for the mean when he does not know the standard deviation of the population. In such a case, he must estimate the standard deviation as $\sigma'_x = s$, as was the case in the test of a hypothesis with the standard deviation unknown. Then his estimate of the standard error of the mean will be, once again, $\sigma'_{\bar{x}} = s/\sqrt{n}$. As before, when s is used as an estimate of σ_x, it is not appropriate to use the normal variate. In its place, the Student's t ratio must be used. Thus, for a level of confidence of β, the value of $t_{\beta/2}$ for $n - 1$ degrees of freedom is required. The confidence interval is then

$$\bar{x} - t_{\beta/2}\frac{s}{\sqrt{n}} \leq m'(X) \leq \bar{x} + t_{\beta/2}\frac{s}{\sqrt{n}} .$$

To illustrate, let us return to the marketing problem of the preceding chapter. It will be recalled that a firm marketing a luxury product believed that a mean income of at least $7,500 was required for its product to be a success in a given marketing area. A test of the appropriate hypotheses on the basis of a sample of 30 incomes led the company to accept the hypothesis that mean income in a new marketing area was above $7,500. Suppose, now, that the firm is not content with the belief, merely, that mean income in the area is "somewhere above $7,500."

They would like to have an estimate of a range within which mean income lies.

A confidence interval for mean income of the area can be constructed on the basis of the information of the sample used in Chapter 6. The sample was of size $n = 30$. The sample mean was $\bar{x} = \$7,766$, and its standard deviation was $s = \$801$. Supposing that we wish a level of confidence of 0.90, we require the value of $t_{0.45}$ with $n - 1 = 29$ degrees of freedom. Table E yields the value of $t_{0.45} = 1.699$. The confidence interval is, then:

$$\bar{x} - t_{0.45}\frac{s}{\sqrt{n}} \leq m'(X) \leq \bar{x} + t_{0.45}\frac{s}{\sqrt{n}},$$

that is,

$$\$7,766 - (1.699)\left(\frac{\$801}{\sqrt{30}}\right) \leq m'(X) \leq \$7,766 + (1.699)\left(\frac{\$801}{\sqrt{30}}\right)$$

that is,

$$\$7,518 \leq m'(X) \leq \$8,014 .$$

The interval stated above amounts to nearly $500. This may seem like an unsatisfactorily large range for the estimate. The remedy is to increase the size of the sample. The effect of the additional information contained in a larger sample is to allow us to reduce the range of the estimate, *for the same level of confidence.* This reduction occurs because of two factors. For one thing, the size of the critical value of $t_{\beta/2}$ is reduced because of the larger number of degrees of freedom. The second factor is the effect of a larger sample size on the estimate of the standard error of the mean. An estimate, $\sigma'_{\bar{x}} = s/\sqrt{n}$, based on a large value of n is very likely[2] to be smaller than an estimate based on a smaller sample size.

Of course, in order to know the size of sample which will lead to a particular range for the confidence interval based on that sample, one would have to know the standard deviation of the population. In cases where the standard deviation is not known, a reasonable and practical procedure to follow is to get an estimate of the standard deviation on the basis of the first portion of the sample selected. Armed with this estimate, the statistician can then arrive at an estimate of a total sample size which will yield approximately the desired range for the confidence interval.

---

[2] Strictly, we cannot say with certainty that an estimate of the standard error of the mean based on a larger sample will be smaller than an estimate based on a smaller sample. It is conceivable that the value of s for a large sample would be enough larger than the value of s for a small sample to offset the reducing effect of the larger value of n. We can say, however, that we *expect,* with a high probability, that an estimate based on a large sample will be smaller than an estimate based on a small sample.

To illustrate this procedure, let us suppose that the sample of 30 income values cited above is considered to be only a part of a larger sample to be taken. We wish an estimate of how large a sample must ultimately be collected in order to give us a level of confidence of 0.90 for a confidence interval with a range of $100. Looking at the general expression given above for the confidence interval, it is evident that the range of the interval will be $2(t_{0.45})(s/\sqrt{n})$. The value of s which will ultimately appear in this expression is the standard deviation of the final sample. At this point that value is not known, however, so we substitute the value of s for the preliminary sample of 30 incomes. This gives us an estimate of the range of $2(t_{0.45})(\$801/\sqrt{n})$. Notice, now, that the value of $t_{0.45}$ is dependent upon the number of degrees of freedom in the final sample, which is unknown to us at this stage. Since the sample which we ultimately will select will be much larger than 30, however, we may use the standardized normal variate, $z_{0.45}$, in place of $t_{0.45}$. Making this substitution, we have an estimate of the range for a given sample size, n, equal to $2(1.645)(\$801/\sqrt{n})$.

It is our desire that the range of the estimate associated with a level of confidence of 0.90 be about $100. To find a sample size that will approximately meet this requirement, we solve for the value of n in the following equation:

$$\text{Range} = \$100 = 2(1.645)(\$801/\sqrt{n}) .$$

Simple algebraic procedure leads to the solution:

$$n = \left[\frac{2(1.645)(\$801)}{\$100} \right]^2 \simeq 695 .$$

On the basis of the preliminary sample of 30 incomes, we estimate that a final sample size of 695 will yield a confidence interval with a range of approximately $100 and a level of confidence of 0.90.

Generally, when one has a preliminary estimate of the standard deviation of the population, σ', (based on a preliminary sample, or judgment from experience), one can arrive at a preliminary estimate of the sample size required to yield a confidence interval of specified range, R, and specified confidence level, β, by solution of the equation:

$$n = \left[\frac{2(z_{\beta/2})(\sigma')}{R} \right]^2 .$$

Problem Set 7–1

1. Suppose that a statistician has the task of estimating the mean of a population. He knows that the standard deviation of this population is $\sigma_x = 150$. If he makes a point estimate of the mean of the population, $m(X)$, on the basis of a sample mean, $\bar{x}$, he knows that this estimate will probably be in

error. The size of this error would be, of course, the difference between the sample mean and the mean of the population, in absolute terms. That is, we can express the error as, error $= |\bar{x} - m(X)|$. With this definition of error in mind, do the following.

a) Suppose the statistician made his point estimate of the population mean on the basis of a sample mean for a sample of size $n = 25$. What are the values for the probabilities listed below:

$$P(\text{error} \leq 10);$$
$$P(\text{error} \leq 30);$$
$$P(\text{error} \leq 60).$$

b) State the probabilities associated with the errors indicated above if the statistician were to base his point estimate on a sample of size $n = 100$.

c) State the probabilities of the errors listed in part (a) if the statistician were to base a point estimate of the population mean on the basis of a sample mean for a sample of size $n = 225$.

d) Comparing the results of parts (a), (b), and (c), comment on the precision to be expected from an estimate as it relates to the size of the sample.

2. Suppose that in the example of problem 1, the statistician took a sample of size $n = 225$ and found the mean of that sample to be $\bar{x} = 1,250$. On the basis of this sample result, establish a confidence interval for which the level of confidence is $\beta = 0.95$.

3. Explain what meaning must be attached to the word "confidence" as it is used in the preceding problem.

4. A sample of lengths of sisal rope is subjected to a breaking test. On the basis of the results listed below, set up a 0.90 confidence interval for the mean breaking strength of this type of rope.

$$n = 25, \bar{x} = 520 \text{ pounds}, s = 15 \text{ pounds}.$$

5. In the coffee-sacking situation described in problem 9, Problem Set 6–2, suppose that you wish to get an estimate of the process mean of the basis of the sample results: $n = 25$, $s = 0.22$ ounce, $\bar{x} = 16.1$ ounce. On the basis of these results, state the confidence interval for which the level of confidence would be $\beta = 0.95$.

6. Using the data of problem 1 in Problem Set 2–4, construct a 0.90 confidence interval for the mean strength of bricks manufactured by firm A.

7. Using the data of problem 1 in Problem Set 2–4, construct a 0.90 confidence interval for the mean strength of bricks manufactured by firm B.

8. One can say that the precision of a statistician's estimate of the population mean based on a sample mean decreases as the confidence he has in that estimate increases. Explain.

9. Discuss the part played by each of the distributions listed below in the process of estimating the mean of a population (that is, how are the three related in the procedure of making the estimate):

a) The population.
b) The sample.
c) The sampling distribution.

10. In problem 6 of Problem Set 6–3, we discussed a manufacturer of light bulbs who guaranteed the life of his bulbs to be at least 3,000 hours. Suppose that a sample of size $n = 30$ yielded a value of $\bar{x} = 3,008.25$ hours and a standard deviation of $s = 6.26$ hours. On the basis of these sample results, set up a 0.99 confidence interval for the mean life of the bulbs produced by the process.

11. In earlier problems we discussed the arms manufacturer who had developed a new powder to be used in rifle shells. Seven of these new shells were subjected to test firings, and the muzzle velocities of these shells were as follows: 3,040; 3,033; 3,029; 3,024; 3,020; 3,017; and 2,997, all values in feet per second. On the basis of these results, establish the 0.95 confidence interval for the mean muzzle velocity of shells that use the new powder.

12. In an attempt to estimate the mean monthly expenditures of families on food, a government agency has selected a random sample of $n = 1,000$ families, for which they find the sample mean to be $\bar{x} = \$160$ with a sample standard deviation of $s = \$12$. Make an estimate of family food expenditures in which your level of confidence is 0.99.

13. Suppose the government agency of problem 12 wished to have an estimate of food expenditures with a precision such that the probability that the estimate would be in error by more than 50¢ will be 0.05 or less. Using the sample standard deviation $s = \$12$, determine the approximate value of the sample size required to assure this level of precision.

14. The arms manufacturer of problem 11 wishes to circulate a brochure to potential customers describing the new shell which he has developed. He would like to include in the description of the shell a figure for the mean muzzle velocity of the shells which are produced by the new process. He would like to have an estimate of the mean muzzle velocity with a level of precision such that the probability is not greater than 0.01, that the estimate will be in error by more than 5 feet per second. On the basis of the data given you in problem 11, determine the approximate size of sample which would be required to meet this level of precision.

Estimating the difference between the means of two populations

From time to time the statistician may be required to estimate the difference between the means of two populations. Such a requirement might arise in trying to estimate the differential effects of two different treatments, for example. The procedure is the same as that described in the preceding section, with obvious modifications. The confidence interval will be estimated on the basis of information from two samples subjected to the two treatments. Specifically, a confidence interval with a level of confidence of β would be constructed as

$$(\bar{x}_a - \bar{x}_b) - t_{\beta/2}\sigma'_{(\bar{x}_a - \bar{x}_b)} \leq [m(X_a) - m(X_b)]' \leq (\bar{x}_a - \bar{x}_b) + t_{\beta/2}\sigma'_{(\bar{x}_a - \bar{x}_b)},$$

where $[m(X_a) - m(X_b)]'$ denotes the estimate of the difference between the population means, and the other symbols have the interpretation given them in Chapter 6, page 208. The critical value of $t_{\beta/2}$ is selected for the total number of degrees of freedom in both samples.

To illustrate the procedure, we use the data on the two training methods discussed in Chapter 2. The required values for the two samples of trainees were developed in Chapter 6, page 207 and following pages:

$$n_a = 6,\ n_b = 6,$$
$$\bar{x}_a - \bar{x}_b = 81 - 66.5 = 14.5,$$
$$\sigma'_{(\bar{x}_a - \bar{x}_b)} = 4.5.$$

In order to construct a 0.99 confidence interval as an estimate of the difference in the mean scores of trainees under training methods A and B, we also require the value for $t_{0.495}$ with $n - 2 = 10$ degrees of freedom. From Table E, we find the required value, $t_{0.495} = 3.169$. Combining this information, we calculate the 0.99 confidence interval:

$$(\bar{x}_a - \bar{x}_b) - t_{0.495}\sigma'_{(\bar{x}_a - \bar{x}_b)} \leq [m(X_a) - m(X_b)]' \leq (\bar{x}_a - \bar{x}_b) + t_{0.495}\sigma'_{(\bar{x}_a - \bar{x}_b)}$$
$$14.5 - (3.169)(4.5) \leq [m(X_a) - m(X_b)] \leq 14.5 + (3.169)(4.5)$$
$$14.5 - 14.3 \leq [m(X_a) - m(X_b)]' \leq 14.5 + 14.3$$
$$0.2 \leq [m(X_a) - m(X_b)]' \leq 28.8.$$

We would estimate that the mean score of trainees trained by method A is somewhere between 0.2 point and 28.8 points higher than the mean score for men trained by method B. The confidence level we associate with this estimate is 0.99.

Problem Set 7–2

1. Using the data of problem 1 in Problem Set 2–4, construct a 0.90 confidence interval for the difference in mean strength of bricks manufactured by firm A and firm B.

2. Using the data for muzzle velocities of the two types of shell which appears in problem 7 of Problem Set 2–4, construct a 0.95 confidence interval for the difference in the mean muzzle velocity of the two types of shell.

3. In problem 4 of Problem Set 6–4, we considered two samples of 9-volt batteries to be used in transistor radios. Sample A consisted of carbon-zinc-type batteries and sample B consisted of mercury-type batteries. For the 13 carbon-zinc batteries tested, the mean lifetime was 300 hours, and the sample standard deviation was 20 hours. For the 14 mercury type batteries tested, the mean lifetime was 500 hours and the sample standard deviation was 18 hours. On the basis of these results, construct a confidence interval for the increased life of mercury batteries over carbon-zinc batteries such that your level of confidence in the estimate will be 0.99.

4. In problem 5 of Problem Set 6–4, we tested the hypothesis that a gasoline additive increased the mileage of the gasoline. On the basis of the data set down there, construct a confidence interval for the difference in mean mileage rates attributable to the gasoline additive such that the level of confidence you hold in the estimate is $\beta = 0.90$.

Estimating the proportion of a population with a given attribute

Construction of a confidence interval for the proportion of a population with a given attribute is more involved than the procedures described above. The greater difficulty arises from the fact that the binomial distribution associated with a given estimate of the population proportion, denoted by p', will be more or less skewed, depending on its distance from the value 0.5. Rather than attempt a development of the procedure here, we refer to the existence of convenient graphs which yield confidence intervals for varying sample results and selected levels of confidence. Two examples of such graphs appear as Figures 7–3 and 7–4. Figure 7–3 is used in arriving at confidence intervals with a level of confidence of 0.95. Figure 7–4 is to be used if a level of confidence of 0.99 is desired.

Notice, in Figure 7–3, that the lower horizontal scale ranges from 0.00 to 0.50, moving from left to right. The top horizontal scale continues from 0.50 to 1.00, moving from right to left. These horizontal scales are of the proportion of the sample with the relevant attribute. The value of r/n is to be located on these scales. Turning now to the heavy curved lines that run across the face of the figure, notice that there is a pair of lines associated with each number. For example, the topmost and bottommost lines are associated with the number 8. The innermost pair of lines is associated with the number 1,000. The numbers represent the sample size, and the two curves associated with each number trace the paths of the upper and lower limits of the confidence intervals related to possible values of r/n. If the value of r/n in the sample result is less than 0.50, it is located on the bottom scale. Projecting a perpendicular from that value, one locates the points at which this perpendicular intersects the pair of curved lines corresponding to the sample size. The values of the limits of the confidence interval are read from the vertical scale to the left of these points of intersection.

To illustrate the procedure, let us use the sample result of the preceding chapter in which the insurance executive found that 6 of 20 policyholders did understand fully the terms of their policies. To get a confidence interval with a level of confidence of 0.95, we locate the value $r/n = 6/20 = 0.30$ on the bottom scale of Figure 7–3. Tracing along the perpendicular rising at the value of 0.30, we find its intersection with the lower of the two lines tagged with the number 20. We read the lower limit of the confidence interval as the value on the vertical scale directly to the left of this intersection, approximately 0.12. Continuing to the second line tagged with the number 20, and reading to the left of that intersection, we estimate the upper limit to be 0.54. Thus, based on a sample of 20 interviewees in which 6 had adequate knowledge of their insurance policies, we estimate the proportion of all

Figure 7-3

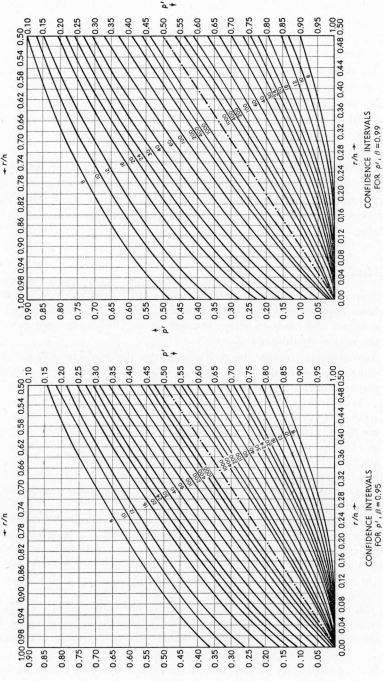

CONFIDENCE INTERVALS
FOR p', $\beta = 0.95$

Figure 7-4

CONFIDENCE INTERVALS
FOR p', $\beta = 0.99$

Source: These figures are adapted from Table 41 of the *Biometrika Tables for Statisticians* (New York: Cambridge University Press, 1954), Vol. I.

policyholders who do understand their policies to be somewhere between 0.12 and 0.54. That is, $0.12 \leq p' \leq 0.54$. The probability that this estimate is correct is approximately 0.95.

If the sample proportion is larger than 0.50, we must start at the top scale of the figure and proceed to values on the right scale. In this case, the lower limit of the confidence interval is read to the right of the top line in the pair, and the upper limit is read to the right of the bottom line in the pair. Suppose that a sample of 100 policyholders yielded 60 who had an adequate understanding of their policies. We locate $r/n = 0.60$ on the top scale and read down to the first (top) line of the pair tagged with the number 100. Reading to the right scale, we estimate the lower limit of the interval to be 0.50. Continuing to the lower line tagged with 100, we estimate the upper limit of the interval as 0.70. The sample result would lead us to believe, with a confidence level of 0.95, that between 50 and 70 percent of all policyholders understand their policies.

Problem Set 7–3

1. Suppose that a coin is tossed 100 times and in those 100 tosses, it lands heads-up 48 times. Using this information, estimate the probability that the coin will land heads-up on any one toss, making the estimate one in which the level of confidence is $\beta = 0.95$.

2. Repeat problem 1, only this time suppose that the coin is tossed 1,000 times and that in 480 of these tosses it lands heads-up. Comment on the level of precision in this case as compared to the situation of problem 1.

   We learned in Chapter 6 that one may use the normal distribution as an approximation of the binomial distribution for tests of hypotheses. It should not be surprising, therefore, that one may also use the normal distribution as a basis for estimating the proportion of a population with a given characteristic. In this procedure, one sets up a confidence interval for the value of p using the appropriate values of the mean and standard deviation for the binomial distribution. An example will serve as adequate explanation of this procedure.

   Consider the situation outlined in problem 1 where, in 100 tosses of a coin, heads appeared on 48 tosses. If we were to make a point estimate of the expected value of r in this experiment, where r is the number of heads occurring in $n = 100$ tosses of the coin, the point estimate would be $(\bar{r})' = 48$. Our point estimate would just be the number of occurrences of heads in the 100 tosses which we observed.

   If we wished a confidence interval for the expected value of r, we should have to make use of the standard deviation of the binomial distribution. We remember that the binomial distribution of r has a standard deviation, $\sigma_r = \sqrt{np(1-p)}$. Of course, we don't know the actual value for p to place in this formula, but we can estimate the value of p as $p' = r/n$. In the present situation, for example, $r = 48$ and $n = 100$. Our estimate of p would therefore be $p' = 48/100 = 0.48$. Substituting this value into the formula for the standard deviation of r, we have: $\sigma'_r = \sqrt{np'(1-p)'} = \sqrt{100(0.48)(0.52)} = \sqrt{24.96} \simeq 5$.

Now, suppose we wished a confidence interval for the value of p, such that the level of confidence is $\beta = 0.95$. Looking to a normal distribution, we know that an interval which extends 1.96 standard deviation on either side of the sample result will give us such a confidence interval. If then, we use our sample result of $r = 48$ and specify an interval which extends 1.96 standard deviations on either side of that value, we will have an approximate confidence interval for $\bar{r}$. Thus, the confidence interval will be:

$$48 - (1.96)(5) \leq (\bar{r})' \leq 48 + (1.96)(5) .$$

That is,

$$38 \leq (\bar{r})' \leq 58 .$$

With a confidence interval for the expected value of r, it is an easy matter to get the corresponding confidence interval for the expected value of p. We know that the relationship between p and r is $p = r/n$. For the confidence interval given above, therefore, we divide the lower limit and the upper limit by $n = 100$ to find a 0.95 confidence interval for the expected value of p or approximately:

$$0.38 \leq p' \leq 0.58 .$$

A comparison of the approximate values for the limits on the confidence interval found for p' above with the values which you read from the table in answering problem 1 above indicates the closeness of the approximation. It should be noted, however, that this form of an approximation will be better for large sample size and a value of p' close to 0.5. As the value of p departs further from 0.5, we have already noted that the binomial distribution takes on a skewness. Attempts to use a symmetrical normal distribution to approximate the binomial distribution becomes more tenuous as p departs from 0.5. We can use the same general rule of thumb in this instance that we developed earlier. That is, the approximations based on this method will probably be satisfactory if

$$np \geq 5 \text{ and } n(1-p) \geq 5 .$$

3. Using the approximate method described in the preceding paragraphs, find approximately the 0.95 confidence interval for the experiment described in problem 2. Compare these approximate values with those that you found from the table of Figure 7–3 in problem 2.

4. In problem 3 of Problem Set 6–5, an experiment was discussed in which 20 persons were asked to indicate their preference for two brands of coffee. The result of the experiment was that 17 of the 20 persons preferred Coffee A to Coffee B. On the basis of these results, construct the 0.99 confidence interval for the proportion of people in the population who would prefer Coffee A. Use Figure 7–4.

5. Repeat problem 4, this time using an approximate method. Compare the results of these two methods.

6. Suppose that the group of persons discussed in problem 4, who were asked to show a preference for Coffee A or Coffee B, were enlarged to include 500 persons. Of these 500 persons, 350 expressed a preference for Coffee A. On the basis of these results, construct a confidence interval for the proportion of the population who prefer Coffee A, such that your level of confidence in the estimate is approximately 0.95.

7. In problem 4 of Problem Set 6–5, a sample of $n = 200$ transistors was considered in which the number of defective transistors was 17. On the basis of this result, form a 0.99 confidence interval for the defective rate of the process at the time the sample was selected. Use Figure 7–4.

8. Repeat problem 8, using an approximate method. Compare the results and comment.

9. If 365 of 1,000 persons randomly selected from an area indicate that they watch a particular television program, estimate the proportion of persons in that area who watch the program. Set a level of confidence in your estimate of 0.99.

10. Repeat problem 9, using an approximate method. Compare results.

Regression and correlation analysis

The estimation procedures described so far can be termed univariate procedures. This is the case because they rely on information concerning only one variable (or variate) in the sample as a basis for making the estimate. Thus, in the marketing problem discussed earlier, the one variable of interest was the income of the households in the sample. Actually, the firm's concern was with the propensity of residents in the proposed new marketing area to buy their luxury product. They chose to look at the income of the residents as a gauge of this propensity to buy. They postulated a rather simple relationship between income and the propensity to buy: that if mean income was above $7,500, the marketing area would be a profitable one. The threshold value of $7,500 presumably was based on information gained from past experience.

It may have occurred to the marketing research staff of the firm that better rules for decision might be possible if some additional information were gleaned from past experience. A rule based on the estimation procedure already discussed would be: If a sample indicates that mean income of the area is greater than $7,500 introduce the product to the area; otherwise, do not. If the propensity of consumers to buy the product is indeed related to their income level, however, might it not be possible to learn a great deal more about this relationship than is implied by the simple rule just stated? An approach to investigating if such a relationship exists is regression and correlation analysis. This term often is shortened to correlation analysis.

Economists have long been concerned with a relationship which they call the "consumption function." The consumption function is the relationship which is assumed to exist between the consumption expenditures of an individual (or a group of individuals) and several other variables related to that individual(s). Some of the "other variables" might include his income, his savings and other liquid assets, past levels of his consumption expenditures, and so forth. The most important of these is his income.

Many investigations to learn the nature of these relationships have made use of the techniques of correlation analysis. In some cases, the investigations have been of the relationship between income and consumption expenditures as they vary over time. In other cases, a method called cross-section analysis has been used. In the latter, a sample is stratified to include persons from different income levels. A relationship between their reported income and their consumption expenditures is then sought. The major difference between the two methods is that, in the cross-section method, the sample results are "frozen" in time. This can be considered an advantage, since any relationship found to exist will not have been influenced by other factors operating through time.

As a vehicle for developing the concepts and techniques of correlation analysis, an example of such a cross-section analysis will be used. Although the techniques of *multiple* correlation (where more than two variables are considered) are a mere extension of the techniques which we shall consider here, we shall content ourselves to concentrate on *simple* correlation (where only two variables are considered). Our first concern is with terminology and notation.

Terminology and notation

In the bivariate relationship which we shall consider, the purpose of the analysis is to determine to what degree variation in one variable (in our case, income) seems to "explain" variation in the other variable (consumption). The variable whose variation is to be explained is called the *dependent* variable. The variable whose variation supposedly constitutes (at least in part) the "explanation" is called the *explanatory* or the *independent* variable.

It should be emphasized that the notion of "explanation" arises prior to the statistical analysis of the data, as does the question of which variable is dependent and which is independent. The answers to these questions come from the theory underlying the relationship to be investigated. Thus, the hypothesis that there exists a relationship between income as an independent variable and consumption expenditures as a dependent variable has its basis in economic theory. The statistical analysis is undertaken merely to determine if the data tend to support that hypothesis or to refute it. If on the basis of the correlation analysis we say that the one variable "explains" the other, we are saying that the data tend to support the existence of the hypothetical relationship. This is not quite the same thing as saying that the sample results are significant in the sense that this word was used in earlier discussions. These points will be clarified as we proceed with the example.

We have already noted that more than one explanatory variable can be considered in the relationship, in which case we would perform a multiple correlation, as opposed to a simple correlation. It is also possible to consider relationships of different forms between the variables. Thus, one might wish to relate the second power of values of the explanatory variable with the first power of values of the dependent variable. Letting X represent the explanatory variable and Y the dependent variable, such a relationship is described by the equation $Y = A + BX^2$. Or one might wish to relate the first powers of the two variables, in which case the equation would be $Y = A + BX$. Equations of the second type, involving only algebraic relationships between first powers of the variables, are called *linear* equations. Equations involving other than first powers are called *nonlinear* equations. We shall be concerned only with the linear relationship. Many useful nonlinear relationships can be treated by the methods for linear relationships, however, if a suitable transformation is first applied to the variables.

Data to be used in testing the relationship are collected through the selection of a stratified sample.[3] For each item in the sample, values for the two variables of interest will be determined. As above, we shall let X denote the explanatory variable and Y the dependent variable. The mean of the values of X *in the sample* will be denoted by $\bar{X}$ (pronounced X-bar), and $\bar{Y}$ will have an analogous meaning. Since it will be useful to discuss at length the deviations of individual values of the variables from their respective means, we let x and y denote these deviations (that is, $x = X - \bar{X}$ and $y = Y - \bar{Y}$).[4] Finally, it will be necessary to discuss the relationship between the values in the sample and values in the population from which the sample is selected. To distinguish the two, the mean values of the variables *for the population* will be denoted by $m(X)$ and $m(Y)$. The relationship between the two variables *in the population* will be written $Y_g = A + BX$, compared to $Y' = a + bX$ *for the sample*.

The model

The example which we wish to use is the "consumption function" of economic theory. In its simplest form, this function is presumed to be a

---

[3] It need not always be the case that the sample is stratified. One may have to be content with a completely random sample if it is not possible, or if it is too costly, to stratify. The procedures and the interpretation of the results of the analysis remain the same in either case.

[4] Note that this differs from earlier practice, where the individual values in the sample were denoted by x and the sample mean was denoted by $\bar{x}$.

linear relationship between income, the explanatory variable, and consumption expenditures, the dependent variable. In general, the relationship between these two variables in the population is taken to be $Y_g = A + BX$. Although this is the general form of the supposed relationship, the economist does not consider it to be exact. That is, he recognizes full well that two individuals with the same income (same value of X) may have different consumption expenditures (different Y values). These differences undoubtedly will be due to many factors, such as differences in age, family size, savings, and so forth. Since we are concerned only with the simple linear model, however, we do not attempt to specify in what way these additional factors may affect consumption expenditures. Rather, we lump all these effects together in one term, called the *error* term, which is added to the right side of the equation, thusly: $Y = A + BX + \epsilon$.[5] For purposes of the analysis, this additional term ϵ, is considered to vary in value from one individual to another in a random manner. In some cases, the value for ϵ will be positive, in other cases it will be zero, and in still others it will be negative. Moreover, the validity of inferences to be discussed later is based on the assumption that this term is distributed normally about a mean of zero.

Let us explore for a moment the meaning of the statements in the last paragraph. Suppose that the coefficients of the hypothetical relationship are given values of $A = 1,000$ and $B = 0.8$. Then the general relationship between income of individuals and their consumption expenditures would be $Y_g = 1,000 + 0.8X$, with X and Y in dollar amounts. We would then *expect* (in the expected value sense) an individual with income of $7,000 to spend $6,600 on consumption $[Y_g = 1,000 + 0.8(7,000) = 6,600]$. The figure of $6,600 would just be the mean consumption expenditures for individuals with $7,000 in income, however. A particular individual with the income might actually spend $6,300, or $300 less than the mean for his income group. In that case, $\epsilon = -300$, so that $Y = A + BX + \epsilon = 1,000 + 0.8(7,000) - 300 = 6,300$. Some individuals with $7,000 of income would have expenditures just equal to the expected value of $6,600 (for them, ϵ would be zero), while others would spend more than the expected value (ϵ positive). Since the expected value of expenditures for $7,000 of income is $6,600, however, these deviations would "average out" (the mean of the values for ϵ is zero).

Figure 7–5 is an attempt to portray graphically the presumed relationship between income and consumption expenditures in the population. The three broken lines running vertically from the axis for X (the convention is to place the explanatory variable on the horizontal axis) repre-

---

[5] Notice that the equation for the *general* relationship has been written with $Y_g (Y_g = A + BX)$, while the relationship for an *individual* is written with $Y (Y = A + BX + \epsilon)$. This allows us to distinguish between expected values, Y_g, and observed values, Y, of consumption.

sent three different levels of income in the population. Consumption expenditures for individuals with a level of income corresponding to one of these vertical lines would be distributed along that vertical line and centered with a mean directly above the line graphing the equation $Y_g = A + BX$. The student should visualize a surface lying above the level of the page. The shape of this surface is conveyed by the distributions drawn to the right of the three vertical lines. These should be visualized as cross sections of the surface which would be produced if one were to slice through the surface to the level of the page. The distributions are of the error term, ϵ, and are assumed to be normal distributions with a variation about the equation line measurable by the standard deviation, σ_ϵ.

Figure 7–5

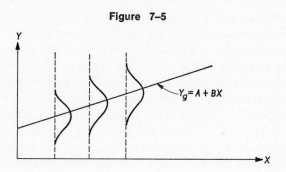

Figure 7–5 depicts a case in which the relationship between X and Y is an increasing one. As successively larger values of X are considered, the general level of Y associated with X, as indicated by the equation line, is also larger. This relationship will be reflected in the equation by a positive value for B. It is possible for the relationship between two variables to be a decreasing one, in which case B would have a negative value and the equation line would slope downward. If there were no relationship between the two variables, this would be reflected in a value of zero for B, and the line would be horizontal. These latter two situations are depicted in Figure 7–6(a) and 7–6(b).

Figure 7–6

(a)   **(b)**

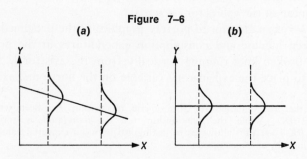

Problem Set 7–4

1. Suppose that we were concerned with the relationship between years of schooling completed by a person and the level of his income.

   a) What, in your opinion, would be the explanatory, or independent, variable in this situation? Why?

   b) Do you believe that a relationship between these two variables would be an increasing one, a decreasing one, or no relationship at all? Why?

   c) To what extent does your answer to (*b*) depend on a sample of observations of education and income levels for various individuals, and to what extent on reasoning concerning the nature of the structure of the economy?

   d) If you believed that the relationship between education and income was, say, an increasing one, of what use could a sample of education-income observations be to you?

2. Suppose that the general relationship between height in inches (X) and weight in pounds (Y) is $Y_g = 10 + 2.2(X)$. Suppose, also, that weights of persons of a given height are normally distributed with a dispersion measurable by $\sigma_\epsilon = 10$ pounds.

   a) What would be the expected weight for a person whose height is 65 inches?

   b) If a person whose height is 65 inches should weigh 161 pounds, what value of ϵ does this represent?

   c) What reasons might account for the value of ϵ for the person of part (*b*)?

   d) What would be the probability that someone whose height is 70 inches would weigh between 124 and 184 pounds?

3. Give one example of a pair of variables which would have

   a) An increasing relationship.

   b) No relationship.

   c) A decreasing relationship.

The scatter diagram

The purpose of the regression[6] analysis is to allow us to estimate the unknown values for A and B in a relationship presumed to exist between the two variables of interest. Thus, regression analysis is an estimation procedure. In the case of simple linear regression, however, we wish to estimate two values rather than one as in earlier procedures. The first step, of course, is to collect the sample. Assume that we have selected a sample of 10 persons, from whom we have learned their income during

---

[6] Henceforth, we shall use the term regression analysis to refer to the procedure for arriving at an estimate of the equation relating the two variables. The estimating equation which we derive from the information contained in the sample will be called the "regression equation." The term "correlation" will be reserved for the procedures by which we judge the significance of the relationship in the sample.

Table 7–1

X *Income* *(Hundreds of Dollars)*	Y *Consumption Expenditures,* *(Hundreds of Dollars)*
41	44
65	60
50	39
57	51
96	80
94	68
110	84
30	34
79	55
65	48

the past year and their consumption expenditures in the same period. We record these values, in hundreds of dollars, in two columns as in Table 7–1. The two columns form a table in which each row contains the income and consumption expenditures for one of the persons interviewed.

A second step which is often useful is to plot the points corresponding to the (X,Y) pairs of the table on the Cartesian plane. The resulting *scatter diagram* gives a visual representation of the relationship which exists between income and consumption expenditures *in the sample*. If there is in fact a relationship between income and consumption expendi-

Figure 7–7

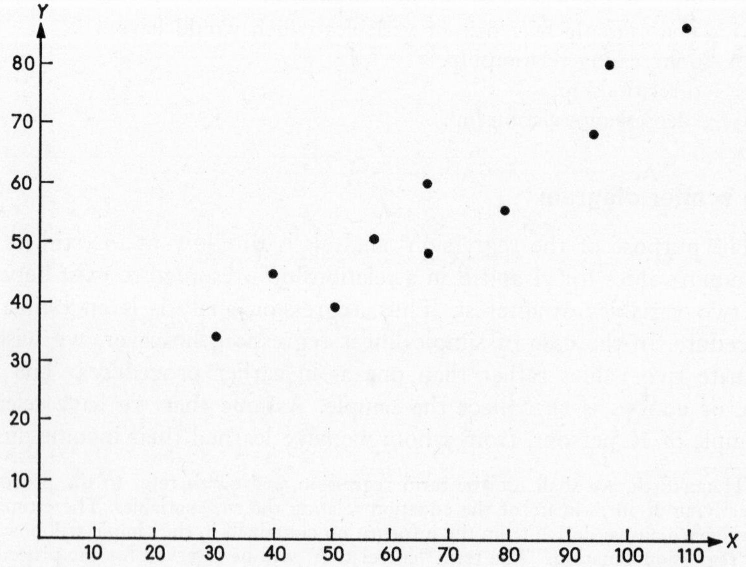

tures in the population, we should expect that relationship to be reflected in the sample data. Thus, visual examination gives our first indication of the tendency of the sample to support the hypothesis that such a relationship does exist. The scatter diagram corresponding to the assumed sample data appears as Figure 7–7. The preliminary indication is that a relationship does exist.

The regression equation

We wish to specify an equation of the form $Y' = a + bX$ which will serve as an estimate of the relationship $Y_g = A + BX$ that we assume exists between income and consumption. This regression equation must take account of the information in the sample. It must, in some fashion, give a "best" fit to the sample data. Said another way, we wish the equation to graph as a straight line that will give a good description of the general relationship which seems to exist between X and Y, as depicted in the scatter diagram of Figure 7–7. It is evident that an indefinite number of equations could be specified which might seem to describe this relationship adequately. Regression analysis is a procedure whereby one unique equation is selected from the infinite number of possible equations. The selection is made according to the criterion of *least squares*.[7]

The question as to what constitutes the "best" fit to a set of data can never be answered finally. Arguments can be made for different criteria of judgment. The criterion which has historically been most widely used is *least squares*. According to this criterion, the equation must be specified so that the resulting line will pass through the points of the scatter diagram in such a fashion that *the sum of the squares of the vertical deviations of these points from the line will be a minimum*. Thus, the line so selected will yield a *least* (sum of) *squares* fit to the data.

The meaning of the least squares criterion can be grasped more easily through reference to Figure 7–8, where the scatter diagram of Figure 7–7 has been reproduced along with a line which represents the least square fit to the data. The vertical deviations of the individual points from the line are shown as the short vertical lines joining the points to the least squares line. These deviations will be denoted by the symbol e. The value of e, of course, varies from one point to another. In some cases it is positive, in others it is negative. The values of e in the sample are analogous to the values of ϵ in the population, as discussed above. If the line drawn in Figure 7–8 is indeed the least squares line, then the value

---

[7] There are other criteria for deriving an equation that gives a "best" fit to the sample data. The least squares criterion is most commonly used and appears to be adequate for most practical situations.

Figure   7–8

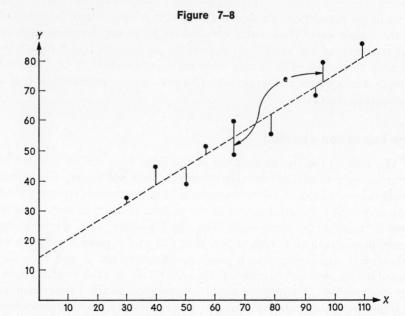

resulting from squaring the individual values of e and summing them, Σe^2, is smaller for that line than would be the corresponding sum for any other line that might be drawn through the scatter diagram.

The regression equation which gives the least squares fit to the data is specified through proper choice of the values of a and b, the coefficients of the equation. Although derivation of the method for choosing these values requires the use of the calculus, which we are not prepared to do, the method itself is very simple and requires only basic algebraic manipulation of the sample data. To specify the proper values for a and b, and thus specify the least squares equation, one need only find the solution for a and b in the so-called *normal equations* given below:

$$\Sigma Y = n \cdot a + b\Sigma X,$$
$$\Sigma XY = a\Sigma X + b\Sigma X^2.$$

Notice that there are two normal equations with two unknowns, a and b. The values for ΣY, ΣX, ΣXY, ΣX^2 (the so-called sums of products and cross products), are calculated from the sample data. The value of n is, of course, just the number of observations in the sample. Although one can proceed to find the values of a and b through solution of the two equations given above, it usually is simpler to express the values for X and Y in terms of deviations from their respective means, x and y. This amounts to a shift of the origin of measurement for the two variables, from the point where each equals zero, to the point $(\bar{X}, \bar{Y})$. The change is indicated by an examination of Figure 7–9. The value of the point

Figure 7–9

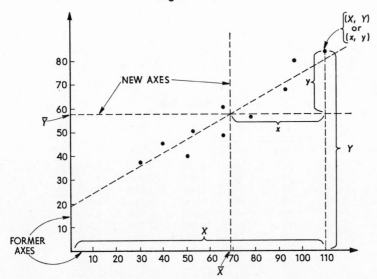

selected there is indicated in terms of both sets of axes, either as (X,Y) or as (x,y).

The effect of the shift of axes on the normal equations is easy to see. Now the equations become:

$$\Sigma y = n \cdot a + b\Sigma x,$$
$$\Sigma xy = a\Sigma x + b\Sigma x^2.$$

Because the sum of the deviations of a variable from its mean equals zero, we have $\Sigma y = 0$ and $\Sigma x = 0$. Substitution of zero at the appropriate places in the above equations reduces them to one equation:[8]

$$\Sigma xy = b\Sigma x^2,$$

or,

$$b = \Sigma xy/\Sigma x^2.$$

If the value of b is found through this equation, the value of a can then be determined through the relation,

$$a = \bar{Y} - b\bar{X},$$

which is a consequence of the fact that the regression equation will pass through the point $(\bar{X},\bar{Y})$. In order to use these latter equations, we require

---

[8] The first equation "drops out" as a consequence of the fact that the regression line passes through the point of the means, $(\bar{X},\ \bar{Y})$. This can be shown by dividing both sides of the equation, $\Sigma Y = na + b\Sigma X$, by n, which leads to $\bar{Y} = a + b\bar{X}$.

Σxy and Σx^2. These values are easily calculated from the original data as $\Sigma xy = \Sigma XY - n\overline{X}\overline{Y}$ and $\Sigma x^2 = \Sigma X^2 - n(\overline{X})^2$.[9]

To illustrate the procedure for arriving at the regression equation, consider the data for the sample. The values of X and Y for the sample are reproduced in the first two columns of Table 7–2. The remaining columns

Table 7–2

X	Y	XY	X²	Y²
41	44	1,804	1,681	1,936
65	60	3,900	4,225	3,600
50	39	1,950	2,500	1,521
57	51	2,907	3,249	2,601
96	80	7,680	9,216	6,400
94	68	6,392	8,836	4,624
110	84	9,240	12,100	7,056
30	34	1,020	900	1,156
79	55	4,345	6,241	3,025
65	48	3,120	4,225	2,304
687	563	42,358	53,173	34,223

of Table 7–2 contain the values for the various products and cross products. The sums of these columns, along with a count of the number of observations in the sample, provide the information we need to calculate the coefficients of the regression equation (a column for Y^2 is included for subsequent use).[10]

First, the means of X and Y are required:

$$\overline{X} = \Sigma X/n = 687/10 = 68.7 \,,$$
$$\overline{Y} = \Sigma Y/n = 563/10 = 56.3 \,.$$

Given the values of the means, and using the sums of cross products in Table 7–2, we next calculate:

$$\Sigma xy = \Sigma XY - n\overline{X}\overline{Y} = 42,358 - (10)(68.7)(56.3) = 3,67.9 \,,$$
$$\Sigma x^2 = \Sigma X^2 - n(\overline{X})^2 = 53,173 - (10)(68.7)^2 = 5,976.1 \,.$$

These values allow us to calculate the value of b:

---

[9] These equivalences are easily demonstrated:

$$\begin{aligned}
\Sigma xy &= \Sigma(X - \overline{X})(Y - \overline{Y}) = \Sigma(XY - \overline{X}Y - \overline{Y}X + \overline{X}\overline{Y}) \\
&= \Sigma XY - \Sigma \overline{X}Y - \Sigma \overline{Y}X + \Sigma \overline{X}\overline{Y} \\
&= \Sigma XY - n\overline{X}\left(\frac{\Sigma Y}{n}\right) - n\overline{Y}\left(\frac{\Sigma X}{n}\right) + n\overline{X}\overline{Y} \\
&= \Sigma XY - 2n\overline{X}\overline{Y} + n\overline{X}\overline{Y} \\
&= \Sigma XY - n\overline{X}\overline{Y}
\end{aligned}$$

Stating Σx^2 as Σxx, the same procedure gives $\Sigma x^2 = \Sigma X^2 - n(\overline{X})^2$.

[10] Appendix B at the end of this chapter contains listings, and descriptions for use, of two computer programs which provide a regression and correlation analysis for two variables.

$$b = \Sigma xy/\Sigma x^2 = 3{,}679.9/5{,}976.1 \simeq 0.616 \ .$$

Finally, the value of a is determined as

$$a = \bar{Y} - b\bar{X} = 56.3 - (0.616)(68.7) \simeq 14.00.[11]$$

These calculated values of the coefficients yield the least squares regression equation,

$$Y' = 14.00 + 0.616X \ ,$$

which may be taken as our estimate of the linear relationship presumed to exist between income and consumption expenditures. Interpretations of the coefficients of the equation are possible, but caution must be used —particularly with regard to the value of a. Looking first at $b = 0.616$, this value indicates that the change to expect in Y, associated with an increase in X of one unit, is an increase of approximately 0.616 unit. Since the units in which both X and Y were reported are hundreds of dollars, this means that, "on the average," \$100 more income seems to be associated with about \$61.60 more in consumption expenditures.

A comparable interpretation of the meaning of the value of a is not usually worthwhile, and in many cases may be quite misleading, unless it happens that the range of the values for X in the sample includes zero. The reason for this can be seen in attempting to interpret the value $a = 14.00$ in our equation. Evidently, this indicates that one should expect that a household with no income $(X = 0)$ would have consumption expenditures of about \$1,400. One can conceive of the possibility that a household without employment, and therefore without income, would continue to maintain some level of consumption. It is doubtful, however, that this level would be predictable on the basis of a relationship which had been fitted to a sample comprised of income-earning individuals. If the sample had consisted largely of persons dependent on welfare programs, the relationship would be more meaningful for the case of zero income.[12]

Problem Set 7–5

1. As personnel manager for a firm that supplies electronic assemblies to the government, one of your concerns is to hire laborers to do the work of assembling these assemblies from their constituent parts. As an aid in selection of workers to perform this operation, you have devised a testing pro-

---

[11] The values for b and a, as they appear here, have been rounded. In performing calculations with these values, as we show later, the figures should be used with more digits than appear in the rounded answers shown here. Thus, further calculations with b were actually made using $b = 0.61577$.

[12] This discussion is predicated on a definition of income as the return to a person which he receives for participation in gainful employment. If the term were defined to include welfare receipts, hopefully, in our society there would be no persons with zero income.

cedure for applicants. The test supposedly relates to the person's manual dexterity and general aptitude for the type of work involved in putting together these assemblies.

In order to test the effectiveness of your testing procedure, you have watched the progress of a "pilot group" of 12 workers. These 12 workers were selected randomly from the list of applicants available at the time you began the experiment, and they were hired after they had taken the proficiency test, no matter what their score was on the test. This was done in order to maintain randomness in the sample and its representativeness of all applicants. The time interval since these workers were hired has been long enough that you feel they are all familiar with the job and are operating at a level which is representative of their ability in the job. Over the past several weeks, you have collected data on the productivity of these workers. This productivity is expressed as the mean number of assemblies completed per week by the individual workers. The table following shows the relevant data for these workers: X is their score on the proficiency test, and Y is the mean number of assemblies completed per week.

X	Y	X	Y
27	31	64	52
30	40	75	55
39	35	75	64
46	45	83	63
52	54	90	70
55	40	97	77

For this set of data, do the following:
a) Graph the scatter diagram for the data.
b) Find the regression equation, $Y' = a + bX$, and draw the line corresponding to the equation on the scatter diagram.
c) Indicate what the values of the coefficients of the regression equation, a and b, tell you concerning the relationship between test scores and worker productivity.
d) Make an estimate, based on your work above, of the productivity of a worker who achieves a score of 70 on the proficiency test.

2. It seems reasonable to suppose that there is a relationship between the level of educational attainment of individuals and their income. The data given below are adapted from Table No. 160, "Lifetime and Mean Income in 1949 to 1965 of Males 25 Years Old and Over, by Years of School Completed," *Statistical Abstract of the United States*, 1967.

X = years of schooling.
Y = mean income per year (\$000).

X	Y
6	3.28
8	4.66
10	5.90
12	6.90
14	8.13
18	10.82

Assuming that each observation is the educational attainment and income of one individual:

a) Set down the data as points in a scatter diagram.

b) Find the regression relationship between X and Y in these data.

c) Draw the line which corresponds to the relationship of part (b) on the scatter diagram of part (a).

d) Given the relationship of part (b), what would you estimate the yearly income to be for a person with a high school education?

3. As a furniture retailer in a certain locale, you are interested in seeing if some relationship might exist between the number of building permits issued in that locale in past years and the volume of your sales in those years. You accordingly collect the data for your sales (Y, in thousands of dollars) and the number of building permits issued (X, in hundreds) in the past 10 years. The results of preliminary calculations appear below:

$$n = 10; \ \Sigma X = 200; \ \Sigma Y = 2,200; \ \Sigma X^2 = 4,600; \ \Sigma XY = 45,800;$$
$$\Sigma Y^2 = 490,400 .$$

a) Calculate the coefficients of the regression equation and write down this equation.

b) It is expected that there will be approximately 2,000 building permits issued next year. On the basis of that estimate, what level of sales can you expect next year?

c) On the basis of the relationship you found in (a), one would expect what change in sales with an increase of 100 building permits?

4. One aspect of the world's hunger problem is that apparently, as per capita income increases for a people, their requirements in grain consumption also increase. At lower levels of income, the total of grain consumption is largely a matter of direct consumption. At higher levels of income, there appears to be a decrease in the total amount of grain consumed directly, but an increase in the amount of grain consumed indirectly through meat products. The data below indicate for 10 different nations the per capita income and the per capita consumption, both directly and indirectly, of grain annually. (Data adapted from Lester R. Brown, "The World Outlook for Conventional Agriculture," *Science*, Vol. 158 (Nov. 3, 1967), p. 605, Fig. 2. Copyright 1967 by the American Association for the Advancement of Science.)

$X = $ Per capita dollar income .

$Y = $ Per capita consumption of grain annually, in pounds .

Nation	X	Y
India...................	75	348
Mexico................	312	452
Japan.................	350	470
Italy..................	512	730
USSR..................	763	974
W. Germany...........	975	739
France................	1,000	930
U.K...................	1,112	792
Canada................	1,525	1,835
U.S.A.................	2,287	1,652

a) Construct a scatter diagram for the data given on page 255.

b) Determine the regression coefficients relating values of X and Y in the data above and write down the regression equation.

c) Draw in the line representing the regression equation on the scatter diagram of part (*a*).

d) On the basis of the relationship which you find to exist between income and grain consumption, approximately what increase in grain consumption per person per year can be expected if the per capita income in a nation were to increase by $100?

5. The data below represent the number of years which 12 different lengths of ¼-inch sisal rope have been in use (X), and the breaking strength of those lengths of rope in hundreds of pounds (Y).

X	Y	X	Y
8	49	18	33
6	48	24	32
11	46	19	29
22	43	23	28
14	40	26	20
17	35	40	17

a) Construct the scatter diagram for these data.

b) Calculate the regression coefficients for these data and write down the regression equation.

c) On the basis of the relationship which you found in part (*b*), what is the approximate loss in strength of this type of rope per year?

6. The data which appear below are the heights in inches (X) and the weights in pounds (Y) of students in one of the author's classes. Below these data appear the values for the sums of products and cross products that are required in order to calculate the regression equation.

X	Y	X	Y
66	150	70	185
72	205	71	181
70	155	72	170
69	175	65*	105
73	165	65	145
68	155	71	165
60*	100	72	183
70	210	72	160
72	160	71	173
64*	130	72	188
73	165	71	165
71	140	69	160
71	165	71	175
68	168		

*Values for young ladies in the class.

$\Sigma X = 1,879,\ \Sigma Y = 4,398,\ \Sigma XY = 307,535\ \Sigma X^2 = 131,021,$
$$\Sigma Y^2 = 732,272,\ n = 27\ .$$

a) Construct a scatter diagram for the above data.

b) Write down the regression equation for the sample observations given above.

c) On the basis of the relationship which you found in part (b), estimate the mean weight of persons who are 68 inches tall.

d) Draw the line through the scatter diagram which corresponds to the regression equation which you found in part (b).

e) What interpretation can you put upon the value of a which you calculated for the regression equation, if any?

7. The data on heights and weights presented in problem 6 include the values for three young ladies (marked in the table of problem 6 with asterisks). If these observations are deleted from the data, the new values become as given below.

$\Sigma X = 1,690,\ \Sigma Y = 4,063,\ \Sigma XY = 286,390,\ \Sigma X^2 = 119,100,$
$$\Sigma Y^2 = 694,347,\ n = 24$$

a) On the scatter diagram which you constructed for problem 6, outline the scatter diagram which is pertinent for the data with the three observations deleted. (Do this by using a different colored pencil or ink.)

b) Calculate the new regression equation and draw in the line corresponding to it on the revised scatter diagram.

c) Comment on the differences you note in the two situations and how they may relate to particular observations deleted from these data.

8. The data appearing in the table below are for disposable personal income per family, thousands of dollars (X), and insurance coverage per family in thousands of dollars (Y). (Data adapted from Table 666, "Life Insurance In Force and Personal Income: 1930–1966," *Statistical Abstract of The United States, 1967.*)

X	Y	X	Y
1.9	2.8	6.1	10.2
1.4	2.4	6.5	11.4
1.7	2.7	6.8	12.2
3.2	3.2	7.3	13.3
4.1	4.6	7.6	14.7
5.1	6.9	8.1	15.9

a) Construct the scatter diagram for the data set out above, being sure to include the origin of the Y and X axes in this diagram.

b) Determine the regression equation which fits these data.

c) What interpretation do you place on the value of the coefficient, a, which you calculated in part (b), above?

d) Based on the relationship which you determined in part (b) above, historically there appears to be about what size increase in insurance coverage related to each $1,000 increase in disposable personal income?

e) Draw the straight line corresponding to the regression equation which you determined in part (*b*) on the scatter diagram which you constructed in part (*a*). Upon examination of this line as it fits the data of the scatter diagram, comment on whether it appears that a linear relationship does indeed exist between levels of disposable personal income and levels of insurance coverage.

The problem of prediction

In the preceding paragraph, reference was made to the ability of the regression relationship to "predict" consumption expenditures. The word "predict" must be used with caution, with the understanding that it relates to a special context. The statistician does not claim a gift of prescience when he uses this word. What he implies, in substance, is that if the relationship $Y = A + BX + \epsilon$ exists as theorized, then the regression equation $Y' = a + bX$ provides a basis for making estimates of the value for Y which will be associated with particular values of X. There is some likelihood that these estimates will be in error, but the size of error to expect is subject to certain probability statements of the type already considered in earlier discussion. In order to exploit the analogy which exists between estimation procedures based on a sample mean and estimates based on a regression equation, the ensuing discussion will parallel that which led to the consideration of confidence intervals.

The regression equation which we fitted to the income and consumption data of our sample is:

$$Y' = 14.00 + 0.616X .$$

On the basis of this equation, we wish to estimate the level of consumption expenditures we would expect of individuals with a certain specified level of income, X_0. One approach is to make an estimate based on a single figure, much like the point estimate discussed earlier. If we wished to estimate the consumption expenditures of individuals with income of $10,000, we substitute $X_0 = 100$ in the equation and receive an estimate of consumption expenditures:

$$Y' = 14.00 + 0.616(100) = 75.6 .$$

Our regression relationship indicates that individuals with $10,000 of income may be expected to spend approximately $7,560 on consumption. This amount is only an expected value, however. We would not be surprised to see the actual consumption expenditures of some individuals with that income to deviate from this amount. The likelihood is high that our estimate will be in error if applied to any one individual.

As in estimating the mean of a population on the basis of the mean of a sample selected from that population, we can have more confidence in an estimate which states an interval in which to expect the consumption expenditures to fall. As in the earlier case, the wider the interval which we use, the greater the level of confidence we can attach to it. Again, as in the earlier case, the width of the interval associated with a specified level of confidence will be dependent on the variability found in the sample. These points are common to the two estimation procedures. There are some points of difference. In order to afford the student a deeper appreciation of the expression which yields the interval estimate associated with a particular value of X_0, it is useful to devote a few paragraphs to an intuitive explanation of the factors affecting what we shall call the *precision*[13] of the estimate.

There are several factors which affect the precision of the estimates yielded by a regression equation. A mathematically sophisticated explanation would be quite different from what is offered here. Our purposes will be adequately served if we consider four different factors relating to our problem.

The first, and most obvious, factor which will affect the precision of our estimates is the variability of consumption expenditures in the population about the general relationship, $Y_g = A + BX$. This variability is measurable, in principle, by the standard deviation of the error term, ϵ, in the "complete" relationship, $Y = A + BX + \epsilon$. Denoting this standard deviation by σ_ϵ, it is obvious that, the smaller the value of σ_ϵ (in graphic terms, the more closely the distributions pictured in Figure 7–5 are dispersed about the line), the more precision we can expect our estimate to have. Since the value of σ_ϵ is unknown to us, we estimate it from the deviations of the sample observations about the regression line. Specifically, we estimate it as:[14]

$$\sigma_\epsilon' = \sqrt{\frac{\Sigma e^2}{n-2}}.$$

A second factor which influences the precision of our estimate is the number of observations on which the estimate is based. This effect is not so strong in this case as it was in the univariate case, however. The reason for this is that in the bivariate case, sample observations are not all presumed to be from the same distribution about one mean value, as was done

---

[13] By the precision of the estimate, we mean the width of the interval associated with a given level of confidence. The wider the interval, the less precise the estimate, and vice versa. We must remember that precision and accuracy are not the same thing.

[14] The fact that $n-2$ is used in the denominator, rather than n, is due to the fact that we lose two degrees of freedom in basing our estimate on the variability of the sample observations about the line whose position is determined by those same sample observations. A close examination of Figure 7–8 should make it clear that the individual values of e associated with the sample observations, and therefore the value of Σe^2, depends on the general level of the line drawn through them and on the line's slope. The general level of the line is specified by the value for a in the regression equation, and the slope of the line is specified by the value for b. The specification of these two values on the basis of the sample observations reduces the degrees of freedom in the sample by two.

in the univariate case. In the bivariate case, we assume that consumption expenditures observed for a particular individual are from a distribution of expenditures uniquely related to the income level of that individual. Since the sample will typically yield various values of income, we do not get a "pooling" of information concerning the distribution of consumption expenditures at any given income level. In other words, all n observations in the sample do not relate to the same distribution of consumption expenditures. An increase in sample size is, therefore, not so powerful an influence on the expected precision of the estimate.

A third factor is the variability in the sample observations of the variable X. Since it is our concern to estimate the relationship relating

Figure   7–10

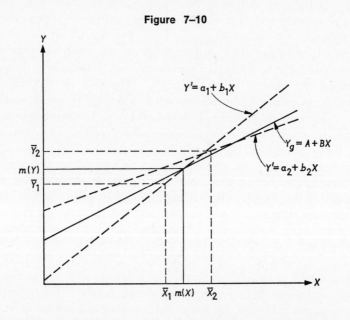

changes in X to changes in Y, our estimate will be better, the wider the variation in X which occurs in our sample. This point can be emphasized by means of an exaggerated example. Suppose that our sample consisted only of individuals with an income of $7,000. Based on that sample, we might get a fairly good estimate of consumption expenditures of persons with $7,000 of income. But the sample would not be very helpful to us in estimating consumption expenditures of persons with income of $10,000.

Finally, an estimate, Y', based on a particular value of X_0 will have a higher degree of expected precision, the closer the selected value of X_0 is to $\overline{X}$, the sample mean. The reason for this is best understood through an examination of Figure 7–10. In that figure, the unbroken lines indicate the true means of Y and X in the population, and the true relationship between these variables. A sample drawn from this population may yield various possible values for $\overline{X}$ and $\overline{Y}$. It is also possible for the sample to yield various values for the coefficients, a and b, in the regression equation. The broken lines indicate two possible extremes among these variations.

If the sample yielded the regression line, $Y' = a_1 + b_1x$, it is evident that point estimates based on it would tend to deviate further and further from the true value as the associated value for X_0 departs further from $\overline{X}$. The same tendency is evident in estimates based on $Y' = a_2 + b_2X$, although the departures are in opposite directions to the first case.

These represent only two possible cases from an indefinite number of possibilities. They were, admittedly, chosen to give the student a predisposition to accept the notion that the width of interval estimates, for any given level of confidence, will be described by a fan-shaped zone which widens as the specified value of X_0 departs from the particular value of $\overline{X}$ yielded by the sample. Figure 7–11 indicates the general

Figure 7–11

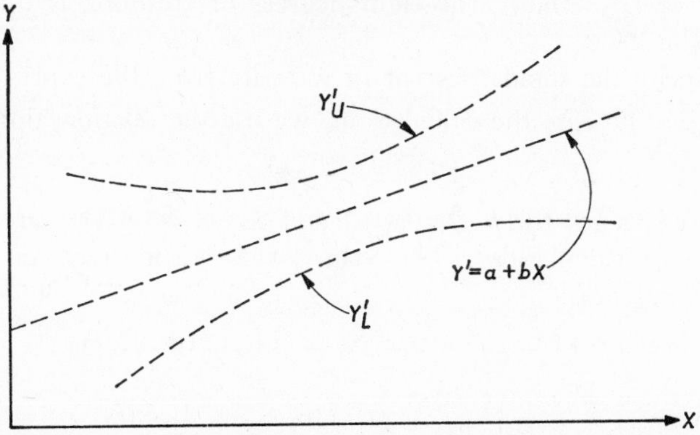

shape of this zone about the regression line associated with a particular sample, where Y'_U and Y'_L trace the paths of the upper and lower confidence limits, respectively.

All of the above considerations are reflected in the expressions which yield the lower and upper confidence limits for the estimate of Y which is associated with a specified value of X_0:

$$Y'_L = Y' - t_{\beta/2}\sigma_\epsilon' \sqrt{\frac{n+1}{n} + \frac{(X_0 - \overline{X})^2}{\Sigma x^2}}.$$

$$Y'_U = Y' + t_{\beta/2}\sigma_\epsilon' \sqrt{\frac{n+1}{n} + \frac{(X_0 - \overline{X})^2}{\Sigma x^2}}.$$

The first term on the right of the equality sign is, of course, the point estimate derived from the regression equation for the specified value of X_0. The value of $t_{\beta/2}$ is Student's t, for $n - 2$ degrees of freedom, associated with a confidence level of β. The use of Student's t is required, since the standard deviation of ϵ must be estimated as $\sigma_\epsilon' = \sqrt{\Sigma e^2/(n-2)}$ (often called the *standard error of estimate*). The first term under the radical, $(n + 1)/n$, is a ratio larger than one which approaches unity as the sample size increases. It reflects the influence of sample size, per se, on the precision of the estimate. The second term under the radical, $(X_0 - \bar{X})^2/\Sigma x^2$, expresses the square of the distance of X_0 from the sample mean as a proportion of the total variation in the sample of the variable X, measured by Σx^2. This term reflects the influence of two factors on the width of the interval: the influence of distance from the sample mean in widening the interval, and the influence of variability of X in the sample in narrowing the interval.

To illustrate the calculation of confidence limits, let us find the confidence interval for consumption expenditures associated with an income of \$10,000, where the desired level of confidence is $\beta = 0.95$. The sample is of size $n = 10$ and contains eight degrees of freedom. The value of $t_{\beta/2} = t_{0.475}$, for eight degrees of freedom, is found from Table E to be 2.306.

We estimate the standard error of estimate from the expression $\sigma_\epsilon' = \sqrt{\Sigma e^2/n - 2)}$. To ease the calculations, we use the relationship:[15]

$$\Sigma e^2 = \Sigma y^2 - b\Sigma xy.$$

The required values for b ($= 0.616$) and Σxy ($= 3,679.9$) are available from previous calculations. The value of Σy^2 is derived in the same fashion as Σx^2, that is:

$$\Sigma y^2 = \Sigma Y^2 - n(\bar{Y})^2 = 34{,}223 - (10)(56.3)^2 = 2{,}526.1 .$$

Combining these values, we have:

$$\Sigma e^2 = 2{,}526.1 - (.616)(3679.9) \simeq 259.3 .$$

Finally, we use this value to find:

$$\sigma_\epsilon' = \sqrt{259.3/8} \simeq 5.7 .$$

---

[15] To see the equivalence expressed in this relationship, note that the deviation, e, of any point in the set of sample observations can be expressed as the difference between the vertical distance of that point from $\bar{Y}$ and the vertical distance of the regression line from $\bar{Y}$ at the value of X associated with the point in question. That is, $e = y - bx$. Turn to Figure 7–13, page 269, to see this. Then,

$$\Sigma e^2 = \Sigma(y - bx)^2 = \Sigma y^2 - 2b\Sigma xy + b^2\Sigma x^2. \text{ But } b = \frac{\Sigma xy}{\Sigma x^2}, \text{ so } \Sigma e^2$$
$$= \Sigma y^2 - 2b\Sigma xy + b\left(\frac{\Sigma xy}{\Sigma x^2}\right)\Sigma x^2 = \Sigma y^2 - b\Sigma xy.$$

The calculation of σ_ϵ' completes the set of values we require in order to determine the confidence limits for consumption expenditures associated with an income of $X_0 = 100$. We catalog them at this point:

$$Y' = 14.00 + (.616)(100) = 75.6, \qquad t_{0.475} = 2.306,$$
$$\sigma_\epsilon' = 5.7, \qquad\qquad\qquad n = 10,$$
$$X_0 - \bar{X} = 100 - 68.7 = 31.3 \qquad\qquad \Sigma x^2 = 5,976.1$$

Substituting these values in the expression for the upper confidence limit, we have:

$$Y'_U = Y' + t_{0.475}\, \sigma_\epsilon' \sqrt{\frac{n+1}{n} + \frac{(X_0 - \bar{X})^2}{\Sigma x^2}}$$

$$= 75.6 + (2.306)(5.7)\sqrt{\frac{11}{10} + \frac{(31.3)^2}{5976.1}}$$

$$\simeq 75.6 + 14.7$$

$$= 90.3 .$$

To determine the lower confidence limit, we subtract:

$$Y'_L = 75.6 - 14.7 = 60.9 .$$

Problem Set 7–6

1. Continuing with the data of problem 1 in Problem Set 7–5, do the following.
   a) Calculate the 0.95 confidence intervals for Y' at the following values of X_0, and join the points obtained to form the "confidence zone" on the graph which you contructed there: $X_0 = 30, 55, 80$.
   b) Comment on the relative width of the confidence intervals calculated in part (a).
2. On the basis of the data and the calculations of problem 2 in Problem Set 7–5, calculate the 0.99 confidence interval which you would assign to the annual income of a person with a high school education.
3. Given the data and the calculations of problem 3 in Problem Set 7–5, give an estimate of the level of sales which you would expect in a year for which the number of building permits issued was 2,000. State your estimate so that the level of confidence you place in it is 0.90.
4. Suppose that India were to quadruple her per capita income from $75 per year to $300 per year. On the basis of the relationship which you calculated in problem 4 of Problem Set 7–5, give an estimate for the per capita consumption of grain per year at this new level of income. Make this estimate one in which your level of confidence is approximately 0.99. You should have gotten a negative value for Y_L'. Looking at the scatter diagram for the data and considering the assumptions of the model, what do you think is wrong here?
5. Assume that the sample given in problem 5 of Problem Set 7–5, represents, accurately, the relationship between age of rope and its breaking strength. Assume, also, that the breaking strengths of rope are normally distributed about the mean in breaking strength for any given age of rope. On the basis

of these assumptions, what is the approximate probability that a rope which is 20 years old will bear a load of 4,500 pounds?

Some uses of regression analysis and a note of caution

Regression analysis has been a powerful tool of businessmen and economists. Its uses in business include diverse examples ranging from models relating unit costs of production to the volume of production, to models which attempt to forecast sales of a firm by relating these sales to some explanatory variable, such as disposable income. In economics, investigations of supply and demand functions often rely heavily on regression equations, as do many other areas of economic research. Usually, more sophisticated business and economic models are designed to include more than one explanatory variable, in an attempt to improve the ability of the model to "explain" variation which has been observed in the dependent variable. Inclusion of a larger number of variables lengthens the procedure of calculation, but it does not change the substantive interpretation of the relationship between the sample observations and the theoretical model. It is usually obvious, in most situations, that the dependent variable is strongly influenced by more than one other variable. If these additional variables can be identified and set in the model, one can expect to improve the "explanation" provided by the regression equation and, hopefully, its predictive ability.

In the last sentence, a distinction was made between *explanation* and *prediction*. Some amplification of that distinction will be helpful, and it will serve as a cautionary note to the student. The regression equation which results from our analysis of the data is our attempt to explain what happened in these sample observations. Notice that it is a description of a *historical* relationship between two variables, *as they appeared in a sample*. Basically, what the regression equation accomplishes is this: It indicates the way in which variation of the variable Y, in the sample, was related to variation in X, in the sample. That is, it allows us to *explain* variation in Y, at least partially, in terms of variation in X.

Prediction is quite different from explanation, as we described it above. In prediction, we wish to relate a value for Y (or range of values for Y) to a value of X which has not, as yet, been observed. Our confidence in using a regression equation as a predictive tool depends largely on two things. One is the faith that we have in the validity of the theoretical model relating the dependent variable to the explanatory variable. The second is the support given to the theoretical model by the degree of explanation that we find in the sample.

The faith which we may have in the theoretical model is related to two aspects of the model. First, we must be convinced that the relationship between variables expressed in the model is the true relationship, or at least that any possible departure of the model from the true relationship would be inconsequential. Second, we must be reasonably certain that the relationship is a relatively stable one. If the regression equation accurately reflected the true relationship existing at the time the sample was selected, but that relationship had since changed, then the predictive ability of the equation is seriously impaired.

The question of support for the model from the sample results is a familiar one. The student has become well aware, at this juncture, of the role of sample variation. It is possible for two variables actually to be unrelated in the systematic fashion envisioned in the theoretical model, even though the sample results may point to such a relationship. The reverse is also possible. The sample results may indicate no relationship between two variables, when such a relationship actually does exist. The problem arising here is the familiar one of determining how well the sample results seem to support the hypothesis that a relationship does, in fact, exist. The answer is found by determining a measure of the degree to which variation in X is explained by variation in Y, and testing this measure for statistical significance. This procedure is explained in the following section.

Correlation

The regression equation derived from the sample results indicates a general relationship between the two variables as they appeared in the sample. It does not tell us directly how well the relationship explains the observed variation in Y. For this, we turn to the *coefficient of correlation*. There are a number of ways in which the coefficient of correlation can be presented. The development below proceeds through explanation of what is called the product-moment formula for the coefficient.

Consider, once again, the scatter of points representing the 10 observations in our sample for income and consumption expenditures. This scatter diagram, shown again in Figure 7–12, traces an area on the X–Y plane which has a distinctly increasing orientation. If we allow the lines corresponding to $\overline{X}$ and $\overline{Y}$ to partition the X–Y plane into four quadrants, we can label these quadrants I, II, III, and IV, as indicated in Figure 7–12. It is apparent that the points of the scatter diagram lie predominantly in the quadrants marked I and III. Only two points lie in the other two quadrants, one in each. Now, if we express the position of any point in the diagram in deviations from $\overline{X}$ and $\overline{Y}$, we find that the points in quadrant I have x and y both positive. The points in quadrant III have x and y both negative. Consequently, for these points, the product xy will be positive in either case. By contrast, points in quadrants II and IV will have x and y of opposite signs and will, therefore, lead to a negative value of xy.

Because of this quality, one can use the sum of these products, Σxy, as an indicator of the orientation of the scatter diagram. If the points tend to be concentrated in an increasing pattern, as in Figure 7–12, this sum should be positive. If the points should be concentrated in a decreasing pattern, falling largely in quadrants II and IV, the sum will be negative. Finally, if there appears to be little consistent orientation in the pattern, the sum might be negative or positive, but it would be close to zero.

Although the value of Σxy gives us the first indication of whether or not a relationship exists in the sample, it is deficient in two respects. First, consider two different scatter diagrams. Suppose that, for both

Figure 7–12

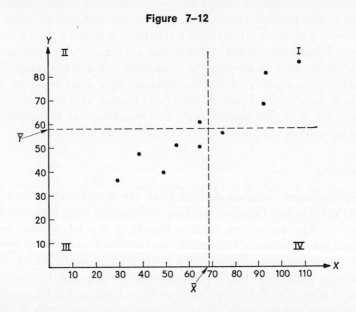

scatter diagrams, the value of Σxy is the same. If we were to be content with Σxy alone as an indicator of the existence of a relationship between X and Y, we should have to say that the strength of the evidence was the same in either case. But suppose that one of the scatter diagrams had, say, twice the observations as the other. With a larger number of observations over which to sum the products, xy, there would be a larger probability that any particular nonzero value of Σxy might occur. Because of this fact, the sum is divided by the number of observations. The result is the mean contribution of each observation in the sample as an indicator of the degree of relationship present.

The second deficiency in Σxy as an indicator of the strength of the relationship between X and Y relates to the units in which those two variables are expressed. Looking back to our calculations preceding

Table 7–2, we note the value of $\Sigma xy = 3679.9$. Now this value is in units of (hundreds of dollars)^2, since both X and Y were reported in Table 7–2 in units of hundreds of dollars. If we had chosen to report the two variables in units of dollars, each value of X and Y would have been one hundred times as large, and the value of Σxy would have been larger by a factor of $(100)^2$. That is, with dollar units, the result would be $\Sigma xy = 36,799,000$. It would be absurd, however, to say that the evidence for a relationship between X and Y was 10,000 times as strong in the second case as in the first. Quite obviously, the units in which the variables are reported should not be allowed to affect our measure of the relationship between the two variables. To avoid the influence of arbitrary selection of units, we *standardize* the values of x and y in the same manner as before. We express the deviations, x and y, in terms of their standard deviations, S_x and S_y.[16] It is not necessary, however, to divide each deviation, individually, by the appropriate standard deviation. The same result is accomplished by dividing the already calculated sum, Σxy, by the two standard deviations.

To summarize what has gone before, the value of Σxy forms a basis for measuring the relationship which exists between X and Y. It is necessary to adjust for number of observations by dividing Σxy by this number. Additionally, to escape the effect of arbitrary selection of units on the resulting measure, we must standardize the result by division with S_x and S_y. The final result is the desired measure. It is called the *coefficient of correlation* and is denoted by the letter, r. We have:

$$r = \frac{\Sigma xy}{n \cdot S_x \cdot S_y}.$$

Noting that $S_x = \sqrt{\Sigma x^2/n}$ and $S_y = \sqrt{\Sigma y^2/n}$, we can also write:

$$r = \frac{\Sigma xy}{\sqrt{\Sigma x^2} \cdot \sqrt{\Sigma y^2}}.$$

The latter form may be more convenient, since we usually have no reason to calculate the values of S_x and S_y directly.

For our example of income and consumption expenditures, the coefficient of correlation is:

$$r = \frac{\Sigma xy}{\sqrt{\Sigma x^2} \cdot \sqrt{\Sigma y^2}} = \frac{3,679.9}{\sqrt{5,976.1} \cdot \sqrt{2,526.1}} \simeq 0.947 .$$

---

[16] Note that S_x and S_y are written with upper-case S to distinguish them from the sample standard deviation defined in an earlier chapter. S_x and S_y are not used as estimates of the respective population standard deviations. We, therefore, do not adjust for degrees of freedom. $S_x = \sqrt{\Sigma x^2/n}$ and $S_y = \sqrt{\Sigma y^2/n}$.

The fact that the value of r is positive reflects the increasing orientation of the scatter diagram. It corresponds to the fact that the value of b in the regression equation is positive. If the scatter diagram had been oriented in a decreasing direction, the values of r and of b would have been negative. We consequently speak of positive or negative correlation, depending on the sign of these two coefficients. The value of r will fall in the range -1 to $+1$, inclusive, as will be shown later. A value for r close to zero lends little support to the hypothesis that a relationship exists between the variables of concern. A value close either to -1 or $+1$ is strong support for the hypothesis of a relationship. We shall discuss a test for significance of the value of r, but before doing so we consider another useful measure of the relationship between variables.

The coefficient of determination

Recalling that, in earlier discussion, we talked of the ability of the regression equation to explain variation in Y in terms of variation in X, let us consider how we might measure the explanation provided. Since our concern is to determine what part of the variation of Y is explained by the regression equation, we need a measure of the total variation exhibited by Y. The obvious choice for this measure is the variance of Y:[17]

$$\text{var}(Y) = \frac{\Sigma(Y - \bar{Y})^2}{n} = \frac{\Sigma y^2}{n}.$$

To get a comparable measure of the amount of variation in Y that has been explained by the regression, we can use a measure of the variation of Y which would have occurred if each observed value of Y had been exactly what we would have expected on the basis of the regression equation. For each observation, the value of Y which we would expect on the basis of the equation is just the estimate $Y' = a + bX$, where the value of X is the one associated with that observation. Then we have as a measure of *explained* variation:

$$\text{var}(Y') = \frac{\Sigma(Y' - \bar{Y})^2}{n} = \frac{\Sigma(y')^2}{n}.$$

The relation between these measures becomes clearer with an examination of Figure 7–13, where the various terms are pointed out, relative to one of the points of the scatter diagram.

By expressing the measure of explained variation as a ratio of the total variation which occurred in Y, we can find what proportion of this variation is explainable by the regression equation. Thus,

---

[17] Once again, we are interested in the variance of Y as it occurs in the sample, not as an estimate for the population. We divide by n, not $n - 1$.

$$\frac{\text{Explained variation}}{\text{Total variation}} = \frac{\Sigma(y')^2/n}{\Sigma y^2/n} = \frac{\Sigma(y')^2}{\Sigma y^2}.$$

Through some manipulation, we can relate this measure of explained variation to the coefficient of correlation. Thus, since $y' = bx$ (see Figure 7–13), we can substitute in the last expression above to get:

$$\frac{\Sigma(y')^2}{\Sigma y^2} = \frac{\Sigma(bx)^2}{\Sigma y^2} = \frac{b^2 \Sigma x^2}{\Sigma y^2}.$$

But $b = \Sigma xy/\Sigma x^2$, which we substitute above:

$$b^2 \cdot \frac{\Sigma x^2}{\Sigma y^2} = \left(\frac{\Sigma xy}{\Sigma x^2}\right)^2 \cdot \frac{\Sigma x^2}{\Sigma y^2} = \frac{(\Sigma xy)^2}{\Sigma x^2 \cdot \Sigma y^2}.$$

This last expression can be seen to be the square of the coefficient of correlation. Thus, the ratio of explained variation to total variation, called the *coefficient of determination,* is denoted by r^2 and is easily calculated as the square of the coefficient of correlation.

Figure 7–13

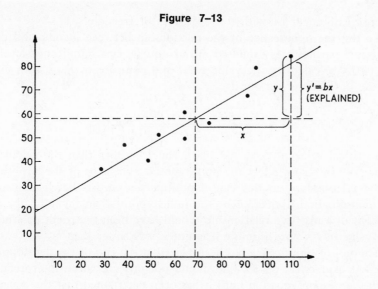

The coefficient of determination by the nature of what it measures necessarily will have a value between zero and one, inclusive. That is, the ratio of total variation in Y "explained" by the regression equation cannot be less than zero or more than one. It follows that the value of r must be in the range -1 to $+1$, as stated earlier. For our particular example, the coefficient of determination is $r^2 = (0.947)^2 \simeq 0.897$. In the sample of 10 observations of income and consumption expenditures, about 90 percent of the variation in consumption expenditures among the persons included is explainable in terms of a linear consumption function, $Y' = 14.00 + (0.616)X$.

A test for the significance of the relationship

The point has already been made that even though no relationship actually exists between the two variables in question, it is possible for a sample of observations from the population to exhibit some relationship. Put another way, a sample of observations almost certainly will yield a nonzero value for r, since the probability of all observations taking such values as to exactly offset each other in Σxy is rather small. On the other hand, large nonzero values (either negative or positive) for r tend to discredit a hypothesis that no relationship exists between the variables. With the by now familiar reasoning, therefore, we can test the null hypothesis of no relationship through the test statistic

$$t = \frac{r\sqrt{n - 2}}{\sqrt{1 - r^2}},$$

where t is Student's t with $n - 2$ degrees of freedom.

To test the significance of the relationship between income and consumption expenditures exhibited in our sample, at a significance level of $\alpha = 0.05$, we calculate the value for t and compare to $t_{0.025}$ with eight degrees of freedom. For our data,

$$t = \frac{r\sqrt{n - 2}}{\sqrt{1 - r^2}} = \frac{(0.947)\sqrt{8}}{\sqrt{1 - 0.897}} \simeq 8.37 .$$

The critical value of $t_{0.025} = 2.306$ is much smaller than the calculated value. We therefore reject the null hypothesis in favor of the hypothesis that a relationship (in this case a positive one) exists between income and consumption. Rejection of the null hypothesis in favor of the hypothesis of a negative relationship would have been the result of a negative value of t whose absolute magnitude was larger than $t_{0.025}$.

The test of significance has been placed at the end of the development here. As a practical matter one should not proceed to an interpretation of the regression equation until it has been determined that the equation does indicate a significant relationship. If one is not able to reject the null hypothesis, he may wish to enlarge the sample, in which case the values calculated for the sums of products and cross products can be saved to be pooled with the additional values.

The development of the correlation analysis has been lengthy, and may appear rather involved at this point. To help the student in getting an overview of the procedure, a flow diagram is provided which outlines the required steps.

FLOW DIAGRAM FOR CORRELATION ANALYSIS

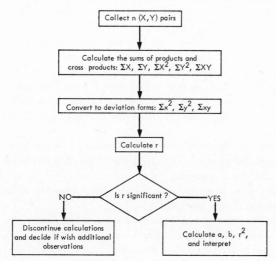

Problem Set 7–7

1. The proficiency test which was discussed in problem 1 of Problem Set 7–5 was devised by the personnel manager as a basis for predicting productivity of workers. On the basis of the data presented there, test for a significant relationship between scores on the proficiency test and productivity of workers at a level of significance of $\alpha = 0.10$. Given the result of this test, would you say that the proficiency examination administered to workers gives a strong basis for estimating productivity?

2. On the basis of the data appearing in problem 2 in Problem Set 7–5, does there appear to be a significant relationship between level of educational attainment and the earning power of an individual? About what proportion of variation in incomes of individuals appears to be explainable in terms of variation in level of educational attainment?

3. Does the level of grain consumption in a country appear to be significantly related to the per capita income in that country? (See problem 4 of Problem Set 7–5.) What proportion of variation in grain consumption from one country to another appears to be explainable in terms of variation in income from one country to another?

4. Test for a significant relationship between weight and height in the data of problem 6 of Problem Set 7–5 (use a level of significance of $\alpha = 0.01$). About what proportion of the variation in weights in the sample of problem 6 is explainable in terms of variation in heights for that sample?

5. Repeat the steps of problem 4 using the data of problem 7 in Problem Set 7–5 in which the weight and height observations for three young ladies were deleted from the data. At what level of α does the relationship between height and weight on the reduced set of data become significant? What does

a comparison of the results in this problem with those of the previous problem suggest to you concerning the level of significance which was achieved in the relationship of the previous problem? Do you think that some factor other than weight may have been instrumental in bringing about the level of significance in that relationship?

6. Examine the following statements and indicate, for each one, whether it is true or false. If you believe that a statement is false, indicate why.

a) One can say generally that if the value for the *b* coefficient in a regression equation is less than 0.5, then the relationship will not be a significant one.

b) If the value of the coefficient of correlation, *r*, is 0.8, then this indicates that 80 percent of the variation in the *Y* variable has been explained by variation in the *X* variable.

c) It would not be possible for a regression relationship to be significant if the value for r^2 was less than 0.50.

d) If the result of a regression analysis on a set of data yields a highly significant relationship between the *X* variable and the *Y* variable, this constitutes conclusive proof that there is a causal relationship between these two variables.

e) Generally, one can say that negative values of the *b* coefficient in a regression relationship indicates a weaker relationship between the variables involved than would a positive value for the *b* coefficient in a regression relationship.

f) Consider two regression relationships for two different samples of observations and suppose that the value of *b* in the first was +4 and the value of *b* in the second was +8. Comparing the values for the *b* coefficient in the two regressions, we note that twice the variation of the *Y* variable in the second regression is explained as in the first regression.

Appendix A

In this appendix, we wish to extend the results concerning regression analysis somewhat further. In the text, it was shown how to find a confidence interval for values of *Y* associated with particular values of *X*. We also learned how to test for a significant relationship through an evaluation of *r*.

Here we wish to consider the value of *b*, the slope of the regression equation. We wish a method of testing for significance of the value of *b* and a method of constructing a confidence interval for *b*. We concentrate on *b* because its interpretation is especially important. The value of *b*, we have seen, provides us with an estimate of the change to expect in *Y*, per unit change in *X*. An estimate of the ratio of change in one variable, relative to another, is often quite important in practical and theoretical problems. To cite one example, the economists' concept of the marginal propensity to consume is such a ratio—the change in consumption expenditures to be expected on the basis of a unit change in income.

The following development makes extensive use of the rules for summation and expected values which were developed in Appendixes A and B of Chapter 3. The results are for the case where the values for X are fixed and only Y is considered free to vary from sample to sample. That is, we assume that for each sample of n observations, the same set of X values occurs each time,[1] but the Y values associated with these values of X are free to vary from one sample to the next. No assumption is required as to the form of probability distribution that Y follows, unless this fact is specifically noted.

Noting that

$$b = \frac{\Sigma xy}{\Sigma x^2} \text{ and } y = Y - \bar{Y},$$

$$b = \frac{\Sigma xy}{\Sigma x^2} = \frac{\Sigma x(Y - \bar{Y})}{\Sigma x^2} = \frac{\Sigma xY}{\Sigma x^2} - \frac{\bar{Y}\Sigma x}{\Sigma x^2}$$

$$b = \frac{\Sigma xY}{\Sigma x^2}, \text{ since } \Sigma x = 0 . \tag{1}$$

To find the sampling distribution of b:
Mean of b:
Substituting $Y = A + BX + \epsilon$ in (1) we have:

$$b = \frac{\Sigma x(A + BX + \epsilon)}{\Sigma x^2}$$

$$= \Sigma \left(\frac{x}{\Sigma x^2}\right)(A) + \Sigma \left(\frac{x}{\Sigma x^2}\right)(BX) + \Sigma \left(\frac{x}{\Sigma x^2}\right)(\epsilon)$$

$$= A\Sigma \frac{x}{\Sigma x^2} + B\Sigma \left(\frac{x}{\Sigma x^2}\right)(X) + \Sigma \left(\frac{x}{\Sigma x^2}\right)(\epsilon) .$$

Note that:

$$\Sigma \frac{x}{\Sigma x^2} = \frac{1}{\Sigma x^2} \Sigma x = 0 \text{ since } \Sigma x = 0 ,$$

and

$$\Sigma \left(\frac{x}{\Sigma x^2}\right)(X) = \frac{1}{\Sigma x^2} \Sigma(x \cdot X) = \frac{1}{\Sigma x^2} \Sigma(X - \bar{X})X = \frac{1}{\Sigma x^2} (\Sigma X^2 - \bar{X}\Sigma X)$$

$$= \frac{1}{\Sigma x^2} (\Sigma x^2) = 1 .$$

Thus,

$$b = A(0) + B(1) + \Sigma \frac{x}{\Sigma x^2} (\epsilon)$$

$$b = B + \Sigma \left(\frac{x}{\Sigma x^2}\right)(\epsilon) . \tag{2}$$

---

[1] It can be shown that the results below apply if the values of X are also allowed to vary, if the distribution of X does not involve the same parameter values as apply to Y.

Now, the mean of b is:

$$E(b) = E(B) + E\left(\Sigma \frac{x}{\Sigma x^2} \cdot \epsilon\right)$$

$$= B + [E(\epsilon)]\left[\Sigma \frac{x}{\Sigma x^2}\right]$$

$$= B \quad \text{since } E(\epsilon) = 0 .$$

So the mean value of b is B.

To find the variance of b:

First note, from (2), that:

$$b - B = \Sigma\left(\frac{x}{\Sigma x^2}\right)(\epsilon) .$$

So,

$$\text{var}(b) = E[(b - B)^2]$$

$$= E\left[\left(\Sigma \frac{x}{\Sigma x^2}\epsilon\right)^2\right]$$

$$= E\left[\left(\frac{x_1}{\Sigma x^2}\right)^2\epsilon_1{}^2 + \left(\frac{x_2}{\Sigma x^2}\right)^2\epsilon_2{}^2 + \cdots + \left(\frac{x_n}{\Sigma x^2}\right)^2\epsilon_n{}^2 + 2\left(\frac{x_1}{\Sigma x^2}\right)\left(\frac{x_2}{\Sigma x^2}\right)\epsilon_1 \cdot \epsilon_2 \right.$$

$$\left. + \cdots + 2\left(\frac{x_{n-1}}{\Sigma x^2}\right)^2\left(\frac{x_n}{\Sigma x^2}\right)^2 \epsilon_{n-1}\epsilon_n \right]^2 .$$

Now the values of ϵ_1 (the error term for $X = X_1$) and ϵ_2 (the error term for X_2) are assumed to be independent of one another. Because of this $E(\epsilon_1 \cdot \epsilon_2) = E(\epsilon_1) \cdot E(\epsilon_2)$ by Rule E–5 in Appendix B of Chapter 3. And since $E(\epsilon_i) = 0$ for all i, $E(\epsilon_1 \cdot \epsilon_2) = 0$. The same result applies for all other pairs ϵ_i, ϵ_j. Thus, all terms with cross products, such as $\epsilon_1 \cdot \epsilon_2$, have an expected value of zero. This leads to:

$$\text{var}(b) = E\left[\left(\frac{x_1}{\Sigma x^2}\right)^2\epsilon_1{}^2 + \left(\frac{x_2}{\Sigma x^2}\right)^2\epsilon_2{}^2 + \cdots + \left(\frac{x_n}{\Sigma x^2}\right)^2\epsilon_n{}^2\right]$$

$$= E(\epsilon_i{}^2)\Sigma\left(\frac{x}{\Sigma x^2}\right)^2 .$$

But,

$$E(\epsilon_i{}^2) = \text{var}(\epsilon_i) \text{ and } \Sigma\left(\frac{x}{\Sigma x^2}\right)^2 = \frac{1}{(\Sigma x^2)^2}\Sigma x^2 = \frac{1}{\Sigma x^2} ,$$

---

[2] To show this for $n = 3$, substitute a_i for $\frac{x_i}{\Sigma x^2}$ and expand:

$$\left(\sum_{i=1}^{3} a_i\epsilon_i\right)^2 + (a_1\epsilon_1 + a_2\epsilon_2 + a_3\epsilon_3)^2$$

$$= a_1{}^2\epsilon_1{}^2 + a_2{}^2\epsilon_2{}^2 + a_3{}^2\epsilon_3{}^2 + 2a_1\epsilon_1a_2\epsilon_2 + 2a_1\epsilon_1a_3\epsilon_3 + 2a_2\epsilon_2a_3\epsilon_3$$

so

$$\text{var}(b) = \sigma_\epsilon^2 \cdot \frac{1}{\Sigma x^2}.$$

The results above show that the statistic, b, has a sampling distribution with a mean equal to B, the parameter which it estimates, and a standard deviation of $\sigma_\epsilon/\sqrt{\Sigma x^2}$. If we assume, further, that the distribution of the values of ϵ (or, the distribution of individual Y values about the line $Y = A + BX$) is normal, we can test for a significant difference between b and some hypothetical value of B, B^*, by forming the t statistic

$$t = \frac{b - B^*}{\sigma_\epsilon'/\sqrt{\Sigma x^2}}.$$

The usual concern will be to test the value of b against $B^* = 0$ (the null hypothesis of no relationship), but we can also test for b significantly different from any value of B^*. As an example, we test for b significantly different from $B^* = 0$, using the values of the problem in the text. The required values are: $b = 0.616$ $\sigma'_\epsilon = 5.7$, $\Sigma x^2 = 5{,}976.1$. Substituting these values, we get:

$$t = \frac{b - B^*}{\sigma_\epsilon'/\sqrt{\Sigma x^2}} = \frac{.616 - 0}{5.7/\sqrt{5{,}976.1}}$$
$$\simeq 8.37 ,$$

which is much larger than a critical value of $t_{0.025} = 2.306$. Note that this result is the same as the test based on $t = r\sqrt{n-2}/\sqrt{1-r^2}$. Later, we show that the tests are equivalent.

Having found that the value of b is significant, we may wish an interval estimate for B. This is easily accomplished in the same manner discussed for finding a confidence interval of $m'(X)$. We find the interval as:

$$b - t_{\beta/2}\sigma_\epsilon'/\sqrt{\Sigma x^2} \leq B' \leq b + t_{\beta/2}\sigma_\epsilon'/\sqrt{\Sigma x^2}.$$

For a confidence level of $\beta = 0.95$, we get an interval:

$$0.616 - (2.306)(5.7)/\sqrt{5976.1} \leq B' \leq 0.616 + (2.306)(5.7)/\sqrt{5976.1}$$
$$0.616 - 0.169 \leq B' \leq 0.616 + 0.169$$
$$0.447 \leq B' \leq 0.785 .$$

The conclusion would follow that the value of B in the consumption function lies somewhere between 0.447 and 0.785 with the usual interpretation of the confidence we place in that conclusion.

We can now show how a test for significant relationship can be based on $t = r\sqrt{n-2}/\sqrt{1-r^2}$. We have, to test significance with b,

$$t = \frac{b - 0}{\sigma_e / \sqrt{\Sigma x^2}} = \frac{\dfrac{\Sigma xy}{\Sigma x^2}}{\sqrt{\dfrac{\Sigma y^2 - b\Sigma xy}{n - 2}} \Big/ \sqrt{\Sigma x^2}}$$

$$= \frac{\dfrac{\Sigma xy}{\sqrt{\Sigma x^2}} \sqrt{n - 2}}{\sqrt{\Sigma y^2 - b\Sigma xy}}.$$

Dividing both numerator and denominator by $\sqrt{\Sigma y^2}$,

$$t = \frac{\dfrac{\Sigma xy}{\sqrt{\Sigma x^2} \cdot \sqrt{\Sigma y^2}} \cdot \sqrt{n - 2}}{\sqrt{1 - b\dfrac{\Sigma xy}{\Sigma y^2}}}$$

which gives, since $b = \Sigma xy / \Sigma x^2$,

$$t = \frac{\dfrac{\Sigma xy}{\sqrt{\Sigma x^2} \cdot \sqrt{\Sigma y^2}} \cdot \sqrt{n - 2}}{\sqrt{1 - \dfrac{(\Sigma xy)^2}{\Sigma x^2 \cdot \Sigma y^2}}}$$

Now,

$$r = \frac{\Sigma xy}{\sqrt{\Sigma x^2} \cdot \sqrt{\Sigma y^2}}$$

so,

$$t = r\sqrt{n - 2} / \sqrt{1 - r^2}.$$

Appendix B

This appendix contains a program in FORTRAN, Figure 7–B–1, which provides the required values in a simple linear correlation. Another program is written in BASIC language, to accomplish the same purpose, Figure 7–B–2. The FORTRAN program is discussed fully in the appendix, Statistical Analysis and the Computer, where it appears as Figure A–4 on page 401. For a discussion of preparation of the FORTRAN program cards, see Appendix C in Chapter 3. We discuss here, for the two programs, the required format for data input.

The program of Figure 7–B–1: Data input for this program is provided on punched cards. The first card must contain the number of X, Y observations in the sample. The first four columns of the card are to contain this number. Thus, if there are 150 observations in the sample, the first card will be punched 0150. The following data cards contain the actual X,Y pairs of the sample observations, one pair on each card. Each value, X and Y, has six columns reserved for it, with the last two of the six reserved for a decimal value. For example, in Table 7–2, the first X,Y pair consists of X = 41 and Y = 44. These values would be recorded on a data card by punching 004100004400 in the first 12 columns (as before, the zeros actually need not be punched).

With this program, no signal card is required to indicate the end of a

Figure 7–B–1

```
C        A PROGRAM TO CALCULATE THE COEFFICIENTS OF A SIMPLE LINEAR REGRESS
C        ION, STANDARD ERROR OF ESTIMATE, COEFFICIENT OF CORRELATION, COEFF
C        ICIENT OF DETERMINATION, AND STUDENTS T FOR TEST OF SIGNIFICANCE
    1    FORMAT(I4)
    2    FORMAT(2F6.2)
    5    READ 1, N
         SUMX = 0.0
         SUMY = 0.0
         SUMXY = 0.0
         SUMX2 = 0.0
         SUMY2 = 0.0
         EN = N
         DO 3 I = 1, N
         READ 2, X, Y
         SUMX = SUMX + X
         SUMY = SUMY + Y
         SUMXY = SUMXY + X*Y
         SUMX2 = SUMX2 + X*X
    3    SUMY2 = SUMY2 + Y*Y
         XMEAN = SUMX/EN
         YMEAN = SUMY/EN
         SUMSXY = SUMXY - EN*XMEAN*YMEAN
         SUMSX2 = SUMX2 - EN*XMEAN**2
         B = SUMSXY/SUMSX2
         A = YMEAN - B*XMEAN
         SUMSY2 = SUMY2 - EN*YMEAN**2
         SUME2 = SUMSY2 - B*SUMSXY
         STERES = SQRTF(SUME2/(EN - 2.0))
         RTSX2 = SQRTF(SUMSX2)
         RTSY2 = SQRTF(SUMSY2)
         R = SUMSXY/(RTSX2*RTSY2)
         R2 = R*R
         RTDEGF = SQRTF(EN - 2.0)
         RT1MIN = SQRTF(1.0 - R2)
         T = R*RTDEGF/RT1MIN
         PRINT 6, SUMX, SUMY, SUMXY, SUMX2, SUMY2
         PRINT 4, A, B, STERES, R, R2, T
    4    FORMAT(2XF10.2, 2XF10.3, 2XF10.2, 2XF6.3, 2XF6.3, 2XF10.4)
    6    FORMAT(5F12.4)
         PAUSE 1
         GO TO 5
         END
```

set of data. The first data card, with the number of observations, serves to indicate the length of the set of data. The program is written to process more than one set of data automatically.

The output, for each set of data, is printed in two lines. The first line contains, in the order given, ΣX, ΣY, ΣXY, ΣX^2, and ΣY^2. The second line includes values for the regression coefficients, a and b, for σ_e', r, r^2, and Student's t, in that order.

The program of Figure 7–B–2: This program is written in BASIC language. Entry of data begins on DATA line 570. This line, 570 DATA

Figure 7–B–2

```
100  REMARKS:  A PROGRAM TO PERFORM A SIMPLE LINEAR CORRELATION
110  DIM X(50),Y(50)
120  READ N
130  LET T1 = 0
140  LET T2 = 0
150  LET T3 = 0
160  LET T4 = 0
170  LET T5 = 0
180  FOR I = 1 TO N
190  READ X(I), Y(I)
200  LET X1 = X(I)*Y(I)
210  LET X2 = X(I)↑2
220  LET Y2 = Y(I)↑2
230  PRINT X(I),Y(I),X1,X2,Y2
240  LET T1 = T1 + X(I)
250  LET T2 = T2 + Y(I)
260  LET T3 = T3 + X1
270  LET T4 = T4 + X2
280  LET T5 = T5 + Y2
290  NEXT I
300  PRINT
310  PRINT T1,T2,T3,T4,T5
320  PRINT
330  LET M1 = T1/N
340  LET M2 = T2/N
350  PRINT "MEAN OF X = "M1, "MEAN OF Y = "M2
360  LET S1 = T3 − N*M1*M2
370  LET S2 = T4 − N*M1 ↑ 2
380  LET S3 = T5 − N*M2 ↑ 2
390  PRINT "SUM XY = "S1; "SUMXSQ = "S2; "SUM YSQ = "S3
400  LET B = S1/S2
410  LET A = M2 − B*M1
420  PRINT
430  PRINT "EQUATION IS Y = "A "+ ("B")X"
440  PRINT
450  LET Y1 = A + B*X(1)
460  LET Y2 = A + B*X(N)
470  PRINT "TWO POINTS ARE X = "X(1)", Y = "Y1
480  PRINT "              AND X = "X(N)", Y = "Y2
490  PRINT
500  LET R = S1/(SQR(S2)*SQR(S3))
510  LET R2 = R↑2
520  LET T = (R*SQR(N − 2))/SQR(1 − R2)
525  LET N1 = N − 2
530  PRINT "R = "R; "R SQUARED = "R2;"T = "T; "DEGREES OF FREEDOM = "N1
540  PRINT
550  LET E = SQR((S3 − B*S1)/(N − 2))
560  PRINT "SIGMA OF ERRORS = "E
570  DATA 27
580  DATA 66,150,72,205,70,155,69,175,73,165,68,155,60,100,70,210
590  DATA 72,160,64,130,73,165,71,140,71,165,68,168,70,185,71,181
600  DATA 72,170,65,105,65,145,71,165,72,183,72,160,71,173,72,188
610  DATA 71,165,69,160,71,175
620  END
```

27 in the case shown, indicates the number of X,Y pairs to be processed. The values of successive X,Y pairs, 27 pairs in this case, follow on successive DATA lines. The data shown in Figure 7–B–2 are the values for height and weight in problem 6, Problem Set 7–5.

If the set of data to be processed contains more than 50 X,Y pairs the line, 110 DIM X(50),Y(50), must be revised so as to indicate the number of pairs. As usual, if the number of DATA lines required to record the data leads to use of the line number, 620, for data, a new END line must be written with a line number higher than the highest numbered DATA line.

The output of this program, for the data included in Figure 7–B–2, is exhibited in Figure 7–B–3. First there appears a table containing columns for X,Y,XY,X², and Y². This table is followed by a separate row which records the sums of the columns. Following this are the relevant values which result from the correlation analysis, as indicated in Figure 7–B–3.

Figure 7–B–3

66	150	9900	4356	22500
72	205	14760	5184	42025
70	155	10850	4900	24025
69	175	12075	4761	30625
73	165	12045	5329	27225
68	155	10540	4624	24025
60	100	6000	3600	10000
70	210	14700	4900	44100
72	160	11520	5184	25600
64	130	8320	4096	16900
73	165	12045	5329	27225
71	140	9940	5041	19600
71	165	11715	5041	27225
68	168	11424	4624	28224
70	185	12950	4900	34225
71	181	12851	5041	32761
72	170	12240	5184	28900
65	105	6825	4225	11025
65	145	9425	4225	21025
71	165	11715	5041	27225
72	183	13176	5184	33489
72	160	11520	5184	25600
71	173	12283	5041	29929
72	188	13536	5184	35344
71	165	11715	5041	27225
69	160	11040	4761	25600
71	175	12425	5041	30625
1879	4398	307535	131021	732272

MEAN OF X = 69.5926   MEAN OF Y = 162.889

SUM XY = 1466.78 SUMXSQ = 256.519 SUM YSQ = 15886.7

EQUATION IS $Y = -235.042 + (5.71801)X$

TWO POINTS ARE X = 66   , Y = 142.346
               AND X = 71   , Y = 170.936

R = .726588 R SQUARED = .52793 T = 5.28756 DEGREES OF FREEDOM = 25

SIGMA OF ERRORS = 17.3201

Note that, following the line which records the regression equation, two X, Y pairs are given. These are two coordinates of the regression line, to be used in plotting the line if that is desired. The value of X in the first of these pairs is the first value of X entered as data in the program. The second X, Y pair has the last value of X entered as data. If one wishes to get a good plot of the line, therefore, he should endeavor to make the first and last X values entered in the data widely separated values. (The point $\overline{X},\overline{Y}$ which is also provided can be used, of course, to plot the line.)

It should be pointed out that the values of SUM XY, SUMXSQ, and SUM YSQ are not ΣXY, ΣX^2, and ΣY^2, but are, rather, Σxy, Σx^2, and Σy^2. In the last line of output, SIGMA OF ERRORS refers to σ_e'.

Fitting a
probability distribution to
a set of data:
The normal distribution,
an example

Introduction

The student who has progressed this far in the study of statistical methods will recognize that much statistical analysis proceeds on the assumption that some statistical model is appropriate. There are several such models available. The particular one to choose, or the question if any is appropriate, depends on the problem at hand. The nature of the problem will often dictate the choice of model. We discussed, in an earlier chapter, conditions that make the binomial model appropriate, for example. We have also illustrated situations in which the normal distribution is appropriate. If space and time permitted, we could describe other probability distributions and the types of situation in which they have been useful.

Much of the choice of a proper probability distribution depends on a priori considerations of what the statistician believes will provide a proper "fit" to the situation. It often is helpful, however, for the statistician to "check out" this belief by seeing how well the chosen probability distribution fits the data at hand. This process of *fitting* a probability distribution to a set of data is accomplished by determining the frequency with which various values of the random variable could be expected to occur if the probability distribution chosen were, in fact, the appropriate one. For most probability distributions, the expected frequencies are easily calculated when one specifies the appropriate values for the parameters of the distribution. The appropriate parameter values usually will just be the values for the corresponding statistics in the data at hand. In this chapter, the process of fitting a probability distribution to a set of data is illustrated for the normal distribution. The general procedure is the same for other distributions although, obviously, the parameters of interest may differ somewhat.

We begin in the following section by showing how one can proceed from the standardized normal distribution to a frequency distribution whose class frequencies are those one would expect of a normal frequency distribution. The second section develops a method by which the ordinates of the "fitted" normal distribution can be determined. A third section repeats these procedures in an example for a given set of data. Finally, a fourth section introduces a test for goodness of fit which allows us to see if the actual set of data differs significantly from a normal distribution. This so-called goodness-of-fit test is applicable to other probability distributions.

Fitting the expected class frequencies

As a first approach, suppose that we have a sample consisting of 1,000 values (denoted by the symbol x) that we believe to be distributed in an essentially normal fashion. Actually, we treat this set of data as if it were a sample from a normal population. Our first concern is to determine the frequencies we might expect in the various classes of a frequency distribution describing these data if the data are, in fact, a sample from a normal population. Assume that a suitable frequency distribution of the data is provided by assigning the 1,000 values to seven classes with *bounds* of 165, 175, 185, 195, 205, 215, 225, and 235 (we do not show the frequency distribution, since the actual frequencies are not required in what follows). Assume, further, that the 1,000 items have a mean of $\bar{x} = 200$ and a standard deviation of $s = 10$.

Now, if we wish to determine the expected frequencies in various classes for a sample selected from a normal population, we must specify the values for the mean and standard deviation of this population. Our best estimates of these parameters will be the mean and standard deviation of our sample of 1,000 values. Thus, letting μ denote the mean of the distribution and σ its standard deviation, we wish to fit a normal distribution with $\mu = \bar{x} = 200$ and $\sigma = s = 10$ to the set of sample data. The resulting fitted distribution will be located, relative to the classes of the sample frequency distribution, much as depicted in the accompanying figure (see page 283).

If the sample frequency distribution *were* a normal distribution with $\mu = 200$ and $\sigma = 10$, we would know exactly what proportion of items to expect in each class. In the class with *bounds* of 195–205, for example,

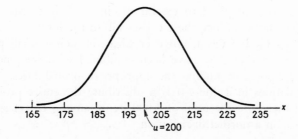

the proportion of items to expect is easily calculated. The upper *bound* of this class is converted to the standard normal variate, *z*, by:

$$z = \frac{205 - \mu}{\sigma} = \frac{205 - 200}{10} = 0.5 .$$

From Table C in the section of tables, we find that the proportion of items to expect within 0.5 standard deviations of the mean is 0.1915. Since the lower *bound* of the class is the same distance below the mean as the upper *bound* is above it, we would expect 0.1915 of the items to fall in this interval also. Thus, the central class should contain a propor-

Table 8–1

Class Bounds	Value of z for Class Bounds		$P(z_l < z < z_u)$	Expected Number in Class f_e
	z_l*	z_u*		
$-\infty$–165	$-\infty$	-3.5 ⎫		
165–175	-3.5	-2.5 ⎬	0.0062	6.2
175–185	-2.5	-1.5	.0606	60.6
185–195	-1.5	-0.5	.2417	241.7
195–205	-0.5	$+0.5$	.3830	383.0
205–215	0.5	1.5	.2417	241.7
215–225	1.5	2.5	.0606	60.6
225–235	2.5	3.5	.0062	6.2
235–$+\infty$	3.5	$+\infty$		
			1.0000	1,000.0

* z_l is z value for lower bound, and z_u is z value for upper bound, of each class.

tion equal to 0.3830 of the total number of items in the distribution. That is, $(0.3830)(1,000) = 383.0$ is the *expected* number of items for this class on the assumption of a normal distribution with $\mu = 200$, $\sigma = 10$. In the same manner, we can calculate the expected number of items in each class of the frequency distribution. This has been done in Table 8–1. Notice that two classes have been added at either end of the distribution. These are required to extend the interval of z from minus infinity to plus infinity. Since these classes fall in the intervals 3.5 standard deviations beyond the mean, however, there is such a small probability attached to them that they have been combined with their neighboring classes for purposes of finding the appropriate probabilities. The effect of the calculations in Table 8–1 is to distribute the entire probability of 1.0000, and therefore the total of 1,000 items, among the classes as they would appear in a normal distribution.

Fitting the ordinates of a normal distribution

In the preceding section, the manner of determining the frequencies associated with a normally distributed frequency distribution was illustrated. It may occasionally be useful to plot the normal curve on a graph alongside (or superimposed on) the graph of the actual frequency distribution, for purposes of visual comparison. To do this, we require the *ordinates* (heights) of the appropriate normal curve at varying distances from the mean of the distribution. These ordinates are easily calculated. To see how this is done, we return to a consideration of the density function, introduced in Chapter 4, for a normal random variable.

The density function of the normal random variable with mean, μ, and standard deviation, σ, is:

$$y(x) = \frac{1}{\sigma\sqrt{2\pi}} e^{-1/2[(x-\mu)/\sigma]^2} .$$

As was pointed out earlier, the density function of a random variable describes the height of the probability distribution associated with a random variable, at all values the random variable may take. Thus, for a given normal random variable, x, substitution of the appropriate values in the equation above will yield the ordinates of the curve for any values of x we might wish. The process can be simplified considerably, however, if we make use of some of the uniformities in characteristics which we have learned to expect of normal distributions.

Looking at the density function once again, we note that it can be viewed as consisting of two parts, as indicated below:

$$y(x) = \left[\frac{1}{\sigma\sqrt{2\pi}}\right] [e^{-1/2[(x-\mu)/\sigma]^2}] .$$

In the term, $1/(\sigma\sqrt{2\pi})$, only the value of σ depends on the particular normal distribution with which we are concerned. The value to use for σ will, of course, be the value calculated for s in the frequency distribution. The value of $\sqrt{2\pi}$ is, of course, constant and equals approximately

2.5067. In fitting a normal curve to a set of data, therefore, we can substitute for this term the value $1/(2.5067 \cdot s)$.

Next, we consider the term, $e^{-\frac{1}{2}[(x-\mu)/\sigma]^2}$. Noting that the standardized normal variate is $z = (x - \mu)/\sigma$, we can write this term as $e^{-\frac{1}{2}z^2}$. This term will remain the same for any normal distribution, regardless of the values of its mean and standard deviation. This fact allows us to use a standardized table for the proportionate heights of a normal distribution which is to be fitted to a set of data. The values in such a table will be those for $e^{-\frac{1}{2}z^2}$. For any value of the random variable, x, the appropriate factor for the relative height at that point can be found merely by transforming x to $z = (x - \mu)/\sigma$ (or, for an actual frequency distribution, $z = (x - \bar{x})/s$) and looking up the appropriate value of $e^{-\frac{1}{2}z^2}$ in the table. A brief table containing selected points appears as Table 8–2.[1]

Table 8–2

z	$e^{-1/2z^2}$
0.0	1.000
0.5	0.883
1.0	0.607
1.5	0.325
2.0	0.135
2.5	0.044
3.0	0.011
3.5	0.002

The right-hand column of Table 8–2 indicates the proportionate height of a normal curve at various distances from the mean, where these distances are expressed in standard deviations. These values do not represent the *density* of the probability distribution, however. To find the density at the selected points, we must evaluate the term $1/(2.5067 \cdot s)$. For our data, we have:

$$\frac{1}{2.5067 \cdot s} = \frac{1}{(2.5067)(10)} \simeq 0.03989 .$$

The density of the distribution at the point $z = 0$ (which, of course, corresponds to the mean of the x values) is easily calculated as:

$$y_0 = \frac{1}{s\sqrt{2\pi}} e^{-1/2z^2} = (0.03989)(1.000) = 0.03989 .$$

That is, the density of the normal curve at the mean of the distribution is always just the value of $1/\sigma\sqrt{2\pi}$, or $1/s\sqrt{2\pi}$ as the case may be. Since all other densities will bear a relation to y_0 as the proportions appearing

---

[1] More extensive tables are readily available in handbooks of statistics. One can also calculate particular values easily, using e $\simeq 2.718$.

in Table 8–2, we find successive densities by multiplying y_0 by these proportions. Thus, the density at $z = 1$ is $y = y_0(0.607) = (0.03989)(0.607) \cong 0.02421$, as it appears in the second column of Table 8–3.

Table   8–3

$z = (x - \bar{x})/s$	$y = y_0 e^{-1/2z^2}$	$f_c = n \cdot w \cdot y$
0.0	0.03989	398.9
0.5	.03523	352.3
1.0	.02421	242.1
1.5	.01296	129.6
2.0	.00539	53.9
2.5	.00176	17.6
3.0	.00044	4.4
3.5	.00008	0.8

The values for the densities of the curve that appear in the second column of Table 8–3 can be considered as analogous, in the continuous case, to the relative frequency per unit width of the classes of the frequency distribution. The student will recall that probabilities are presented graphically as areas, not heights. Also, given the probability associated with a particular interval, one must multiply this probability by

Figure   8–1

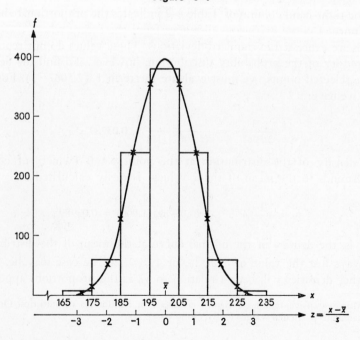

the total number of items included in the distribution in order to arrive at the expected frequency to associate with that interval. Bearing these two facts in mind, we note that the densities in column two of Table 8–3 must be "scaled up" by two factors: the width, w, of the classes in the frequency distribution and the total number, n, of items in the distribution. The final result of this scaling procedure will be the appropriate set of ordinates for a normal distribution fitted to the frequency distribution. Since $n = 1,000$ and $w = 10$ in our example, we multiply each entry of the second column in Table 8–3 by $n \cdot w = 10,000$ to get the appropriate ordinates in column three.

In order to see the relationship between the ordinates of the normal curve and the expected frequencies of the classes of the frequency distribution, Figure 8–1 presents the graph of the frequency distribution derived in Table 8–1. Superimposed on this graph is the continuous normal curve whose probabilities were used in deriving the expected frequencies of Table 8–1. It is plotted from the points, marked on the graph by x's, of Table 8–3.

Fitting the normal distribution to a set of data: A practical example

It was pointed out in an earlier chapter that statistical quality control of manufacturing processes often relies on the assumption that the relevant dimension of the parts being manufactured is distributed in a normal fashion about the mean value. As a practical illustration, suppose we wish to determine if it is reasonable to assume that a manufacturing process that produces machine bolts does so with the diameters of these bolts normally distributed. To that end, we select a random sample of 1,000 bolts from a day's[2] production; and on the basis of the sample result, we test the hypothesis that the sample was selected from a normal distribution.

For the 1,000 bolts included in the sample, the diameters at the threaded end are measured to the nearest one hundredth of a millimeter. Suppose that the 1,000 measurements are assigned to a frequency distribution as shown in Table 8–4. A graph of this frequency distribution appears in Figure 8–2. The sample values appear to be distributed in a fashion generally similar to a normal distribution, although some skewness to the right seems to be present. Our task at this point is to determine the class frequencies we should expect if a normal distribution is fitted to the sample.

The first step in fitting the data is to calculate the sample mean and

---

[2] The point should be emphasized that the test to be described is a test for some particular time period (in this case, some day). A further question of whether the process is stable, relative to the type of distribution taken by the diameters, will not be discussed here.

Figure   8–2

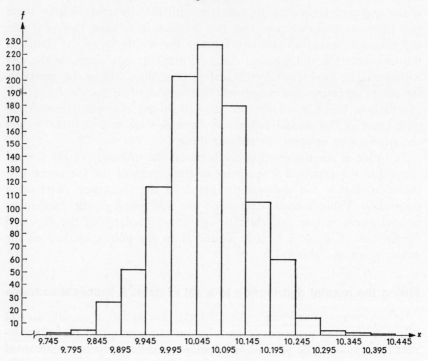

standard deviation. These calculations appear below the frequency distribution in Table 8–4. The sample mean is $\bar{x} = 10.066$mm. The sample standard deviation is $s = 0.092$ mm.

The second step is to determine the expected frequencies for the classes of the distribution if the sample results had been distributed according to a normal distribution, $N(10.066, 0.092)$. This step is accomplished in Table 8–5, with classes to $-\infty$ and $+\infty$, respectively, added at each end of the distribution. To illustrate the manner in which z_l and z_u are determined, consider the entries on the second row of the table. The lower bound of the class is 9.745 which yields:

$$z_\ell = \frac{9.745 - 10.066}{0.092} \simeq -3.49 \ .$$

The upper bound of the class is 9.795, giving:

$$z_u = \frac{9.795 - 10.066}{0.092} \simeq -2.95 \ .$$

Continuing across the row to the next column, and noting that the probability $P(z < -3.49)$ is added to the probability of this class, we find $P(z < -2.95) = 0.0016$. Multiplying this probability by $n = 1,000$, we

Table 8–4

x = Diameter in Millimeters	f	x_c	$f \cdot x_c$	$f \cdot x_c^2$
9.745– 9.795	2	−6	−12	72
9.795– 9.845	5	−5	−25	125
9.845– 9.895	27	−4	−108	432
9.895– 9.945	52	−3	−156	468
9.945– 9.995	117	−2	−234	468
9.995–10.045	203	−1	−203	203
10.045–10.095	228	0		
10.095–10.145	180	1	180	180
10.145–10.195	105	2	210	420
10.195–10.245	60	3	180	540
10.245–10.295	14	4	56	224
10.295–10.345	4	5	20	100
10.345–10.395	2	6	12	72
10.395–10.445	1	7	7	49
	1,000		−73	3353

$$x' = 10.070 \qquad \bar{x}_c = \frac{\Sigma f \cdot x_c}{n} = -0.073$$

$$\bar{x} = x' + w \cdot \bar{x}_c = 10.070 + (0.05)(-0.073) \simeq 10.066$$

$$s_c = \sqrt{\frac{3353}{999} - \frac{(-73)^2}{(1000)(999)}} \simeq 1.831$$

$$s = w \cdot s_c = (0.05)(1.831) \simeq 0.092$$

find the expected frequency to be $f_e = 1.6$. The other entries of Table 8–5 are determined in like manner.

Comparison of the expected class frequencies, f_e, of Table 8–5 with the actual frequencies, f, of Table 8–4 indicates considerable agreement.

Table 8–5

Class	z_ℓ	z_u	$P(z_\ell < z < z_u)$	f_e
− ∞− 9.745	− ∞	−3.49		
9.745– 9.795	−3.49	−2.95	0.0016	1.6
9.795– 9.845	−2.95	−2.40	.0066	6.6
9.845– 9.895	−2.40	−1.86	.0232	23.2
9.895– 9.945	−1.86	−1.32	.0620	62.0
9.945– 9.995	−1.32	−0.77	.1272	127.2
9.995–10.045	−0.77	−0.23	.1884	188.4
10.045–10.095	−0.23	+0.32	.2165	216.5
10.095–10.145	0.32	0.86	.1796	179.6
10.145–10.195	0.86	1.40	.1141	114.1
10.195–10.245	1.40	1.95	.0552	55.2
10.245–10.295	1.95	2.49	.0192	19.2
10.295–10.345	2.49	3.03	.0052	5.2
10.345–10.395	3.03	3.58	.0012	1.2
10.395–10.445	3.58	4.12		
10.445– + ∞	4.12	+ ∞		
			1.0000	1000.0

The larger discrepancies appear toward the middle of the distribution. In order to get a visual comparison of the sample frequency distribution and the normal distribution we have fitted to it, we can plot the ordinates of the normal distribution at various values of x, the diameters of the bolts. The ordinates for selected values of x are calculated in Table 8–6. They are distinguished from the expected frequencies of Table 8–5 by denoting them f_o.[3] The values of x used in the table are those that correspond to values of z that are multiples of one half. That is each successive x value is one half standard deviation removed from its neighbors. The first value, $x = 9.744$, is found by solving the equation:

$$z = -3.5 = \frac{x - 10.066}{0.092} ,$$

$$x = 9.744 .$$

Successive values of x can be determined by adding $s/2 = 0.092/2 = 0.046$, successively. Thus, the next larger value is $x = 9.744 + 0.046 = 9.790$.

The value of x associated with $z = 0.0$ is, of course, the mean of the set of data, $\bar{x} = 10.066$. The maximum ordinate of the fitted normal curve will appear at this value of x and is calculated in Table 8–6 as $y_0 = 4.336$. The remaining values of y appearing in the third column of Table 8–6

Table 8–6

$z = \dfrac{x - 10.066}{0.092}$	x	$y = y_0 e^{-1/2z^2}$	$f_c = n \cdot w \cdot y = 50y$
−3.5	9.744	0.009	0.45
−3.0	9.790	0.048	2.40
−2.5	9.836	0.191	9.55
−2.0	9.882	0.585	29.25
−1.5	9.928	1.409	70.45
−1.0	9.974	2.632	131.60
−0.5	10.020	3.829	191.45
0.0	10.066	4.336	216.80
0.5	10.112	3.829	191.45
1.0	10.158	2.632	131.60
1.5	10.204	1.409	70.45
2.0	10.250	0.585	29.25
2.5	10.296	0.191	9.55
3.0	10.342	0.048	2.40
3.5	10.388	0.009	0.45

$$y_0 = \frac{1}{(2.5067)(0.092)} \simeq 4.336, \ w = 0.05, \ n = 1{,}000$$

[3] We do not plot the values for f_e found in Table 8–5 because these frequencies would be represented by a set of vertical bars. Actually, a normal distribution is a smooth curve with its peak at the mean. We use the values of f_e later in a goodness-of-fit test.

are the result of multiplying $y_0 = 4.336$ by the appropriate value of $e^{-\frac{1}{2}z^2}$. The values of $e^{-\frac{1}{2}z^2}$ are found in Table 8–2. Thus, for $z = -0.5$ and $z = +0.5$, $e^{-\frac{1}{2}z^2} = 0.883$. The appropriate value of y to associate with $x = 10.020$ and $x = 10.112$ is, therefore,

$$y = y_0 e^{-1/2z^2} = (4.336)(0.883) = 3.829 .$$

Finally, to determine the value of the ordinate at these values of x, we multiply the y values by the sample size and the class width:

$$f_c = n \cdot w \cdot y = (1,000)(0.05)(3.829) = 191.45 .[4]$$

The ordinates of Table 8–6 are plotted at the appropriate values of x in Figure 8–3. These points are joined by a smooth curve, superimposed on the frequency distribution of the sample. Visually, the fit appears satisfactory. We have learned not to put great faith in judgments based on visual comparisons, however. The following section describes a method for testing the goodness of fit.

Figure 8–3

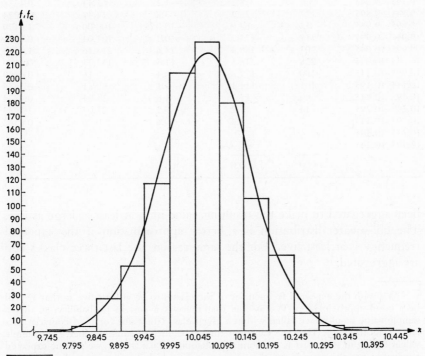

---

[4] The calculations of Table 8–6 are presented in this way to emphasize the rationale underlying the procedure. An easier method for calculating the ordinates, f_o, is first to calculate f_o for $\bar{x}$ as before and then to multiply this value by the entries of $e^{-\frac{1}{2}z^2}$ from Table 8–2. Thus, f_o for $x = 10.020$ and $x = 10.112$ will be:

$$(0.883)(216.8) \simeq 191.43.$$

The chi-square test for goodness of fit

The student will recall that the chi-square statistic, χ^2, was used in Chapter 6 to test for a difference between proportions. The same statistic can be used to test for goodness of fit, since we wish once again to compare expected frequencies with actual frequencies. The expected frequencies were calculated in Table 8–5, on the assumption that the sample data were drawn from a normal distribution with mean $\mu = 10.066$ and standard deviation $\sigma = 0.092$.

We test the hypothesis that the sample values were randomly selected from a normal distribution, $N(10.066, 0.092)$, by calculating the value of χ^2 in Table 8–7. The values of f and f_e in the first two classes have

Table 8–7

Class	f	f_e	$f - f_e$	$(f - f_e)^2$	$(f - f_e)^2/f_e$
9.745– 9.795					
9.795– 9.845	7	8.2	−1.2	1.44	0.1756
9.845– 9.895	27	23.2	3.8	14.44	0.6224
9.895– 9.945	52	62.0	−10.0	100.00	1.6129
9.945– 9.995	117	127.2	−10.2	104.04	0.8179
9.995–10.045	203	188.4	14.6	213.16	1.1314
10.045–10.095	228	216.5	11.5	132.25	0.6109
10.095–10.145	180	179.6	0.4	0.16	0.0009
10.145–10.195	105	114.1	−9.1	82.81	0.7258
10.195–10.245	60	55.2	4.8	23.04	0.4174
10.245–10.295	14	19.2	−5.2	27.04	1.4083
10.295–10.345	7	6.4	0.6	0.36	0.0562
10.345–10.395					
10.395–10.445					
	1,000	1,000.0			$\chi^2 = 7.5797$

been aggregated to make the resulting value of f_e at least as large as five. The chi-square distribution is a better approximation if the expected frequency is at least five.[5] For the same reason, the last three classes also are aggregated.

---

[5] We wish the expected frequencies of the classes to be at least five so that χ^2 will be a good approximation. We assume that there is a certain probability, p, that a sample value would have fallen within a given class (the value for p, of course, varies from class to class). Then we can treat the probability of some number, r, of sample values falling in that class as a binomial probability. That is why we say the expected frequency for the class is np, the mean of a binomial distribution with parameters n and p. The differences $f - f_e = f - np$ are then treated as a deviation of the sample result for a binomial distribution. But, technically, the χ^2 statistic is appropriate only if the deviations are for a normal distribution. Thus, we wish the binomial deviations to be good approximations of normal deviations, and we have noted earlier that this

The resulting value of the chi-square statistic is $\chi^2 = 7.5797$. We compare this value with the critical value of χ^2 for *eight* degrees of freedom. There are eleven classes on which the value of χ^2 is calculated, but only eight degrees of freedom. We lost two degrees of freedom because we fitted the data to estimates of two parameter values, $\mu = 10.066$ and $\sigma = 0.092$, which were determined by the sample data. We lost a third degree of freedom because of the fact that the sum of the expected frequencies must equal $n = 1,000$.[6] The critical value of χ^2 with eight degrees of freedom and a level of significance of $a = 0.05$ is found in Table F in the section of tables to be $\chi^2 = 15.507$. The calculated value is much below the critical value, and we therefore accept the hypothesis that the sample comes from a normal distribution.

Our test of the sample data indicates that they do not vary significantly from expectations of a random sample drawn from a normal distribution. The term "significantly" relates, as always, to the value of a. Having set a at a relatively low level in this test, we run a fairly high risk of committing a Type II error. In the present circumstance Type II error consists of deciding the population is a normal one when it actually is not. If action based on the assumption of normality might lead to seriously adverse consequences when the population is, in fact nonnormal, we might wish to reduce the risk of these consequences.

It was pointed out in Chapter 6 that the risk of Type II error can be reduced by increasing the value of a. In the present test, the calculated value of χ^2 was much below the critical value. We can ease any lingering misgivings by asking what is the maximum value of a that would have been possible, with the sample result still leading to acceptance of the hypothesis of normality. This amounts to determining critical values of χ^2 which "bracket" the sample result.

The table for χ^2 indicates that, for eight degrees of freedom, $\chi^2 = 7.344$ is the critical value associated with $a = 0.50$ and $\chi^2 = 9.524$ is the critical value associated with $a = 0.30$. These values bracket the calculated value of $\chi^2 = 7.5797$, with the calculated value rather close to

---

requires n and p to be of certain sizes. If $np \geq 5$, we are reasonably assured of a good approximation.

If it should happen that the value of f_e in the "class" with a lower bound of $-\infty$ is a value of at least five, then we should treat it as an additional class and calculate the difference, $f - f_e$, in the same way as with the other classes. The value of f for this class will, of course, be zero, since there will have been no observed values which actually fell in this class. The same comments apply to the upper "class" which extends to $+\infty$. In determining number of degrees of freedom, each of these classes must be counted if they are used to calculate the value of χ^2.

[6] Generally, in fitting a probability distribution to a set of data, the number of degrees lost is one (for the number of values in the sample) plus the number of parameters used to fit the data, if these parameter values are estimated from values summarized for the sample data.

7.344. Evidently, the sample result lends strong support to the normality assumption. We could have accepted the hypothesis with a nearly as large as 0.50. At this significance level, the probability of Type II error would have been relatively small if the population did in fact vary widely from a normal distribution.

Problem Set 8–1

1. A manufacturer of men's hats desires some basis for estimating about what proportion of customers will require each different hat size. It would be most helpful to him if he could determine that hat sizes for individual men were subject to some general probability distribution for which probabilities associated with different sizes could easily be associated. He decides, therefore, to examine data which he has on past sales of hats by his firm in an attempt to see if it would be reasonable to suppose that hat size is a normal random variable. Suppose that an examination of these historical data show a breakdown on sales of hats of different sizes as indicated in the table below.

Hat Size	f
6	6
$6\frac{1}{8}$	23
$6\frac{1}{4}$	96
$6\frac{3}{8}$	217
$6\frac{1}{2}$	462
$6\frac{5}{8}$	768
$6\frac{3}{4}$	1,170
$6\frac{7}{8}$	1,450
7	1,615
$7\frac{1}{8}$	1,426
$7\frac{1}{4}$	1,176
$7\frac{3}{8}$	789
$7\frac{1}{2}$	439
$7\frac{5}{8}$	235
$7\frac{3}{4}$	94
$7\frac{7}{8}$	25
8	9
	10,000

a) Graph the frequency distribution for the data set out above, setting up the class boundaries so that the successive hat sizes act as class midpoints for these classes.

b) Calculate the values of $\bar{x}$ and s using coded values.

c) Calculate the values of the ordinate, f_o, for a normal curve fitted to the data above. Plot these fitted ordinates to the frequency distribution which you constructed in part (*a*).

d) Test the null hypothesis that these data are a sample taken from a normal population with a mean and standard deviation as calculated in part (*b*) above (use a significance level of $a = 0.05$). On the basis of the result of this test, does it appear that the hat manufacturer might get good results by estimating what proportion of each hat size he should manufacture on the basis of a normal distribution with mean and standard deviation as computed above?

e) If the hat manufacturer were to assume that a normal distribution represents well the distribution of hat sizes among individual men, about what proportion of hats he produces should have a hat size of 7, of 7¼, of 6⅛?

2. An electronics manufacturer is attempting to reevaluate his work-scheduling procedure associated with the manufacture of a particular assembly. In one phase of the problem, he has attempted to divide the whole operation of manufacturing the assembly into a number of separate tasks. The attempt is then made to determine if the times required to perform these tasks by individual workmen seem to follow a particular probability distribution. There is one task for which he believes it may be reasonable to suppose that the time required to finish the task can be considered to be approximately a normal random variable. In pursuing this assumption to put it to the test, he has asked that the time required to complete the task, by the workmen who perform it, be observed until a large sample of such times has been collected. Suppose that the data set out below are the results of those observations.

Number of Seconds to Complete Task	f
29.0–29.9	4
30.0–30.9	33
31.0–31.9	85
32.0–32.9	119
33.0–33.9	89
34.0–34.9	39
35.0–35.9	11
36.0–36.9	5
	385

a) Find the values of $\bar{x}$ and s, using coded values.

b) Find the values of f_e on the assumption that the population from which the sample was drawn is $N(\bar{x}, s)$, where $\bar{x}$ and s have the values which you calculated in part (a) above.

c) Test for goodness of fit of the normal distribution to the data set out above.

d) Find f_e for $|z| = 0, \frac{1}{2}, 1, 1\frac{1}{2}, 2, 2\frac{1}{2}$.

e) Graph the frequency distribution and the values of f_e from part (d). Connect the points for the values of f_e to get a normal distribution superimposed on the histogram of the frequency distribution.

f) Can you think of any reason, given the nature of the data, why the frequency distribution should tend to skew to the right more than the fitted normal curve?

3. The data in the table appearing below indicate the approximate breakdown of wage rates which would be paid to 100 workers if these 100 workers were representative of the total population of wage earners in the United States (data adapted from Table 336, "Production Workers, Manufacturing Industries—Percentage Distribution by Average Hourly Earnings, by Regions: 1958 and 1964," *Statistical Abstract of the United States*, 1967). We note that

the distribution shown is an "open-end" distribution, that is, the lowest and highest classes are not enclosed by a lower boundary and an upper boundary, respectively. If we were to use fictional midpoints for these classes, however, so that the widths of these classes would be assumed to be the same as for the other classes, that is, $w = \$0.20$, we could get approximate values for $\bar{x}$ and s. The values calculated in this manner are $\bar{x} = \$1.949$ and $s = \$0.586$.

Wages	f
$1.19	13
$1.20– 1.39	10
1.40– 1.59	9
1.60– 1.79	10
1.80– 1.99	10
2.00– 2.19	12
2.20– 2.39	12
2.40– 2.59	9
2.60– 2.79	6
2.80– 2.99	4
3.00	5
	100

a) On the basis of the data set out in the table above and the values for $\bar{x}$ and s indicated earlier, test the null hypothesis that the data are a random sample from a normal distribution with mean = $1.949 and standard deviation = $0.586 (use a significance level of $a = 0.05$).

b) Examining the formula for the chi-square statistic, $\chi^2 = \Sigma([f - f_e]^2/f_e)$, we note that if we were to consider a sample which is, say, 10 times as large as the one set down above with the same proportions of frequencies in each class, the value of χ^2 would be 10 times as large. This is so since the values of f in the data would be 10 times as large and the value of f_e also would be 10 times as large. Since the value of χ^2 is determined as the sum of ratios where the numerator is in units of f and f_e, squared, and the denominator is in units of f_e unsquared, it follows that the value of χ^2 will be 10 times as large.

   i. This being the case, suppose that we had considered a sample of 1,000 workers with a representation in each class proportionate to that of the total population of wage earners in the United States. On that assumption, and noting the result in part (a) above, what would be the value of χ^2?

   ii. If you were to test the hypothesis of part (a) on the basis of this value of χ^2 would you accept or reject the null hypothesis?

   iii. Given that the total population of the wage earners in the United States consists of many millions of workers, what do you conclude regarding a hypothesis that the distribution of wages paid to wage earners in the United States is approximately a normal distribution?

chapter 9

Simulation, Monte Carlo methods

Introduction

The discussion of the foregoing chapters has emphasized inferential statistical procedures in those situations where one is reasonably certain of the appropriate statistical model to apply. The point was stressed throughout that proper use of a particular probability distribution—the normal distribution, for example—relies on certain assumptions concerning the characteristics of the data and the processes which generate them. There are many situations in which assumptions of this type seem reasonable. In those situations, the procedures outlined in prior chapters have been very usefully employed. In other situations, it may not be clear that the required assumptions are satisfied. Chapter 8 developed a test procedure by which the underlying assumptions, themselves, can be subjected to a test on the basis of the data at hand. Although the test procedure was illustrated in terms of the assumption of normality, the test has wider application than just to the normal distribution.

We wish to introduce, in this chapter, a different class of procedures also designed to arrive at solutions to problems involving uncertainty. These procedures are useful in situations where the complexity of the problem does not lead readily to generalized assumptions concerning the probability distribution governing the situation. They rely on the so-called "Monte Carlo" technique. The essence of the Monte Carlo technique is to design a game which models the real-life problem situation. Any one play of the game will result in an outcome which will be determined by the values taken by the relevant variables affecting the situation. The particular values taken by these variables in any one play of the game will, in turn, be determined by a random selection process. The selection will be made randomly, but in such a way as to reflect the probability distributions of the variables. The probability distributions of the relevant variables may be dictated by theoretical considerations, in which case they might be selected from the body of distributions whose characteristics are largely known, or they may reflect the empirical evidence available to date in the form of a distribution of relative frequencies. All of this sounds rather complex, but in reality the basic concept is quite simple.

In order to illustrate the procedure, we use as an example a manufacturing process which produces steel balls. These balls are required to meet a certain specification with respect to their diameters, and we restrict our attention to this one specification only. In the next section, the problem is described. The situation described there is simplified to the point that an analytical solution is easily available on the basis of the characteristics of probability distributions which were discussed in earlier chapters. This will allow us to develop a general solution in the section following description of the problem, so that we may know what to expect of the simulation which is developed in following sections.

The problem

Let us suppose that when the process of concern to us is in control, it produces balls with a diameter of 10.0 millimeters (mm.) and a standard deviation of 0.1 mm. Experience has shown, however, that this process does change from time to time, depending on the initial setup of the process, the operator currently supervising the process, and the materials being used in the manufacture of the balls. As a simplification, we shall assume that the process may be in any one of three states and that it will continue in that state until the current production run is completed. In any one state of the process, the diameters of the balls produced in that state constitute a random variable with a normal distribution. The three states differ from one another with respect to the mean diameter of the balls produced while the process is in each state. When the process is in control, the balls are produced with a mean of 10.0 mm. and a standard deviation of 0.1 mm. The process may be out of control on the low side, in which case the mean is 9.9 mm. The process may also be out of control on the high side, when the mean diameter is 10.1 mm. In all three states the standard deviation is 0.1 mm.

If the process is in control, virtually all of the balls produced will have diameters that are satisfactory. If the process is in one of the other two states, however, a certain proportion of the balls can be expected to be defective because of too small or too large diameters. Specifically, let us suppose that a ball with a diameter of less than 9.8 mm is considered defective and that the same is true of balls with diameters in excess of 10.2 mm. Our problem is to determine the probability that a ball produced under these circumstances will be defective.

The analytical solution

The information contained in the preceding section can be presented graphically as in Figure 9–1. The figure depicts three different normal

Figure 9–1

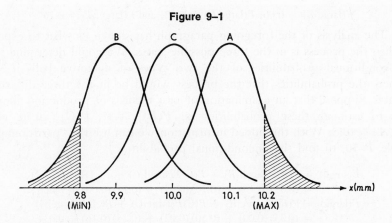

distributions, representing the three states of the process, with x symbolizing the diameter of the balls. The letters, B, C, and A, appearing above the distributions designate them as being *b*elow control, in *c*ontrol, and *a*bove control, respectively. In addition to the marks on the horizontal axis which locate the three means, a mark corresponding to the minimum acceptable diameter of 9.8 mm. and one for the maximum acceptable diameter of 10.2 mm. are shown. The shaded portions of the graph appearing below and above these marks, respectively, indicates the area corresponding to defective balls.

If the process should be in state B, it is evident that the probability a ball will be too small is approximately 0.16, since in this case

$$z = \frac{9.8 - 9.9}{0.1} = -1.0$$

and $P(z < -1.0) \simeq 0.16$. If the process should be in state C, however, the probability that a ball would be too small drops to approximately 0.02:

$$z = \frac{9.8 - 10.0}{0.1} = -2.0, \quad \text{and} \quad P(z < -2.0) \simeq 0.02 .$$

Finally, if the process should be in state A, the probability that a ball would be too small is virtually nil:

$$z = \frac{9.8 - 10.1}{0.1} = -3.0, \quad \text{and} \quad P(z < -3.0) \simeq 0.00 \,.$$

Letting "small" indicate that a ball is too small, this information can be summarized succinctly as:

$$P(\text{small}|B) = 0.16; \; P(\text{small}|C) = 0.02; \; \text{and} \; P(\text{small}|A) = 0.00 \,.$$

In the same manner, it is easy to determine that:

$$P(\text{large}|B) = 0.00; \; P(\text{large}|C) = 0.02; \; \text{and} \; P(\text{large}|A) = 0.16 \,.$$

The analysis of the foregoing paragraph has shown us what to expect when the process is in the three possible states. We could determine the unconditional probabilities of the two types of defective balls if we knew the probabilities that the process would be in the three different states. Suppose that an examination of past records of production allows us to estimate these probabilities as: $P(B) = 0.35$, $P(C) = 0.50$, and $P(A) = 0.15$. With this added information we can use the "partitioning" rule, P–10, to find the unconditional probabilities:

$$\begin{aligned}
P(\text{small}) &= P(B)P(\text{small}|B) + P(C)P(\text{small}|C) + P(A)P(\text{small}|A) \\
&= (0.35)(0.16) + (0.50)(0.02) + (0.15)(0.00) = 0.066 \,; \\
P(\text{large}) &= P(B)P(\text{large}|B) + P(C)P(\text{large}|C) + P(A)P(\text{large}|A) \\
&= (0.35)(0.00) + (0.50)(0.02) + (0.15)(0.16) = 0.034 \,.
\end{aligned}$$

Combining these, we find the probability of a defective ball to be:

$$P(\text{defective}) = P(\text{small}) + P(\text{large}) = 0.066 + 0.034 = 0.100 \,.$$

The analysis above indicates that in a long sequence of production runs we should expect about 10 percent of the balls produced to be defective, so long as the situation continues as described above. Moreover, approximately 6.6 percent of the balls produced should be too small, and about 3.4 percent of them should be too large.

The relation of a simulated solution to the analytical solution

The analytical solution presented above is an exact solution, in the sense that it follows from the logic of the rules of probability. It represents our expectation for the process in the probabilistic sense, and it also represents our expectation in the long-run sense. The defective rate of 10 percent is a norm about which we would expect the results of successive runs to vary, according to changes in the underlying conditions which determine the particular defective rate in any one production run. Consequently, we should expect a random sample of balls produced by the process under the varying circumstances which affect it to provide a reasonably good estimate of this defective rate. We have discussed in earlier chapters procedures for making estimates on the basis of a sample taken from the output of a process. In estimation by simulation, the basic idea is much the same. In simulation, however, the sample is artificially generated through successive trials of an experiment. The outcome of any one trial of the experiment is subject to the varying circumstances affecting the process, with the same probabilities as those estimated to hold in the case of the process.

In our present problem, there are two circumstances that will affect the diameter of a ball produced by the process. One of these is the particular state the process is in at the time the ball is produced. The other is the influence of randomness in the production process in determining where the diameter of the ball will fall within the relevant distribution of diameters.

In order to simulate the process we must determine, on each trial of our experiment, in which state the process is assumed to be, and given that state, where the diameter of the ball resulting from this trial will fall in the relevant distribution. Each of these determinations must be made in a random manner, and in such a way as to be subject to the underlying probabilities associated with each circumstance. Thus, we will wish to choose a state for the process in each trial in such a manner that the probability of choosing state B is 0.35, the estimated probability that that state will occur in the real situation. The probability of choosing state C should be 0.50, and of state A, 0.15.

Having chosen an assumed state of the process for the trial, we must than randomly select a value for the diameter of the simulated ball. This selection must be accomplished randomly, and in such a manner that the probability of the diameter falling in a specified range will be the probability associated with a normal random variable, of appropriate parameter values, for that same range. For the diameter of the simulated ball arising from each trial, we merely compare its value to the minimum and maximum values, in order to classify it as defective or nondefective. In a long series of such trials the proportion of defective and nondefective simulated balls is expected to approach the probabilities associated with these two outcomes in the real process. We can thus take the proportions generated in the simulation to be estimates of the real probabilities. Of course, the longer the series of simulated trials, the better we can expect the estimates to be.

The simulation procedure, then, proceeds in three stages:

1. Simulation of the process state.
2. Simulation of a random normal *variate*[1] with values of the mean and

---

[1] The term "variate" refers to a particular value taken by a random variable. Thus, the standardized normal random variable has a mean of 0 and a standard deviation of 1.0. A particular value of this random variable, say, $z = 0.2$, is called a variate.

standard deviation equal to those of the process state determined in stage (1).

3. Combining the results of these two stages for a series of trials, to arrive at an estimate of the defective rate.

Paralleling this outline of the stages in the simulation, our first task is to describe the procedure for simulating the state of the process.

Monte Carlo simulation of the process state

A critical element in the simulation procedure is that the selection of the process state should be accomplished in a random manner. This element of randomness is achieved through the use of random numbers, in much the same manner that they are used to select a random sample. Truly random numbers are distributed according to a uniform probability distribution, however. This means that the probability of any one digit, 0 through 9, appearing in the random sequence of numbers is equal to that for any other digit. For any one digit, the probability would be one tenth. The same property would hold for all possible two-digit numbers, which would have a probability of one hundredth $\left(\frac{1}{10} \cdot \frac{1}{10}\right)$, and so on for numbers consisting of longer sequences of digits.

We require the random numbers which we select to lead to state B with probability 0.35, to state C with probability 0.50, and to state A with probability 0.15. Accordingly, we must devise a technique whereby random numbers with a uniform distribution can be used to indicate these three states with the appropriate probabilities. Consider, then, random numbers formed from two random digits. The possibilities are 00 through 99. As was indicated above, each of these numbers will have the same probability of being selected: $P(00) = P(01) = \ldots = P(99) = 0.01$. It follows from application of probability rule P–4 that the probability of a given two-digit random number, say, xx, falling in the interval from 00 to 34 is: $P(00 \leq xx \leq 34) = 0.35$, since the interval contains 35 values. By the same reasoning, $P(35 \leq xx \leq 84) = 0.50$ and $P(85 \leq xx \leq 99) = 0.15$.

Noting that these probabilities are equal to those associated with the three states, we have a rule for determining the state of the process. If a two-digit number selected has a value 00 through 34, the simulated process is in state B with a mean diameter of 9.9 mm.; if the number has a value 35 through 84, state C applies with a mean of 10.0 mm.; if the value is 85 through 99, the state is A with a mean of 10.1 mm. This rule allows us to convert a random variable with a uniform probability distribution into a random variable with the same probability distribution as the mean of the process, μ.

It is possible to represent this conversion process graphically, and such a representation should help to clarify the process. In Figure 9–2, a table for the cumulative probability distribution of μ, the mean of the production process, appears above a graph of this distribution. Notice that the height of each of the "steps" in the graph is equal to the probability that the mean of the process will have the value lying below that step. Thus,

Figure 9–2

μ	$P(\mu \leq \mu_0)$
9.9	0.35
10.0	0.85
10.1	1.00

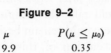

the height of the first step is $0.35 - 0.00 = 0.35$, which is the probability that μ will have a value of 9.9 mm.

Now, if we think of the numbers appearing on the vertical axis as representing uniformly distributed random numbers of two digits (since we are considering two-digit numbers, we must disregard the maximum value of 1.00 on this axis, but we replace it with the minimum value of 0.00), we see that the probability of a number falling in any one of the intervals marked in brackets is just the height of the corresponding step.

We convert a number selected on the vertical axis to a number appearing on the horizontal axis by projecting a line from that point on the vertical axis, to its intersection with the graph, and thence down to a point of the horizontal axis. In this manner, for example, the random number 65 would convert to a value of $\mu = 10.0$, as indicated in the figure. If we wished to get a somewhat "finer" discrimination in the values of the random numbers, we could take three-digit numbers ranging from 000 through 999. The outcome would remain basically the same.

To recapitulate the discussion of this section, the first stage of the simulation consists in determining the state of the process (that is, its mean) for each trial. This can be done through selection of random numbers and the conversion of these random numbers to the appropriate state by the rule: if the value of the random number:

1. Is from 00 to 34, $\mu = 9.9$ mm.
2. Is from 35 to 84, $\mu = 10.0$ mm.
3. Is from 85 to 99, $\mu = 10.1$ mm.

The next step is to select a value for the normal variate. This procedure is explained in the next section.

Monte Carlo simulation of a random normal variate

As in the first stage of the simulation, we must convert a uniformly distributed set of random numbers into another random variable with a different distribution. In this case, we wish the second random variable to have a normal distribution. This can be easily accomplished with the aid of a table for the standardized normal distribution, such as Table C in the section of tables. We note that the values appearing in the body of Table C are four-digit numbers. The first row of Table C is reproduced below, from which we see that the four-digit numbers of that row range from .0000 to .0359.

First Row of Table C

z	.00	.01	.02	.03	.04	.05	.06	.07	.08	.09
0.0	.0000	.0040	.0080	.0120	.0160	.0199	.0239	.0279	.0319	.0359

Thus, in the interval of z from 0.00 to 0.09, there are 359 possible four-digit numbers (0359–0000 = 359).

Contrast the first row of Table C with, say, the 16th row, which is reproduced below. In this row, there are 93 possible four-digit numbers (4545–4452 = 93) corresponding to the interval of z from 1.60 to 1.69. The 16th row of the table indicates a density of four-digit numbers only about one fourth of that of the first row ($93/359 \simeq 1/4$), even though both rows represent the same width of interval for z ($0.09 - 0.00 = 1.69 - 1.60 = 0.09$). This means, of course, that the probability that a four-digit random number would fall in the interval of the 16th row is only about one fourth of the probability associated with the first row. The student can verify that similar general relationships exist between any other pair of rows he might choose.

Sixteenth Row of Table C

z	.00	.01	.02	.03	.04	.05	.06	.07	.08	.09
1.6	.4452	.4463	.4474	.4484	.4495	.4505	.4515	.4525	.4535	.4545

Let us be more specific about the relationship between the four-digit numbers appearing in these rows and the probabilities attaching to the associated value of z. If we wished to determine the probability that a randomly selected four-digit number would fall in the intervals represented by these rows, we could use Rule P–4. Since there are 359 numbers in the row corresponding to the interval $0.00 < z \le 0.09$, and since there are a total of $10^4 = 10,000$ possible four-digit sequences, the probability that such a number will be selected is 0.0359. By the same reasoning, we find that the probability of selecting a four-digit random number in the row corresponding to the interval $1.60 < z \le 1.69$ is 0.0093. But these are exactly the probabilities, $P(0.00 < z \le 0.09)$ and $P(1.60 < z \le 1.69)$, respectively. Thus, we have a rule for converting a four-digit number from a uniform probability distribution into a standardized normal variate: Upon selection of a four-digit number, find the value of z associated with it in Table C.

The cumulative probability distribution for a standardized normal distribution is shown in Figure 9–3. Because a normal random variable is continuous, this curve does not proceed by steps but is a smooth curve. The intervals a and b selected on the vertical axis are the same width, which means that the probability is equal that a four-digit random number would fall in either of these intervals. Notice, however, that the corresponding intervals on the horizontal axis, a' and b', are not of equal width. The smaller width of b' reflects the greater density of the distribution at that interval than at a'. Figure 9–3 illustrates graphically how our conversion rule supplies a normal random variate from a random number.

Having described a conversion rule, let us see how it works in some examples. Suppose, for example, that a random four-digit number selected is 0199. The position of 0199 in the first row of Table C is at the value $z = 0.05$. Thus, for a trial in which the random number is 0199, the value of z would be set at 0.05. As another example, suppose that the random number is 4479. This value falls between 4474 and 4484 in the 16th row of Table C, corresponding to values for z of 1.62 and 1.63, respectively. We can interpolate to find the approximate value of z to associate with the number 4479:

$$z = 1.62 + \frac{4479 - 4474}{4484 - 4474}(1.63 - 1.62) = 1.62 + (0.5)(0.01) = 1.625 .$$

It may have occurred to the student that some values of four-digit numbers do not appear in Table C. Suppose we were to get a number equal to 9515, for example. Table C is meant to show areas (probabilities) only on the right side of $z = 0$ (i.e., positive values of z). Because of this fact, the largest four-digit number that would appear in the table, if we could extend it far enough, would be .5000. The answer to the dilemma

Figure 9–3

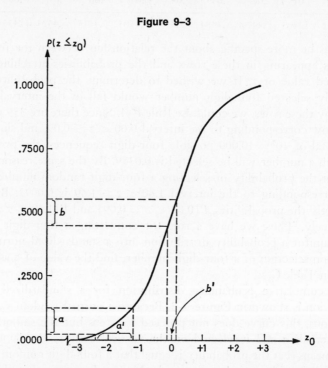

is to use four-digit numbers larger than 5000 to represent values of z below $z = 0$. If we take the difference between 9515 and 5000, we get $9515 - 5000 = 4515$. We see that the value 4515 is associated with a value of $z = 1.66$ in Table C. Since the original number was larger than 5000, however, we give z a negative sign and get a random value for z of -1.66.[2]

The values of z which our conversion rule provides us are for the standardized normal variable with mean zero and standard deviation of one. But the values which we require for the diameters of the balls will

---

[2] With this procedure for interpreting values from Table C, the vertical axis of Figure 8–3 is changed somewhat. In effect, we look at only the top half of the graph, and then convert to negative z values if the random number is greater than 5000. Interpreted this way, the zero values for the vertical axis of Figure 8–3 would appear where the value 0.5000 now does. At the present value of 1.0000, we would place +0.5000. And at the point which at present carries the value 0.0000, we would place −0.5000.

have a mean of 9.9, 10.0, or 10.1, depending on the state of the process, and a standard deviation of 0.1. So we must make one final conversion, from the standardized normal variate provided us by Table C to a normal variate from a distribution with the appropriate mean and standard deviation. Noting that the standardized normal distribution is related to any other normal distribution through the relationship $z = \dfrac{x - \mu}{\sigma}$, we can by algebraic manipulation show that $x = z \cdot \sigma + \mu$. This last expression tells us that we can convert a standardized normal variate to a normal variate with mean μ and standard deviation σ simply by multiplying z by σ and adding the resulting product to μ.

To see how this works, suppose that for a given trial of the simulation the state of the process is B so that the mean is $\mu = 9.9$ and the standard deviation is $\sigma = 0.1$. Then let us assume that the value of the four-digit number drawn in order to find z is 9515, so that $z = -1.66$, as described earlier. Using the conversion relationship of the last paragraph to find the simulated diameter of the ball, we have:

$$x = z \cdot \sigma + \mu$$
$$= (-1.66)(0.1) + 9.9$$
$$= 9.734 \text{ mm.}$$

In this particular trial, the simulated ball would have a diameter of 9.734 mm., which is too small to meet the manufacturer's specifications. We would record that this trial led to a defective ball.

The foregoing discussion has been somewhat involved with the various aspects of the simulation procedure. The flow diagram of Figure 9–4 summarizes the essential aspects of the procedure in a manner easy to follow and to understand.

Estimating the defective rate from the results of a simulation

The flow diagram of Figure 9–4 summarizes the simulation procedure for one trial. The outcome of any one trial will be either "defective" or "not defective." The result of one trial hardly allows us to form an estimate of the defective rate of the process being simulated; the estimate could be only 1.0 or 0.0 on the basis of that result. But as the number of trials increase, we can expect the cumulative result to provide an increasingly better basis for such an estimate. The number of trials usually must be rather large to provide good estimates, however. For this reason, as well as the fact that most simulations are of very complex situations, effective simulation procedures usually rely on a computer to perform the work.

The situation we have been discussing in this chapter was purposely kept simple so that we might work through a series of trials with no undue hardship, even though we were not to avail ourselves of a computer. Such a series of trials perform a useful teaching function, but because of the necessarily limited number of trials, they have little value as a basis for estimating the defective rate. Consequently, the results of a more extensive number of trials generated by a computer program are presented

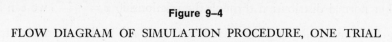

Figure 9–4

FLOW DIAGRAM OF SIMULATION PROCEDURE, ONE TRIAL

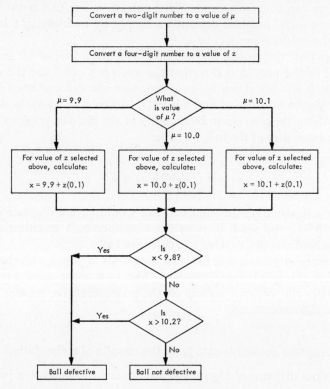

following our discussion of the limited number of trials which we present below. The program by which the results were generated is presented in Figure 9–A–1 of Appendix A at the end of this chapter.

Table 9–1 records the results of 20 trials of the simulation problem. The first column records two-digit random numbers. These were converted to corresponding values of μ, as indicated in the second column of the table. The third column contains four-digit numbers. These four-digit numbers were converted to the corresponding values for z appearing in the fourth column in Table 9–1. The values for z were not interpolated to the third decimal place; rather, each one is the nearest value of z

which appears in Table C. The fifth column of Table 9–1 expresses the conversion, for each trial, of the standardized normal variate, z, into a ball diameter, x, based on the mean of the process, μ, recorded in the second column of the table. The final column of Table 9–1 records whether the resulting diameter was defective, D, or not defective, N.

It should be pointed out that, in the interest of ease and efficiency, one would record all the random numbers required in the first and third

Table 9–1

| State | | z | | | Defective (D) or |
No.	μ	No.	z	$x = \mu + z(0.1)$	Not defective (N)
25	9.9	3824	+1.19	$x = \ 9.9 + 1.19(0.1) = 10.019$	N
20	9.9	8159	−0.90	$x = \ 9.9 − 0.90(0.1) = \ 9.810$	N
96	10.1	9354	−1.52	$x = 10.1 − 1.52(0.1) = \ 9.948$	N
93	10.1	6842	−0.48	$x = 10.1 − 0.48(0.1) = 10.052$	N
23	9.9	2286	+0.61	$x = \ 9.9 + 0.61(0.1) = \ 9.961$	N
00	9.9	5804	−0.21	$x = \ 9.9 − 0.21(0.1) = \ 9.879$	N
48	10.0	4531	+1.68	$x = 10.0 + 1.68(0.1) = 10.168$	N
36	10.0	4323	+1.49	$x = 10.0 + 1.49(0.1) = 10.149$	N
86	10.1	3693	+1.12	$x = 10.1 + 1.12(0.1) = 10.212$	D
53	10.0	4642	+1.80	$x = 10.0 + 1.80(0.1) = 10.180$	N
37	10.0	4616	+1.77	$x = 10.0 + 1.77(0.1) = 10.177$	N
90	10.1	7029	−0.53	$x = 10.1 − 0.53(0.1) = 10.047$	N
22	9.9	3297	+0.95	$x = \ 9.9 + 0.95(0.1) = \ 9.995$	N
23	9.9	1286	+0.33	$x = \ 9.9 + 0.33(0.1) = \ 9.933$	N
40	10.0	4021	+1.29	$x = 10.0 + 1.29(0.1) = 10.129$	N
81	10.0	5192	−0.05	$x = 10.0 − 0.05(0.1) = \ 9.995$	N
39	10.0	5936	−0.24	$x = 10.0 − 0.24(0.1) = \ 9.976$	N
82	10.0	5462	−0.12	$x = 10.0 − 0.12(0.1) = \ 9.988$	N
93	10.1	1686	+0.44	$x = 10.1 + 0.44(0.1) = 10.144$	N
18	9.9	6893	−0.49	$x = \ 9.9 − 0.49(0.1) = \ 9.851$	N

columns prior to performing the other operations required in the table. Although, conceptually, the procedure of a trial follows the outline of the flow diagram in Figure 9–4, it would be wasteful of time and effort to select a two-digit number, then convert it to μ, then select a four-digit number, convert it to z, and so forth.

Looking at the results of Table 9–1, we find that only one of the simulated balls was defective. This occurred on the ninth trial, and the resulting ball was too large, having a diameter of 10.212 mm. None of the trials resulted in a diameter that was too small. On the basis of these 20 trials, we should have to estimate the defective rate to be $1/20 = 0.05$. A point estimate of the defective rate for balls that are too small would be $0/20 = 0.0$, and for balls that are too large, $1/20 = 0.05$. Since we have already worked out the analytical solution to this problem, we know that these estimates would be substantially in error. The overall defective rate is 0.10; the rate for too small balls is 0.066; and the rate for too large balls is 0.034.

The fact that estimates based on these results are so wide of the mark is due, in large part, to the small number of trials. In order to get more realistic estimates, 100 trials of the simulation were performed with a computer. The results of these 100 trials were: the number of balls too small was seven; the number of balls too large was two. Estimates based on these results would be: overall defective rate, $9/100 = 0.09$; rate of too small balls, $7/100 = 0.07$; and rate of too large balls, $2/100 = 0.02$. The estimates in this case are, of course, much closer to the true values.[3]

A note of caution on the use of simulation procedures

Simulations of the type described in this chapter are very powerful tools in seeking solutions to complex problems involving elements of uncertainty. They should be used only in situations where a satisfactory analytical solution is not possible, however, or where the difficulties and costs attending such a solution are prohibitive. One must recognize that simulations, too, can be very difficult if they are to be designed properly. Thus, in choosing between the two methods of arriving at a solution, one must look to relative costs of the two methods. An exact analytical solution will be better, if it is possible, and this fact must be taken into account in weighing the merits of the two methods. A better analytical solution should be worth somewhat more in cost and effort than a solution produced by simulation.

A second important point for caution is that one must be careful that the simulation is a reasonably accurate representation of the real process. In very complex situations, this becomes a difficult problem. Of course, the same caution is required with analytical solutions, too. But in the latter case, one often has various checkpoints available in the construction of the analytical model. These checks are provided by considerations of logic and consistency that follow from the known characteristics of the elements—for example, the known probability distributions—of the model being constructed. Because simulation procedures are most valuable in situations where elements with known characteristics cannot be used, such checks are absent. As a result, one may arrive at simulation results which look quite reasonable, and which actually reflect the model constructed very well, but which represent only poorly the real process. The upshot of this discussion is that extremely careful consideration must be given to all elements of a simulation model and the way in which they are combined.

---

[3] Appendix A at the end of this chapter contains two computer programs, either of which can be used to perform this simulation.

Problem Set 9–1

1. Simulate the toss of a coin by selecting two-digit random sequences. Let the rule be: If the two digits have a value between 00 and 49, the coin is heads; otherwise, it is tails. Perform 20 simulations, and calculate the ratio of number of heads to total number of trials as you proceed through the 20 trials. Plot the ratio on a graph in which the vertical axis is the ratio and the horizontal axis is the number of trials. Comment on the results.

2. Simulate the toss of two dice by determining the outcome on each die with a three-digit random sequence. Note that you must simulate the result on each die separately. Perform 36 trials and note the number of each possible sum that occurs, e.g., the number of times the sum is two, three, etc. In class, compare the results of your simulation with other members of the class.

3. Suppose that the number of cars approaching a toll bridge in any one minute is a random variable, C, with the probability distribution shown below. Assume that the toll gate is able to pass 10 cars per minute, at a constant rate. There are times, of course, when cars are backed up and other times when no cars are waiting. Simulate this situation by assuming that cars arrive at the gate "simultaneously" at the beginning of a "minute" and that no additional cars may arrive until the start of the next "minute." Keep a count of the number of cars still waiting at the end of each "minute," and the number of "minutes" that the approach to the toll gate is empty by the time the next "minute" begins. Perform the simulation 50 times.

C	$P(C)$
7	0.10
8	.20
9	.35
10	.15
11	.15
12	.05

4. In the problem above, calculate the total length of time that the toll gate attendant was idle, during the simulated period. (That is, total the time, throughout the overall period, when no cars remained in line for some part of a "minute.")

5. A telephone booth in the lobby of a men's dormitory receives heavy use. In any one minute, the number of arrivals at the booth may vary from zero to three. The probability distribution for the number of arrivals, A, is given below. Any individuals entering the phone booth will talk an integral number of minutes ranging from one minute through three minutes, as indicated in the probability distribution of M below. Simulate the number of people who will be waiting to use the phone in each successive minute. Assume that at the beginning of the first minute, a person has just entered the booth and that no one was waiting behind him at the time he entered. Assume, also, that no one tires of waiting in line. Assume that all arrivals are "simultaneous" at the beginning of each minute and that if no one is in line at that time, one of the arrivals immediately enters the booth. Perform the simu-

lation 20 times. On the basis of the results of the simulation, would you say that another booth should be installed in the lobby?

A	P(A)	M	P(M)
0	0.40	1	0.50
1	.30	2	.30
2	.20	3	.20
3	.10		

6. An airline has found that its flight number 201 is very popular. As a matter of fact, it often happens that there will not be room for all passengers who have purchased tickets on the flight. The airplane used on the flight seats 100 passengers. The probability distributions below are for the number of tickets sold for the flight (T) and the number of cancellations (C). Using two-digit random sequences, simulate the numbers of vacancies or oversales. Perform the simulation 50 times.

T	P(T)	C	P(C)
98	0.15	0	0.30
99	.25	1	.40
100	.40	2	.20
101	.15	3	.10
102	.05		

7. Suppose that two bags each contain 10 marbles. The colors of the marbles are red and green. The compositions in the two bags are: Bag I has six red and four green marbles; Bag II has eight red and two green marbles. A marble is to be drawn at random from one of the bags. To determine from which bag the marble is to be drawn, two coins are tossed. If the two coins land heads up, the draw is to be made from Bag I, otherwise from Bag II. Simulate 20 draws under these conditions and note the number of red and green marbles that are drawn.

Appendix A

Two computer programs are presented in this appendix, both of which are designed to perform the simulation discussed in Chapter 9. The first of these, exhibited as Figure 9–A–1, is reproduced from Figure A–8 of the appendix, "Statistical Analysis and the Computer," where it is discussed in detail. The second program, shown in Figure 9–A–2, is written in BASIC language and makes use of a "canned" program to generate random numbers which are required in the simulation.

The program of Figure 9–A–1: The listing shown here actually consists of the main program followed by a FUNCTION subprogram. The student is referred to the appendix on the computer, "Statistical Analysis and the Computer," for detailed understanding of the program.

The first data card must be punched with the values of the mean for

Figure 9–A–1

```
C       A PROGRAM TO SIMULATE A PROCESS THAT MANUFACTURES A PART. THE DIM
C       ENSION OF THE PART IS N (U,S). THE VALUE OF S IS STABLE. THE VAL
C       UE OF U VARIES ACCORDING TO A DISCRETE PROBABILITY DISTRIBUTION.
C       P(U = B) = PB, P(U = C) = PC, P(U = A) = PA. IF DIMENSION OF
C       PART IS LESS THAN 9.8 OR MORE THAN 10.2 THE PART IS DEFECTIVE.
   10   FORMAT (3(F5.1, F4.4), F7.3)
        READ 10, B, PB, C, PC, A, PA, S
   20   FORMAT (F4.4)
        NA = 0
        NB = 0
    1   READ 20, RANX
        DO 40 I = 1, 50
        RAN1 = RAND(RANX)
        RANX = RAN1
        IF (PB - RAN1) 3, 3, 2
    3   IF (PB + PC - RAN1) 5, 5, 4
    2   U = B
        GO TO 6
    4   U = C
        GO TO 6
    5   U = A
    6   RAN1 = RAND(RANX)
        RAN2 = RAND(RAN1)
        RANX = RAN2
        STDNOR = (-2.0*LOGF(RAN1))**0.5*COSF(6.283*RAN2)
        VNORM = STDNOR*S + U
        PRINT 30, VNORM
   30   FORMAT (F10.3)
        IF (10.2 - VNORM) 50, 40, 60
   60   IF (9.8 - VNORM) 40, 40, 70
   50   NA = NA + 1
        GO TO 40
   70   NB = NB + 1
   40   CONTINUE
        PRINT 80, NA, NB
   80   FORMAT (2I4)
        GO TO 1
        END
        FUNCTION RAND(X)
        XSQ = X*X
        INITL2 = XSQ*100.0
        FLINL2 = INITL2
        DECIN2 = FLINL2/100.0
        XLAST6 = XSQ - DECIN2
        RAND = XLAST6*100.0
        RETURN
        END
```

each state of the ball-producing process, and the corresponding probability of that state, in pairs. The format for each pair requires nine punches. The first five columns are for the mean in state B, with the fifth column reserved for a decimal place. The following four columns are for the value of $P(B)$, all four columns representing successive decimal places. This pattern is repeated in the next nine columns for the values of state C, and again for the values of state A. To illustrate, the values for the three states, as used in the chapter, were:

State	μ	$p(\mu)$
B	9.9	0.35
C	10.0	0.50
A	10.1	0.15

In order to enter these values as input, a data card is required with punches in the first 27 columns as given below:

000993500001005000001011500 .

In addition to the values associated with the three states of the ball-producing process, the first card must also contain the punched value of the standard deviation common to all three states. In the example of the chapter, this value was $\sigma = 0.1$. The columns 28–34 are reserved for this

Figure 9–A–2

```
100  REM:  A PROGRAM TO SIMULATE A PROCESS THAT MANUFACTURES
110  REM   A PART. THE DIMENSION OF THE PART IS N (U,S). THE VALUE
120  REM   OF S IS 0.1. THE VALUE OF U VARIES ACCORDING TO A DISCRETE
130  REM   PROBABILITY DISTRIBUTION. P(U = B) = M1, P(U = C) = M2,
140  REM   P(U = A) = M3. IF DIMENSION OF PART IS LESS THAN 9.8
150  REM   OR MORE THAN 10.2 THE PART IS DEFECTIVE.
160  READ M1, M2, M3
170  LET N1 = 0
180  LET N2 = 0
190  DIM V(100)
200  FOR I = 1 TO 100
210  LET Y = RND(X)
220  IF Y < M1 THEN 260
230  IF Y < (M1 + M2) THEN 280
240  LET U = 10.1
250  GO TO 290
260  LET U = 9.9
270  GO TO 290
280  LET U = 10.0
290  LET V(I) = (.1)*(−2)*(−LOG (RND(X))) ↑ .5*COS(6.283*RND(X)) + U
300  PRINT V(I);
310  IF V(I) < 9.8 THEN 340
320  IF V(I) > 10.2 THEN 360
330  GO TO 370
340  LET N1 = N1 + 1
350  GO TO 370
360  LET N2 = N2 + 1
370  NEXT I
380  LET N = N1 + N2
390  PRINT
400  PRINT
410  PRINT "NUMBER OF PARTS TOO SMALL = "N1
420  PRINT "NUMBER OF PARTS TOO LARGE = "N2
430  PRINT "TOTAL DEFECTIVE = "N
440  DATA .35,.50,.15
450  END
```

value, with the last three columns to represent decimal places. Consequently, the fully punched data card, using the values of the text, would be

000993500001005000001011500000000100 .

Because of the limitations of the quasi-random number generator employed in this program (see the computer appendix for detailed explanation), a separate data card must be provided for each multiple of 50 simulation trials that is desired. Each of these cards will contain a number, punched in the first four columns, to initiate a new cycle of the random number generator. If 100 trials are desired, for example, two cards must be provided. It is suggested that these cards be punched with the values 5555 and 4832, respectively.

The output of this program consists of simulated values of the diameter of a ball, and the cumulated number of balls which are too small and too large. Each successive simulated value is printed on a separate line. After each 50 simulated values, the cumulated number of balls too large and the number too small are printed on a separate line, in that order.

The program of Figure 9–A–2: This BASIC language program performs the same simulation as the first program, except that it is restricted to the mean values for the three states as used in the chapter and a common standard deviation of 0.1. With these restrictions, the only data input required are the values for $P(B)$, $P(C)$, and $P(A)$. These values are entered in DATA line 440. In the present case, the values shown are those used in the chapter.

In order to allow for variable input of mean values and standard deviation, the following additional lines, and modifications of existing lines, are suggested:

```
165  READ B,C,A,S
240  LET U = A
260  LET U = B
280  LET U = C
290  LET V(I) = (S)*(−2)*(−LOG(RND(X))) ↑ .5*COS(6.283*RND(X)) + U
```

A new data line will then be required, say,

$$445 \quad \text{DATA B,C,A,S}$$

where the values of the three means and the standard deviation are entered as indicated.

The output of the program is exhibited in Figure 9–A–3. The program is written to provide 100 trials of the simulation. The 100 corresponding values of the simulated ball diameter are listed in rows as shown. Follow-

Figure 9–A–3

9.88744	9.8951	9.73457	9.88073	9.91153	10.0359	10.122	10.0865
9.97674	9.80891	10.0657	10.096	9.99539	9.92322	10.0761	10.03
10.0634	10.0028	9.94438	9.97266	9.86745	10.0889	9.83035	9.85197
9.71463	10.098	9.91043	10.1017	10.0206	10.2658	9.97212	9.77804
9.80599	9.84753	10.0335	9.87733	10.0676	10.3054	9.78166	9.91052
9.96858	9.8598	10.135	10.4455	9.86473	9.86046	10.0953	9.98155
9.8783	9.91798	10.1802	9.85697	9.95867	10.0116	9.80284	10.1532
9.89356	10.0995	10.0354	10.3888	10.0699	10.0247	9.90323	9.99566
9.86668	10.0673	9.87178	9.87157	10.1217	10.3231	9.98349	10.04
9.61487	9.9012	9.9155	10.1033	9.9412	9.85663	10.1209	9.81376
9.93321	10.0537	9.94181	10.0868	9.87021	10.1701	10.0838	10.0215
9.8509	10.2129	10.0619	9.90622	9.8819	9.80477	9.6768	9.8507
10.312	9.91008	9.97064	10.0763				

NUMBER OF PARTS TOO SMALL = 6
NUMBER OF PARTS TOO LARGE = 7
TOTAL DEFECTIVE = 13

ing this list, the number of balls too large and too small, and the total number defective, are listed.

If a larger number of trials than 100, say N, are desired, the program must be modified as follows:

```
190   DIM  V(N)
200   FOR  I = 1  TO  N
```

Finally, because of the nature of the "canned" random number generator used in the program, a rerunning of the program will result in the same values of random numbers generated. If one wishes a "fresh start," he can provide it by making the generator generate a certain number of random numbers which are not used, prior to beginning the portion of the program where successive random numbers are used. Suppose, for example, that one wished to generate 100 unused random numbers. This can be accomplished by adding the following lines to the program:

```
181   FOR  I = 1  TO  100
182   LET  Y = RND(X)
183   NEXT  I
```

chapter 10

Some elements of statistical decision theory

Introduction

We began our discussion of statistical methods with the observation that most business and economic decisions were necessarily made under conditions of uncertainty. On the assumption that probability statements could effectively serve as indexes of the level of uncertainty attaching to events, we have devoted much effort to gaining an understanding of the concepts, probability, random variable, and probability distribution. Simple illustrations of applications of these concepts have, hopefully, helped to crystallize this understanding and to persuade the student of the practical importance of the concepts.

On a number of occasions, however, it must have been obvious to the student that the treatment in these illustrations was less than complete. Perhaps the situation in which this incompleteness is most easily shown is the test of a hypothesis. In the discussion of this procedure, the logic of the testing procedure was carefully developed, the probabilities of Type I and Type II errors were highlighted, and some indication of the practical importance of these errors was given. The observation was also made that more precision in a testing procedure was possible if we were willing to increase the size of the sample on which the test was based. The question of determining the levels of these important factors was dismissed with the general statement that "it depends on the relative consequences associated with these factors." Whether to decrease the probability of Type I error at the expense of an increased probability of

Type II error was said to depend on the relative costs of the two types of error. Whether to increase the sample size depended on balancing benefits of increased precision against the rising cost of larger samples.

The purpose of this chapter is to develop a basis for evaluating the consequences associated with possible alternative decisions. In doing so, we shall focus our attention on two fundamental elements in statistical decision theory: the expected monetary value of a decision, and the so-called Bayesian analysis. There is much more to statistical decision theory than we shall consider here, so that the picture will remain somewhat incomplete. However, the outline of a complete solution to a decision problem under conditions of uncertainty should be discernible to the student upon completion of this chapter.

Our first concern will be with the principle of using the expected monetary value of a decision (or, more exactly, a decision to take a certain action among a number of alternative actions) as a criterion for selecting the best decision (or action). Discussion of this principle will range from a gaming situation, through a simplified "practical" example, to a consideration of the test of a hypothesis. We shall then turn our attention to the Bayesian analysis, which will be developed in a similar fashion.

Expected monetary value of a decision: A criterion for choice

The notion of using expected monetary value as a criterion for choosing among alternative decisions is a powerful one. Surprisingly, it is also a simple idea of strong intuitive appeal. The principle is just this: Among alternative decisions available to the decision maker, he should choose the one which yields the highest expected monetary return. Notice that the use of the word "return" refers to the net relationship between monetary inflows and outflows arising as the consequence of a particular decision. Thus, if the inflow arising from a decision is $100 and the outflow occasioned by implementation of the decision is $80, the return accruing from the decision is calculated as $100 − $80 = $20. It is quite possible, therefore, for the return associated with a particular decision to be a negative amount. Determination of the actual values of inflows and outflows associated with a particular decision is, of course, largely a function of accounting and budgeting procedures. For our purposes, these values will be assumed to have been suitably determined prior to the statistical analysis which we illustrate.

As a first illustration of the principle set forth above, suppose that you are given the choice of playing one of two games. In each game you are allowed to draw a marble from a bag which is enclosed in such a fashion that you are unable to see the marble until you have withdrawn it from the bag. The bag associated with each game contains 10 marbles, some of which are white and the remainder of which are red. In Bag I, the bag used in one game, there are nine white marbles and one red marble. In Bag 11, which is used in the other game, there are eight white marbles and two red marbles. In either game, if you should draw a white marble, you will be given $2.50. If you should draw a red marble, however, you must pay the operator of the game $2.50. In order to play either game, you must pay the operator $1.75. We wish to determine whether you should decide to play game number one or game number two, according to the principle of maximizing expected monetary return.[1]

The characteristics of game number one are summarized in the table below. The first two columns of the table indicate the probability distribution of drawing a white or a red marble from Bag I. The third column indicates the monetary return associated with the events, "a white marble is drawn" and "a red marble is drawn." The returns associated with these events are the net value of the inflows and outflows which will accrue to a player if the events should occur. Thus, drawing a white marble will lead to the player receiving $2.50. He will have paid the operator $1.75 in order to play the game, however, so that the return to him is $2.50 − $1.75 = $0.75. If he should draw a red marble in a play of the game, his return is negative, since he must pay the operator $2.50 in addition to the admission charge of $1.75: −$2.50 − $1.75 = −$4.25.

Bag I	P	Return	Return · P
W	0.9	$2.50 − $1.75 = $0.75	$0.675
R	0.1	− 2.50 − 1.75 = − 4.25	− 0.425
	1.0		$0.25
			= expected
			monetary
			return

The returns associated with the events "white" and "red" constitute a random variable. The probability distribution of this random variable is just the distribution associated with the events "white" and "red." We can, therefore, determine the expected value of this random variable, which will be the expected monetary return of the game. The fourth column of the table contains the products of the returns and their respective probabilities. The total of this column is, then, the expected monetary return of the game, which is $0.25.

The same procedure applied to game number two is summarized in the table on page 320. The result of the calculations indicates that the expected monetary return for this game is −$0.25.

---

[1] We should note that there is a third possible decision: to play neither game. The decision to do nothing is always a possible alternative decision. In business situations the decision "do nothing" usually has rewards and penalties associated with it, and it can therefore be treated in the same fashion as any other decision.

Bag II	P	Return	Return · P
W	0.8	$2.50 − $1.75 = $0.75	$0.60
R	0.2	− 2.50 − 1.75 = − 4.25	− 0.85
	1.0		−$0.25
			= expected monetary return

Having determined the expected monetary return associated with each game, we are now in a position to make a choice as to which game should be played. According to the principle of maximizing expected monetary return, game number one should be chosen. With this game, we "expect" a return of $0.25. In a long-run context, this means that we should gain an average of $0.25 per game if we should play the game long enough. By contrast, in game number two an average loss of $0.25 should develop in the long run. Game number one is, accordingly, the better choice.

The student may be aware of some philosophical difficulties involved in the explanation of the basis for choice given above. One immediate question is, What if the decision is a one-time-only situation? Does the concept of the expected return of a decision have any meaning in a situation where the decision situation will not be repeated, and where the "long-run average return" is, therefore, not applicable? A final answer to this question is not possible here because it is, truly, a philosophical question. The two possible answers, "Yes, expected return is meaningful in such a situation" and "No, the concept has no meaning in such a situation," have been subject to lengthy debate. A discussion of the debate is beyond the scope of this book.

A practical answer to the question seems to be that whether or not the principle of maximizing expected return is to be used as a criterion of choice is up to the decision maker faced with the decision. It is necessary that some criterion, or set of criteria, be used in making the decision. In the particular game situation illustrated, it would be difficult to argue that the principle of maximizing expected return is not a sufficient criterion. But let us consider another game in which there might be more room for doubt.

Suppose that the player once again has a choice between two games. The first game is the same as game number one described above, with an expected monetary return of $0.25. In place of game number two we substitute a third game. In game number three a marble is drawn from Bag III, which has the same composition as Bag I; that is, there also are nine white and one red marbles in Bag III. The difference in the two games is that upon drawing a white marble from Bag III, the player will receive $2,500. If he should draw a red marble from Bag III, however, the player is obliged to pay the operator $22,480. As before, the admission charge for each game is $1.75. Which game should the player choose?

The table below outlines the information concerning game number three. We see that the expected return of this game is $0.25.

Bag III	P	Return	Return · P
W	0.9	$ 2,500 − $1.75 = $ 2,498.25	$2,248.425
R	0.1	− 22,480 − 1.75 = − 22,481.75	− 2,248.175
	1.0		$ 0.25
			= expected monetary return

The expected monetary returns to games number one and number three are the same, $0.25. If we were to choose which game to play according to the principle of maximizing expected monetary return, we should have to say that it is a matter of indifference to us as to which game we played. For most of us, however, it is probably true that we would find game number three somewhat less desirable than game number one. The possibility of winning $2,500 is a very tempting one, but the possibility of losing $22,480 is positively horrifying! Game number one is considerably "safer," and it would probably appeal more strongly to most persons for this reason.

This is not to say that *no one* would find game number three as appealing as game number one. If a person were wealthy enough that a loss of $22,480 was not appalling to him, he might be indifferent between the two games. As a matter of fact, game number three might involve somewhat more of a thrill for him than game number one. There is also the possibility that a person might have a "go-for-broke" attitude that would lead him to prefer game number three to game number one, even though he could not afford a loss of $22,480.

What we are saying is, in essence, that whether or not a decision maker will be willing to make a decision according to the principle of maximizing expected return will depend on his attitude concerning the rewards and penalties arising from the different possible decisions. For any decision maker, there will probably be certain limits in the size of these rewards and penalties beyond which he may not wish to rely on expected monetary return as a basis for choice. Conversely, there will almost certainly be a large class of decision situations in which the decision maker will be content to follow expected monetary return as a criterion. The concepts and procedures which follow in this chapter are applicable in those decision situations.[2]

Another difficulty with the criterion of expected monetary return

---

[2] A more thorough discussion of these concepts is available in Robert Schlaifer, *Probability and Statistics for Business Decisions* (New York: McGraw-Hill, 1959). Professor Schlaifer has played a fundamental role in the strong resurgence over the past 10 years of concepts which we sketch briefly in this chapter.

was hinted at above, where it was suggested that the wealthy man might prefer game number three because of the greater thrill he would get from playing it. It is obviously true that in many decision situations monetary return is not the only—in some cases, perhaps, not even the most important—benefit presumed to arise from the possible decisions. In a gaming situation, the thrill of the game may be paramount to monetary considerations. In a business decision, other factors may play large roles: the challenge of a particular alternative, feelings of responsibility to public interests, desires for stability in the business, and so forth. Monetary return may share the stage with a number of such factors, or even play a secondary role, when time comes for the final decision to be made. Once again, however, considerations of these other factors will vary from one decision maker to the next and from one decision situation to the next. For a large class of problems, however, monetary return can probably be assumed to be the primary or the sole criterion for choice.

Problem Set 10–1

1. In the traditional game of shooting dice, one person is the shooter, and there may be several persons who can bet that the shooter will win or that he will lose. For the shooter, the probability that he will win is approximately 0.49293. The probability that he will lose, therefore, is approximately 0.50707. Suppose the game is to be played by you and one other person and that in each play of the game each person is to put up $10. If the shooter wins, he retrieves his $10 and also his opponent's $10. If the shooter loses, his opponent retrieves his $10 and the shooter's $10. Answer the questions which follow on the assumption that we are concerned with one play of the game only. (In the real game of shooting dice, of course, a person continues as the shooter until he loses in a given play. At that point, the position of shooter is rotated to another person.)

    a) On any given play, which would you prefer to be, the shooter or his opponent? Why?

    b) Set up a table for both the shooter and his opponent indicating the possible gains or losses for each with the corresponding probabilities and determine the expected gain for each player.

    c) In part (*b*), you have found that the expected monetary return to each player has the same value except that there is a difference in sign. Give an interpretation of the expected monetary return for each player. For example, is the expected monetary return the amount that each player will win (or lose) in any given play of the game?

2. In the game of dice described in problem 1, consider the following questions.

    a) Would you be willing to play this game if you were required to bet $10? Why?

    b) Suppose that you were required to bet $1,000 each time that you played the game. Would you be willing to play the game in this circumstance? Would you be more or less willing to play the game under the circumstances of this part as compared to part (*a*)?

c) Assuming that you would be willing to play the game where the bet is $10 each time, would you be more willing to play the game a large number of times or only one or two times? Why?

d) Discuss these questions in class and determine if your answers appear to reflect the majority opinion.

3. Consider the following two games: In Game I, one is allowed to draw a marble from Bag I, which contains three green, five red, and two black marbles. The admission charge for Game I is $0.10, and the person playing the game will be given $0.50, $0.10, or fined $0.25, if he draws a marble which is green, red, or black respectively. In Game II the admission charge is $0.15, and the rewards associated with the different colored marbles are the same as in Game I, except that a green marble wins $0.60. Draws are made from Bag II which contains four green, three red, and three black marbles. Which of the two games would you prefer to play, and why?

4. Consider the following situations and indicate some of the factors (monetary return, prestige, tradition) which you consider may have been important in the decision involved.

a) It is reported that in the period immediately following World War II, automobile manufacturers charged lower prices than immediate demand conditions would have allowed.

b) It is a well-known fact that among the members of a President's cabinet, there often will be found individuals who have joined the cabinet at a considerable financial loss.

c) It is a widely recognized fact that some colleges and universities are able to hire faculty members to fill particular positions at substantially lower salaries than would be required for the same type of person in other colleges and universities.

A simple pricing decision

As a second illustration of the principle of maximizing expected monetary return, we turn to a pricing decision in a simple business situation. In economic theory, we are taught to think of the demand for a product as a function in which there will be associated with each possible price a certain quantity which will be demanded by the consuming public at that price. The usual demand function will be one in which at higher prices a smaller quantity of the product will be demanded, and at lower prices a larger quantity will be demanded. These demand functions are usually discussed as if they were deterministic in nature. That is, it is assumed that at a given price a certain quantity will be demanded, and there is no consideration given to the possibility that the quantity demanded at that price might be subject to variation.

Actually, the quantity of a product demanded from day to day at a given price will almost certainly be subject to some variation.[3] Recognizing that such variation does occur, it can be useful to regard the quantity demanded of a product at a given price as a random variable. The probability distribution of the random variable can then be thought of as conditional on the price at which the product is offered for sale. In this context, it becomes meaningful to discuss pricing decisions as subject to the principle of maximizing expected monetary return. We illustrate with a much simplified example.

Suppose that our decision maker is the operator of a popcorn stand situated in a large amusement park. He is faced with the decision problem of determining what price he should charge for the bags of popcorn which he sells (for simplicity, we assume he sells only one size bag). He is familiar enough with his business that he knows about what variation in daily sales to expect at various prices. We assume that he has narrowed his decision problem to one of considering three possible prices: 15 cents, 20 cents, and 25 cents. At these three prices he judges that the daily quantity demanded is subject to the probability distributions set in the table, where q represents the number of bags demanded.

Price = $0.15		Price = $0.20		Price = $0.25	
q	$P(q)$	q	$P(q)$	q	$P(q)$
100	0.05	100	0.10	100	0.25
150	.10	150	.15	150	.35
200	.10	200	.20	200	.25
250	.20	250	.25	250	.10
300	.35	300	.20	300	.05
350	.15	350	.10	350	.00
400	.05	400	.00	400	.00
	1.00		1.00		1.00

The influence of price on sales is easily noted by a comparison of the three probability distributions. Although the operator judges that it is certain his daily sales will fall between 100 and 400 bags at any of the three prices, the probabilities associated with smaller quantities tends to increase with increasing price. At the same time, the probabilities associated with high daily sales tends to decrease with increasing price. Our concern is to see how this price influence affects the operator's expected daily return from the popcorn stand.

In order to determine the return to the operator of the popcorn stand, we must take into account the costs of operating the stand, as well as the price of the popcorn. The costs of doing business for a popcorn

---

[3] The economist will be inclined to describe this variation as due to a shift in the demand function itself from day to day. We are not concerned here with an explanation of the reasons for the variation. We wish only to recognize that such variation can be expected to occur.

stand, as well as any business, should be separated into the two classes of fixed and variable costs. The unit cost (the mean cost per bag of popcorn) associated with a given volume of sales would almost certainly vary from one sales volume to the next, due to the relative contributions of fixed and variable costs. We shall assume here, as a matter of simplification, that the unit cost of a bag of popcorn remains stable at 5 cents, no matter what the sales volume might be.

With this information concerning costs, we are ready to determine which price the operator should charge per bag of popcorn. The three tables which appear below summarize the relevant information. The first two columns repeat the pertinent probability distribution at each price level. The third column in each table indicates the daily profit accruing from popcorn sales at the given price and assuming sales in that day equal to the amount in the same row of the first column. Thus, at a price of $0.20 per bag, the unit profit per bag will be $0.20 − $0.05 = $0.15. If sales for the day should be 100 bags, as indicated in the first row of the first column, total profit for the day would be $(100)($0.15) = 15, as indicated in the first row of the third column

Price = $0.15
(Unit Profit = $0.10)

q	$P(q)$	Profit	Profit · $P(q)$
100	0.05	$10.00	$ 0.50
150	.10	15.00	1.50
200	.10	20.00	2.00
250	.20	25.00	5.00
300	.35	30.00	10.50
350	.15	35.00	5.25
400	.05	40.00	2.00
	1.00		$26.75
			= expected daily profit

Price = $0.20
(Unit Profit = $0.15)

q	$P(q)$	Profit	Profit · $P(q)$
100	0.10	$15.00	$1.500
150	.15	22.50	3.375
200	.20	30.00	6.000
250	.25	37.50	9.375
300	.20	45.00	9.000
350	.10	52.50	5.250
400	.00	60.00	–0–
	1.00		$34.500
			= expected daily profit

Price = $0.25
(Unit Profit = $0.20)

q	$P(q)$	Profit	Profit $\cdot$ $P(q)$
100	0.25	$20.00	$ 5.00
150	.35	30.00	10.50
200	.25	40.00	10.00
250	.10	50.00	5.00
300	.05	60.00	3.00
350	.00	70.00	–0–
400	.00	80.00	–0–
	1.00		$33.50 = expected daily profit

of the table for a price of $0.20. These daily profits associated with the daily sales volume constitute a random variable, so that we can calculate the expected daily profit as is accomplished in the fourth column of each table.

A comparison of the expected daily profits at the three alternative prices indicates that the operator of the popcorn stand should charge a price of 20 cents a bag. At this price, his expected daily profit is $34.50.

Problem Set 10–2

1. In the example of the popcorn stand used in the text, we assumed that the unit cost of a bag of popcorn was $0.05 and that this was a stable cost which did not vary with changes in the quantity of popcorn sold. It is well known, however, that the unit costs of production for a commodity typically tends to follow a U-shaped curve. Suppose, therefore, that the unit cost for a bag of popcorn followed a function as outlined in the table appearing below.

q	Unit Cost
100	$0.07
150	.06
200	.05
250	.06
300	.07
350	.08
400	.09

a) Given the cost function as outlined above and the demand conditions specified by the tables of the text in the preceding section, determine at what price the operator of the popcorn stand should sell his popcorn if his sole concern is to maximize expected monetary return.

b) Suppose that in your discussion with him, you have learned that the operator of the popcorn stand is very much concerned about the number of customers he has per day. He has complained that if there are too few customers, he becomes bored with the job, but if there are too many customers, he is much too tired by the end of the 12-hour day which he puts in. In questioning him a little closer, you learn that he believes the optimum number of customers would be about 20 customers per hour on the average. In answer to your questions, he specifies that he would rather give up $1 of his profit daily in order to maintain an average rate of customers of about 20 per hour rather than see the rate depart from that figure. On the basis of this added information concerning his preferences, would you change your recommendation as to the price he should charge per bag of popcorn? If so, why?

2. Suppose that a contractor wishes to submit a bid in competition with other contractors for a construction project to be performed for the city. Having studied the situation carefully, he has decided that the possible cost of the project can be represented by the probability distribution which appears in the left half of the accompanying table. He is, at present, considering three different possible bids which he might make for the project. The probability that he will be awarded the contract for the project is dependent upon his bid, and he believes that the probabilities associated with these bids are as set out in the probability distribution which appears in the right half of the accompanying table. If the contractor is willing to use expected monetary return as a criterion for selecting which bid he should submit, which of the three bids indicated should he submit?

Hint: Note that for whatever bid the contractor submits, he may or he may not get the contract. If he does not get the contract, his return of course, will be zero. If he should get the contract, however, his return will depend upon the difference between the amount which he bids and the actual cost to him of carrying out the project. There will, therefore, be three possible returns associated with each possible amount which he might bid. For example, if he were to bid $12,000 for the project and the actual costs of the project should turn out to be $10,000, his return would be $+2,000. The probability that this would be the return to him is the probability of the *intersection* of the events "he gets the job" *and* "the cost of the project is $10,000." This probability then would be $P(\text{job}) \, P(\text{cost is } \$10,000) = (0.6) \, (0.1) = 0.06$. In a similar fashion, all of the possible returns and the probabilities associated with them can be determined for each possible amount bid and the expected return associated with each bid can then be determined on the basis of this information.

Cost	P(Cost)	Bid	P(Job)
$10,000	0.1	$12,000	0.6
12,000	.7	13,000	.3
15,000	.2	14,000	.1
	1.0		

3. Mr. Jones has a small bakery in which he produces doughnuts for sale, as well as other bakery items. The cost to him of making doughnuts is $0.30 per dozen, and he sells them at a price of $0.50 per dozen. The number of dozens of doughnuts which he sells varies from day to day and is subject to

the probability distribution set down in the accompanying table, where D is the quantity demanded. The routine of the bakery requires him to bake as many doughnuts as he wishes in any one day at the beginning of the day. His problem, therefore, is to determine how many dozens of doughnuts he should bake each morning. If the demand for doughnuts on any one day should be less than the number he bakes, he will, of course, have a surplus of doughnuts at the end of the day. He has made arrangements for these surplus doughnuts to be sold to a "thrift" shop at a price of $0.10 per dozen. If, on the other hand, the demand for doughnuts on any given day is greater than the number he has baked, he will have missed an opportunity to sell more doughnuts than he has available. Given this information, and using the principle of maximizing expected monetary return, advise Mr. Jones as to how many dozens of doughnuts he should bake each morning.

Hint: The different actions available to Mr. Jones are to "bake 13," "bake 14," . . . , "bake 17." These are the possible actions he should consider, since this is the range of demand as shown in the probability distribution. For any one of these actions, the return would be equal to the difference between the inflow and the outflow. The outflow would, of course, be equal to the number of dozens of doughnuts which he baked, times $0.30. The inflow, however, is conditional upon what the demand is on any given day. Suppose, for example, that the action, "bake 15," is being considered. If Jones should bake 15 dozen doughnuts and demand is only for 13 dozen that day, the inflow would be composed of the amount gained from selling thirteen dozen doughnuts at $0.50 per dozen plus the gain from selling the surplus two dozen doughnuts to the thrift shop at $0.10 per dozen. Thus, the inflow for that level of demand would be $13($0.50) + 2($0.10) = 6.70 and since the outflow associated with baking 15 dozen doughnuts would be $15($0.30) = 4.50, the return in this situation would be $R = $6.70 - $4.50 = 2.20. The probability that this return would be realized is just the probability that the quantity demanded would be $D = 13$, or $P(R) = $2.20 = 0.10$.

Another possibility is that Jones would sell all 15 dozen doughnuts. This would occur if demand on that day were equal to or greater than 15 dozen. In that case, the inflow would be $15($0.50) = 7.50, and the return would be $R = $7.50 - $4.50 = 3. The probability that Jones will realize this return is the probability that demand is greater than or equal to 15 dozen, that is, $P(R = $3) = 0.65$. In a similar fashion, all of the other possible returns associated with a given act can be determined and the expected monetary return associated with any act can, therefore, be determined. The calculations are easily carried out if one sets up a table as in the example given below for the act "bake 15."

D	Inflow	R	$P(R)$	$R \cdot P(R)$
13	$13($0.50) + 2($0.10) = 6.70	$2.20	0.10	$0.22
14	$14($0.50) + 1($0.10) = 7.10	$2.60	.25	$0.65
15 or more	$15($0.50) = 7.50	$3.00	.65	$1.95
				$2.82

The expected monetary return of the act "bake fifteen" is, therefore, $2.82.

D	P(D)
13	0.10
14	.25
15	.30
16	.20
17	.15
	1.00

Testing for control in a ball-and-socket assembly, a third example

In Chapter 9, we discussed a procedure for simulating the production of a steel ball whose mean diameter was desired to be 10 millimeters. Our concern there was to estimate, through a Monte Carlo procedure, the proportion of defective balls the process would produce. In this section, we wish to return to the example of the steel ball and elaborate on it. Our concern here, however, will be to consider the means by which a satisfactory procedure can be developed to determine if the process producing the steel ball is in control or not.

We suppose, as before, that the process producing the ball can be in one of three states, B, C, and A. It will be recalled that in each of these states the ball is produced with diameters falling in a normal distribution with a standard deviation of 0.1 millimeter. The states differ from one another with respect to the mean diameter of the balls: in state B the mean is 9.9 millimeters, in state C the mean is 10.0 millimeters, and in state A the mean is 10.1 millimeters. The probabilities associated with these three states are $P(B) = 0.35$, $P(C) = 0.50$, and $P(A) = 0.15$.

In the earlier chapter, it was assumed that a ball was defective if its diameter fell below 9.8 millimeters or above 10.2 millimeters. We drop that assumption here, and instead describe the use of the steel balls produced by the process. We shall assume that these steel balls are to be fitted into a steel socket, to form a part of a large assembly. In order for this ball-and-socket unit to perform adequately, the difference between the diameter of the ball and the diameter of the socket containing it must fall within the interval of 0.05 to 0.15 millimeters. It is obvious, of course, that whether or not this condition is met will depend on the diameter of the ball selected to be fitted to a socket, and the diameter of the socket. We need, therefore, to know something about the process which produces the sockets.

We shall assume that the process by which the sockets are produced is capable of producing them with a standard deviation in the diameters of 0.05 millimeters. These diameters are normally distributed about a mean value of 10.1 millimeters. Now, we have come to expect any process of the type described here to be subject to some variability in its mean. For purposes of simplification, however, we shall assume that the process producing the sockets is stable with respect both to the mean and the standard deviation of the diameters of the sockets. In other words, it is always in control. This assumption will allow us to concentrate our attention largely on the process producing the steel balls.

Our goal is to specify a procedure by which we can test to determine whether or not the ball-producing process is in control. There are several aspects to this problem. Perhaps the first is the question of which of the three states is the most desirable. That is, what should be the "target" value for the mean diameter of the steel balls? In order to answer that question adequately, we need to know what costs are associated with the different states of the process.

Once we have determined a target value for the mean diameter of the balls, we still must decide on a sampling plan by which we shall test to determine if the process is in control at this target value. A complete specification of the sampling plan would have to include determination of the size of the sample, determination of how often such a sample should be selected from the production stream, and the significance level at which the test should be performed. Once again, in order to simplify the presentation, we shall consider only the last of these three factors. We assume, then, that the steel balls are produced in production "runs" of 1,000. At the beginning of each run, a sample of size $n = 16$ is taken, on the basis of which a test is made to determine if the process is in control. If we decide on the basis of the sample that the process is out of control, the process will be adjusted. This adjustment will, we assume, always leave the process in control if it is performed. If it is not performed, the process will continue in whichever state it was in, initially.

Determination of the costs associated with each state of the process

It has been assumed that the difference between the diameters of the ball and the socket must be in the interval 0.05 and 0.15 millimeters in order for the ball-and-socket unit to be satisfactory. Let us suppose further that if this difference for a particular unit is below this interval (the difference is less than 0.05 millimeters), then the fit of the unit can be made satisfactory by remilling the socket until it is large enough to accommodate the ball. The cost of this operation is $3. If the difference in diameters is larger than 0.15, however, it is not possible to rework the pieces, and the whole unit (the ball and the socket) is scrapped. The cost associated with scrapping a unit is $4, which represents the lost effort and resources which were required to bring the components to that stage in the production process.[4]

---

[4] It may be less expensive, in some situations of this type, to make a conscious effort to match the diameters of the components, rather than to select the components randomly from the separate production streams. Such an assumption would introduce a level of complexity that we are well advised to avoid.

The overall costs of a production run will tend to vary with the state in which the ball-producing process is operating. We need to determine the expected cost associated with each of these states before we can determine which of the three states is the most desirable. Actually, however, it is not necessary to calculate *total* costs for a run of 1,000 units in each state. We can concentrate our attention on the additional costs arising from reworking units with too tight a fit and from scrapping units with too loose a fit. It is assumed that these conditions are the only basis for differences in the costs of production in each state. Moreover, we can express the additional costs associated with each state on a per unit basis in order to make a comparison of the three states.

Since we require the expected (additional) cost for a unit produced in each possible state of the process, it is necessary for us to determine the probability distribution for the differences in diameters which would exist between the ball and the socket in a pair which has been randomly selected from the production stream of each component. We are able to do this on the basis of facts developed in earlier portions of the book.

Let us designate the diameter of a socket by X_s and the diameter of a ball by X_b. Both X_s and X_b are random variables with a normal distribution. It will, therefore, be true that the random variable, $X_s - X_b$, the difference in diameters, will also be a random variable with a normal distribution. We need, in addition to this fact, to know the mean and the standard deviation of $X_s - X_b$. We know that the mean of $X_s - X_b$ will equal the difference of the means of X_s and X_b. That is, $m(X_s - X_b) = m(X_s) - m(X_b)$. This value will vary, of course, depending on the value of $m(X_b)$, the mean diameter of the balls in the different states. The standard deviation of the random variable, $X_s - X_b$, can be determined on the basis of the fact that $\text{var}(X_s - X_b) = \text{var}(X_s) + \text{var}(X_b)$. The standard deviation of X_b is given as $\sigma_b = 0.1$, so that $\text{var}(X_b) = \sigma_b{}^2 = (0.1)^2 = 0.01$. Also, the standard deviation of X_s is $\sigma_s = 0.05$, so that $\text{var}(X_s) = (0.05)^2 = 0.0025$. We have $\text{var}(X_s - X_b) = \text{var}(X_s) + \text{var}(X_b) = 0.01 + 0.0025 = 0.0125$. Therefore, the standard deviation of $X_s - X_b$ is:

$$\sigma_{X_s - X_b} = \sqrt{\text{var}(X_s - X_b)} = \sqrt{0.0125} \simeq 0.1118 \,.$$

The distribution of the difference in diameters in ball-socket units will have a standard deviation of approximately 0.1118 millimeters. The mean of the distribution, $m(X_s - X_b) = m(X_s) - m(X_b)$ will vary with the different values of $m(X_b)$. The table on page 332 indicates the different possible values of $m(X_s - X_b)$ [bear in mind that $m(X_s)$ is assumed stable at a value of 10.1 millimeters].

Let us look, first, at the situation when the ball-producing process is in state B. The graph of Figure 10–1(a) represents the distribution of the differences in diameters, $X_s - X_b$. It is a normal distribution with a mean of 0.2 millimeters and a standard deviation of 0.1118 millimeters. The broken vertical lines of the graph are placed at the points 0.05 millimeters and 0.15 millimeters. They indicate the interval within which the difference in diameters of the ball-socket unit will be satisfactory. The arrows indicate areas within the distribution of these differences in

Process State	$m(X_b)$	$m(X_s - X_b) = m(X_s)$ $- m(X_b) = 10.1 - m(X_b)$
B	9.9	$10.1 - 9.9 = 0.2$ mm.
C	10.0	$10.1 - 10.0 = 0.1$ mm.
A	10.1	$10.1 - 10.1 = 0.0$ mm.

which the unit will need reworking, will be acceptable as is, or will need to be scrapped. These areas represent the probabilities associated with reworking, accepting, or scrapping the unit, respectively. The values of these probabilities are easily calculated:

$$P(\text{rework}) = P\left(z < \frac{0.05 - 0.20}{0.1118}\right) \simeq P(z < -1.34) = 0.0901;$$

$$P(\text{accept}) = P\left(\frac{0.05 - 0.20}{0.1118} \leq z \leq \frac{0.15 - 0.20}{0.1118}\right) \simeq P(-1.34 \leq z \leq -0.45)$$
$$= 0.2363;$$

$$P(\text{scrap}) = P\left(z > \frac{0.15 - 0.20}{0.1118}\right) \simeq P(z > -0.45) = 0.6736.$$

If the ball-producing process is in state C, however, the graph of the distribution of $X_s - X_b$ will appear as in Figure 10–1(b). With the mean of the distribution at 0.1 millimeters, the "acceptable" interval extends equal distances on either side of the mean, as indicated again by the broken lines. In this situation, the probabilities of rework, accept and scrap are:

$$P(\text{rework}) = P\left(z < \frac{0.05 - 0.10}{0.1118}\right) \simeq P(z < -0.45) = 0.3264;$$

$$P(\text{accept}) = P\left(\frac{0.05 - 0.10}{0.1118} \leq z \leq \frac{0.15 - 0.10}{0.1118}\right) \simeq P(-0.45 \leq z \leq 0.45)$$
$$= 0.3472;$$

$$P(\text{scrap}) = P\left(z > \frac{0.15 - 0.10}{0.1118}\right) \simeq 0.3264.$$

Finally, if the ball-producing process is in state A with a mean of 10.1 millimeters, the mean difference in diameters in the ball-socket pairs will be zero. This case is illustrated in Figure 10–1(c). As before,

Figure 10–1

(a)

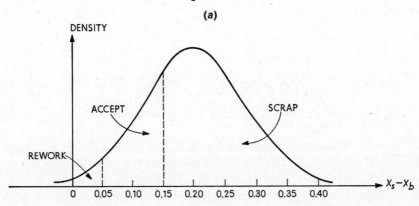

(b)

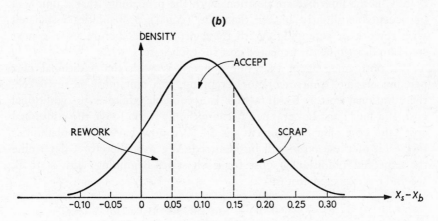

(c)

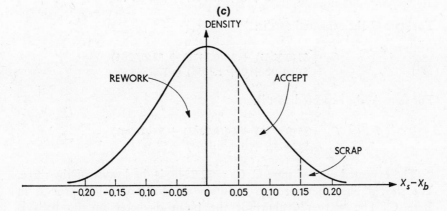

the broken vertical lines indicate the acceptable interval on $X_s - X_b$. The probabilities are:

$$P(\text{rework}) = P\left(z < \frac{0.05 - 0}{0.1118}\right) \simeq P(z < 0.45) = 0.6736 ;$$

$$P(\text{accept}) = P\left(\frac{0.05 - 0}{0.1118} \leq z \leq \frac{0.15 - 0}{0.1118}\right) \simeq P(0.45 \leq z \leq 1.34) = 0.2363 ;$$

$$P(\text{scrap}) = P\left(z > \frac{0.15 - 0}{0.1118}\right) \simeq P(z > 1.34) = 0.0901 .$$

By way of summary, we notice that if the ball-producing process is in state B, the probability of rework is low, but the probability of scrapping a unit is rather high. In state A, the positions are reversed, with the probability of rework high and the probability of scrapping low. State C is the intermediate position, with the probability that a unit will be acceptable slightly higher than the (equal) probabilities associated with rework or scrapping. With these probabilities before us, the next step is to determine the expected cost for each state.

We note once again that our concern is with the additional cost per unit arising from rework or scrapping. If a unit must be reworked, the additional cost is $3. If a unit is acceptable, there is no additional cost. If a unit must be scrapped because the fit is too loose, the additional cost (the cost of a replacement) is $4. We now have the probabilities that each of these costs will be incurred. We can, therefore, determine the expected (additional) cost for each state. Beginning with state B, we find the expected cost is:

$$C_B = \$3\,(0.0901) + \$0\,(0.2363) + \$4\,(0.6736)$$
$$= \$(0.2703 + 0 + 2.6944) = \$2.9647 .$$

For state C, the expected cost is:

$$C_C = \$3\,(0.3264) + \$0\,(0.3472) + \$4\,(0.3264)$$
$$= \$(0.9792 + 0 + 1.3056) = \$2.2848 .$$

For state A, the expected cost is:

$$C_A = \$3\,(0.6736) + \$0\,(0.2363) + \$4\,(0.0901)$$
$$= \$(2.0208 + 0 + 0.3604) = \$2.3812 .$$

The expected cost of state C, $C_C = \$2.2848$, is the lowest of the three. We should like, therefore, to maintain the ball-producing process in state C. The "target" value for the mean diameter of the balls is $m(X_b) = 10.0$ millimeters. Our next problem is to determine a testing procedure which is best for maintaining the process in control at a mean of 10.0 millimeters. We consider this problem in the next section.

Problem Set 10–3

1. In the text we assumed that the socket-producing process was in a state such that the mean diameter of the sockets was 10.1 mm. On the basis of that assumption, we tested to determine what would be the best state for the process which produced the steel balls. This best state proved to be state C, for which the mean diameter of the steel balls is 10.0. Of course, it is entirely possible that the process for producing sockets could be adjusted to different levels. Suppose, then, that such adjustment were to be made so that the mean diameter of sockets is as shown in the parts below. For each case, determine which state, B, C, or A, would be the proper target level for the ball-producing process and show the expected costs associated with each of the three states.

   a) $m(X_s) = 10.2$.
   b) $m(X_s) = 10.0$.

2. In the text, it was assumed that specifications for the ball-socket assembly required that the difference between the mean diameter of the socket and the mean diameter of the ball must fall in the range 0.05 mm. to 0.15 mm. The specification of tolerances is ordinarily considered to be a question of engineering. It should be recognized, however, that such specifications do have an influence on cost. To illustrate this point, suppose that the tolerance on the difference in the dimensions were to be set at 0.05 mm. to 0.25 mm. Assuming once again that $m(X_s) = 10.1$ mm., determine the best state for the ball-producing process and the expected costs associated with each of the three possible states for that process. Based on your findings and comparing these with the results shown in the text, does it appear that a loosening of the tolerance of the difference in mean diameters would be beneficial from the point of view of production costs?

Determination of the conditional costs resulting from the testing procedure

The analysis of the preceding section indicates that if the ball-producing process is in either state B or state A, the costs of production will be higher than in state C. At the beginning of each production run, we have the opportunity to adjust the process. If we do so, we can be sure that the process will operate throughout the run in state C. If we do not adjust the process, it may operate throughout the run in any of the three states, with the probabilities that it will be in each of these states 0.35, 0.50, and 0.15 for B, C, and A, respectively. Our problem is to determine if we can save on the costs of production by taking a sample from the initial stream of the process and to decide on the basis of the sample result whether or not we should adjust the process. We shall assume that the adjustment process can be accomplished at a cost of $200 and that the sample can be collected at no cost. Moreover, we shall ignore the fact that the initial few balls produced in the run will become part of the sample and will not, therefore, be influenced by the adjustment process, should it be undertaken.

Suppose that it has been decided that the size of the sample to be collected is $n = 16$.[5] Let us consider, first, a two-tail test, in which we guard against the process being in either state B or state A by dividing the value of a equally between the two tails of the sampling distribution. We wish to determine, under these circumstances, the value of a which will minimize the expected (additional) costs.

Since we wish to minimize expected cost, we must know the level of costs we can expect under all the different conditions that might arise in our testing procedure, and we must know the probabilities associated with those costs. First, let us consider the costs to expect in different circumstances.

Table 10–1

EXPECTED COSTS RESULTING FROM REJECT-
ING OR ACCEPTING THE HYPOTHESIS OF
CONTROL, WHEN THE PROCESS IS IN
STATES B, C, A

	Real Situation		
Decision	B	C	A
	(1)	(2)	(3)
Reject	$2,484.80	$2,484.80	$2,484.80
	(4)	(5)	(6)
Accept	$2,964.70	$2,284.80	$2,381.20

We know that the state of the process at the time the sample is taken will be one of the three, B, C, and A. These three "real situations" correspond to the columns of Table 10–1. We are also aware of the fact that, regardless of the real situation, we cannot be certain that our decision on the basis of the sample result will be the correct one. There will be only two possible decisions on the basis of the sample result: We must accept the hypothesis that the process is in control, or we must reject that hypothesis. These two decisions correspond to the rows of Table 10–1.

The rows and columns of Table 10–1 partition the total possible experience that can arise from the testing procedure into six different circumstances. These have been numbered (1) through (6). Circumstance number (1) is the case where the process is in state B and the

---

[5] The sample size is, of course, a variable in a real sampling plan. The expected savings arising from a sampling plan would almost certainly be affected by the sample size. We use $n = 16$ as another simplification of the problem.

result of our sample leads us to reject the hypothesis that the process is in control. Circumstance number (2) is the case where the process is in state C (in control), but the sample result leads us to reject the hypothesis that it is in control. That is, circumstance number (2) is the case in which we will have committed a Type I error. The other numbered circumstances of Table 10–1 have similar interpretations. Thus, circumstances number (4) and number (6) are the cases in which we will have committed a Type II error, since the process will not be in control in these cases, but the sample result will lead us to accept the hypothesis that it is.

For each of the six circumstances depicted in Table 10–1, we need the resulting cost which we could expect if that circumstance should arise. Let us direct our attention first to circumstance number (5). This is the circumstance in which the process is in control and our sample result leads us to accept the hypothesis of control. If our sample result leads us to accept the hypothesis of control, of course, this means that we do not adjust the process, thereby avoiding the cost of $200 required to make that adjustment. It follows that the expected (additional) cost in this circumstance will be $C_C = \$2.2848$ per unit as determined earlier. Since there are to be 1,000 units produced per run, this means that the expected (additional) cost per run will be $2,284.80. This latter amount is the value which appears in Table 10–1 under circumstance (5).

Consider now circumstance (4). This is a circumstance once again where the hypothesis of control is accepted, although in this case the process actually has shifted to state B. Since no adjustment of the process will be made in this circumstance, the expected cost will be 1,000 times the value of C_B, that is $1,000(\$2.9647) = \$2,964.70$. This value is the entry in Table 10–1 under circumstance (4). By similar reasoning, the entry under circumstance (6) is calculated as $1,000(\$2,3812) = 2,381.20$.

Turning our attention now to the top row of Table 10–1, which contains the circumstances in which the sample result leads to rejection of the hypothesis of control, we reason in the following way. In all three of these circumstances, (1), (2), and (3), we are led to reject the hypothesis of control. This means that we undertake to adjust the process. It has been assumed that adjustment of the process always will lead to the process being in control in state C. This means in turn that the expected additional costs due to reworking or scrapping of the units will be $C_C = \$2.2848$ per unit. Consequently, the expected costs per run from these factors will be $2,284.80. In addition to this cost, however, we will have incurred the cost of $200 required to adjust the process. Thus, the total expected cost per run in circumstances (1), (2), and (3) will be the same amount of $2,484.80 in all three circumstances.

The cost figures which constitute the entries to Table 10–1 represent the conditional costs of the six possible circumstances which might arise.

From these conditional costs, we shall want to calculate the expected costs associated with the testing procedure. Before doing so, however, it will be instructive to point out some comparisons between these conditional costs.

Looking first at the column of Table 10–1 headed by C, we note that the conditional cost in circumstance (2) is $200 more than the conditional cost in circumstance (5). This difference of $200 reflects the fact that in circumstance (2) we will have committed a Type I error. We will have adjusted the process even though it was in state C to begin with. The sample has misled us and caused us to incur additional unnecessary costs.

Turning now to the column headed with B, we note that the cost associated with circumstance (4) is greater than the cost associated with circumstance (1). Circumstance (4) corresponds to the situation in which the process actually is in state B, but our sample result misleads us and we commit a Type II error. In this circumstance we will proceed with a run when the process is out of control, thereby incurring rather heavy costs of reworking and scrapping. If the sample had led us to reject the hypothesis of control, as in circumstance (1), we would have adjusted the process. This action would have reduced the cost of reworking and scrapping, while incurring an additional cost of adjustment of $200. The relative costs are such in these two circumstances that the reduced costs of scrapping and reworking more than offset the added cost of adjusting the process.

We turn now to a consideration of the column in Table 10–1 headed A. Circumstance (6) is, like circumstance (4), a situation in which the process actually is out of control, but the sample result leads us to a Type II error. In this circumstance, then, we once again would incur costs of reworking and scrapping that are greater than could be realized if the process were in state C. In circumstance (3), the sample result would have caused us, correctly, to reject the hypothesis of control and to adjust the process.

Notice, however, that unlike the circumstances appearing in column B, the conditional cost associated with adjusting the process to a state of control is greater than the conditional cost of not adjusting the process and leaving it out of control. In other words, if the process happens to be in state A, our expected costs would be lower if the sample result misled us into committing a Type II error than if it correctly signaled us to adjust the process! This points up the fact that what is a "correct" decision from the point of view of the sample result alone may not be a correct decision when one considers the costs involved.

At this point it would be obvious that it is not worthwhile to make our testing procedure one involving a two-tail test. We not only have nothing to gain by attempting to guard against the process being in state A but we actually will be incurring unnecessary costs by so doing. We shall continue the analysis for the two-tail test, however, before considering a one-tail test. It is hoped that a comparison of the two results will be useful to the student in gaining an appreciation of the factors involved in arriving at a proper solution.

Problem Set 10–4

1. In problem 1 of Problem Set 10–3, you determined the expected costs associated with each state, given that $m(X_s) = 10.2$ and $m(X_s) = 10.0$. For each of these situations, set up the table of conditional costs, as in Table 10–1.

2. In problem 2 of Problem Set 10–3, you determined the expected costs associated with each state, given a tolerance of 0.05 mm. to 0.25 mm. on the value of $X_s - X_b$ and a value of $m(X_s) = 10.0$ mm. Set down, for this situation, a table corresponding to Table 10–1.

3. Considering the conditional cost tables which you constructed in problem 1 above, determine whether it would be beneficial to adjust the process if it is in each of the two out-of-control states. Do this for:
    a) $m(X_s) = 10.2$.
    b) $m(X_s) = 10.0$.

4. Would one wish to use a one-tail or a two-tail test in the situations considered in problem 1? Why?

5. Repeat problem 3 above, this time considering the table of conditional costs which you set up in problem 2.

6. Repeat problem 4, in the situation considered in problem 2.

Procedure for minimizing expected cost

The entries of Table 10–1 are the (additional) costs to expect in each of the six circumstances. In order to determine the expected cost from the testing procedure, we need to multiply these figures by the probabilities associated with the various circumstances, and form the sum of these products. That is, letting $P(1)$ denote the probability that circumstance number (1) will occur, $P(2)$ denote the probability that circumstance number (2) will occur, and so forth, we can calculate the expected cost of the testing procedure as

$$C = (\$2,484.80)P(1) + (\$2,484.80)P(2) + (\$2,484.80)P(3)$$
$$+ (\$2,964.70)P(4) + (\$2,284.80)P(5) + (\$2,381.20)P(6) . \qquad (1)$$

It is evident that in addition to the net cost figures for the different circumstances, we need also the probabilities, $P(1), P(2), \ldots, P(6)$.

Before we attempt to evaluate a specific sampling plan to be used in the testing procedure, that is, before we specify a value for α, let us decide how we can determine the values of $P(1)$, $P(2)$, and so forth.

$P(1)$ is the probability that circumstance number (1) will occur. Looking at Table 10–1, again, this is the circumstance in which the process is in state B *and* the sample result leads us to reject the hypothesis that the process is in control at state C. Notice, then, that circumstance number (1) is the *intersection* of the two events "process in state B" and "the hypothesis of process control is rejected." Using the rule for the probability of an intersection, Rule P–7, we have:

$$P(1) = P(B)P(\text{reject}|B) . \tag{2,a}$$

Circumstance number (2) occurs when the process is in state C (in control) *and* the sample result leads us to reject the hypothesis of process control. It follows that

$$P(2) = P(C)P(\text{reject}|C) . \tag{2,b}$$

By similar reasoning the other probabilities can be shown to be:

$$P(3) = P(A)P(\text{reject}|A) . \tag{2,c}$$
$$P(4) = P(B)P(\text{accept}|B) . \tag{2,d}$$
$$P(5) = P(C)P(\text{accept}|C) . \tag{2,e}$$
$$P(6) = P(A)P(\text{accept}|A) . \tag{2,f}$$

It is obvious that the various probabilities, $P(1), \ldots, P(6)$, will depend upon the value of α specified in the testing procedure. This is true because the probability of rejecting or accepting the hypothesis of process control will differ with different values for α. And since the probabilities will vary with different values of α, it will also be true that the expected savings for the testing procedure will be different for different values of α. Our problem is to find a value for α that will minimize expected costs.

We do not have available to us the mathematical techniques which would allow us to find the precise value of α that will minimize expected costs, but we can proceed through a trial-and-error procedure to an answer as close as we like. In this procedure, we specify a value for α. For this value of α, we calculate the probabilities of equations (2). Substituting these probabilities in equation (1), we then calculate the expected cost associated with the testing procedure using that value for α. By repeating this procedure for several different values of α, we shall be able to determine an approximate value of α which minimizes expected costs.

Calculating expected cost, $\alpha = 0.01$

On the first trial, let us try the value $\alpha = 0.01$. Then our sampling plan will be to collect a sample of 16 balls at the beginning of a production run and to calculate their mean diameter. If the resulting value of $\bar{x}$ is enough above or below the target value of 10.0 millimeters, we shall have the process adjusted. Otherwise, we shall allow the process to continue through the run without adjustment. The value of $\bar{x}$ will be considered too far removed from the target value of 10.0 millimeters if such a result could be expected to occur with a probability of less than $\alpha = 0.01$, given that the process is in control.

With a significance level of $\alpha = 0.01$, we find from Table C in the section of Tables that the values of z which will lead to rejection of the hypothesis are those greater than 2.575 or less than -2.575. Thus, if the value of $\bar{x}$ for the sample is more than 2.575 standard errors away from the target value of 10.0 millimeters, we shall assume that the process is out of control and have it adjusted. Now, since the sample size is $n = 16$ and the standard deviation of the process is $\sigma = 0.1$, the standard error of the mean is:

$$\sigma_{\bar{x}} = 0.1/\sqrt{16} = 0.025 .$$

Therefore, values of $\bar{x}$ that are greater than $10.0 + 2.575(0.025) = 10.064375$, or smaller than $10.0 - 2.575(0.025) = 9.935625$, will lead us to have the process adjusted.[6]

Figure 10–2

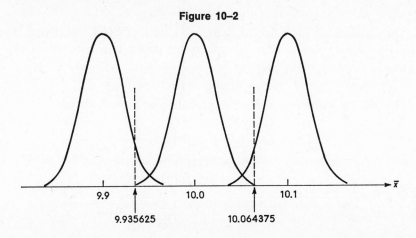

The graphs of Figure 10–2 portray the situation. The three curves represent the *sampling distributions of* $\bar{x}$ in the three possible states of the process. The center distribution is the one we expect if the hypothesis of control is correct, and its mean is 10.0 millimeters. The two other

---

[6] It should, perhaps, be noted that since the diameters of the balls are assumed to be measured in hundredths of millimeters, it follows that the possible values of $\bar{x}$ will necessarily be some multiple value of 0.000625. This is so because $\bar{x} = \Sigma x/n$. The value of Σx will be in hundredths of millimeters, and $n = 16$. Dividing one hundredth by 16 yields $0.01/16 = 0.000625$. Thus, the critical values of $\bar{x}$ developed in the analysis indicated above may not be "possible" values of $\bar{x}$. We can still use these critical values, however, as the rejection limits.

distributions have means of 9.9 millimeters and 10.1 millimeters, corresponding to states B and A, respectively. The vertical broken lines indicate the lower and upper rejection limits for the test with $\alpha = 0.01$.

The first step is to calculate the probabilities associated with the various circumstances, $P(1), \ldots, P(6)$. We shall work through the determination of $P(1)$ in some detail, in order to get the procedure firmly in mind. The other probabilities will be determined in similar fashion, but with some of the detail omitted. Equation $(2,a)$ states:

$$P(1) = P(B)P(\text{reject}|B) .$$

The value of $P(B) = 0.35$ is given by past experience with the process. The value of $P(\text{reject}|B)$ must be calculated. From Figure 10–1 we see that $P(\text{reject}|B)$ is the area in the leftmost distribution, below the value 9.935625. To determine this probability, we note that $\sigma_{\bar{x}} = 0.025$, so that:

$$P(\text{reject}|B) = P\left(z < \frac{9.935625 - 9.9}{0.025}\right) \simeq P(z < 1.42) = 0.9222 .[7]$$

We substitute the values of $P(B)$ and $P(\text{reject}|B)$ into the equation for $P(1)$ to get:

$$P(1) \simeq (0.35)(0.9222) = 0.32277 .$$

In determining the value of $P(2)$, we note that $P(C) = 0.50$ and that $P(\text{reject}|C)$ is just the level of significance of the test, $\alpha = 0.01$. Therefore,

$$P(2) = (0.50)(0.01) = 0.005 .$$

By similar reasoning, the other probabilities are calculated:

$$P(3) = P(A)P(\text{reject}|A) = (0.15)P\left(z > \frac{10.064375 - 10.1}{0.025}\right)$$
$$\simeq (0.15)P(z > -1.42)$$
$$= (0.15)(0.9222) = 0.13833 ;$$
$$P(4) = P(B)P(\text{accept}|B) = (0.35)P\left(z > \frac{9.935625 - 9.9}{0.025}\right)$$
$$\simeq (0.35)P(z > 1.42)$$
$$= (0.35)(0.0778)$$
$$= 0.02723$$
$$P(5) = P(C)P(\text{accept}|C) = (0.50)(1.0 - \alpha) = (0.50)(0.99)$$
$$= 0.495 ;$$
$$P(6) = P(A)P(\text{accept}|A) = (0.15)P\left(z < \frac{10.064375 - 10.1}{0.025}\right)$$
$$\simeq (0.15)P(z < -1.42)$$
$$= (0.15)(0.0778) = 0.01167 .$$

---

[7] In this calculation we ignore the very minute probability that the process in state B would yield a value for $\bar{x}$ above the upper rejection limit. The same thing is done in the calculations following this one, also.

Having determined the values of the probabilities, we substitute them into equation (1) to find the expected cost for a testing procedure with $\alpha = 0.01$:

$$C = (\$2,484.80)(0.32277) + (\$2,484.80)(0.005) + (\$2,484.80)(0.1383)$$
$$+ (\$2,964.70)(0.02723) + (2,284.80)(0.495) + (\$2,381.20)(0.0116)$$
$$\simeq \$2,397.66 .$$

This value indicates that a test of process control at the beginning of each production run of 1,000 units, with $n = 16$ and $\alpha = 0.01$, can be expected to lead to a cost of approximately \$2,397.66 per run. It is not clear at this point if we might expect to do even better with some other value for α.

Problem Set 10–5

1. In the calculation of C, in the text, the value is determined to be $C = \$2,397.66$. Explain, in its full context, what this figure represents.
2. Suppose that the socket-producing process is set so that the mean diameter is $m(X_s) = 10.2$ mm. In this situation, determine the expected additional costs associated with a two-tail testing procedure with a sample of size $n = 16$ and a significance level of $\alpha = 0.01$.
3. Which situation is preferable: the sampling plan outlined in the preceding section with a value of $m(X_s) = 10.1$, or the situation you worked out in problem 2? What criterion do you use in making this judgment? What factors account for the difference in expected costs associated with these two situations?

Choosing the best value for α

If we were to increase the value for α, this would correspond to a movement of the rejection limits of Figure 10–1 in toward the target value of 10.0 millimeters. The result would be, of course, to increase the probability of rejecting the hypothesis of process control and to decrease the probability of accepting this hypothesis. These effects would lead, for example, to a larger probability being associated with the cost figure of \$2,484.80 in circumstances number (1), (2), and (3). In terms of these circumstances, therefore, there will be a tendency for expected costs from the testing procedure to rise with an increase in α. On the other hand, the effect of an increase in α on circumstances number (4), (5), and (6) will be to decrease the probability associated with those circumstances. Through circumstances number (4), (5), and (6), therefore, there will be a tendency for any increase in α to lower the expected cost of the testing procedure.

The net result of these varying influences will depend on the degree to which the various probabilities respond to an increase in α. We shall find that the behavior of expected cost will be to decrease at first with larger values of α, but then to increase as α continues to grow. We can improve expected cost, then, by choosing a value for α larger than, but not too much larger than, 0.01.

Consider, now, a value of $\alpha = 0.05$. We indicate, without showing the calculations, that for $\alpha = 0.05$:

$$P(1) = 0.34276; \ P(2) = 0.025; \ P(3) = 0.14690 \ ;$$
$$P(4) = 0.00724; \ P(5) = 0.475; \ P(6) = 0.00310 \ .$$

Substituting these values into equation (1), we have:

$$C = (\$2,484.80)(0.34276) + (\$2,484.80)(0.025) + (\$2,484.80)(0.14690)$$
$$+ (\$2,964.70)(0.00724) + (\$2,284.80)(0.475) + (\$2,381.20)(0.00310)$$
$$\simeq \$2,392.95 \ .$$

Comparing the expected cost for $\alpha = 0.05$ with those for $\alpha = 0.01$, we note that the increase in α has led to an improvement of expected cost of nearly $5 per run.

Next, let us try $\alpha = 0.10$ and see what cost can be expected at this level. The values of the relevant probabilities are:

$$P(1) = 0.34682; \ P(2) = 0.05; \ P(3) = 0.14864 \ ;$$
$$P(4) = 0.00318; \ P(5) = 0.45; \ P(6) = 0.00136 \ .$$

The expected cost for $\alpha = 0.10$ is then:

$$C = (\$2,484.80)(0.34682) + (\$2,484.80)(0.05) + (\$2,484.80)(0.14864)$$
$$+ (\$2,964.70)(0.00318) + (\$2,284.80)(0.45) + (\$2,381.20)(0.00136)$$
$$\simeq \$2,396.19 \ .$$

An increase of α from 0.05 to 0.10 will lead to a rise in expected cost per run.

From calculated values for expected costs which we have for $\alpha = 0.01$, 0.05, and 0.10, we judge that the minimum expected cost will be for a value of α between 0.01 and 0.10. We cannot be sure, however, if it is a value of α less than or more than 0.05. The next step would be to try values of α close to 0.05 on either side, in order to determine in which direction the minimizing value of α would lie. Then, through successive

Table 10–2

Value of α	Expected Cost per Run
0.01	$2,397.66
.02	2,394.04
.03	2,392.92
.04	2,392.70
.05	2,392.95
.06	2,393.39
.07	2,393.98
.08	2,394.66
.09	2,395.43
.10	2,396.19

Figure 10–3

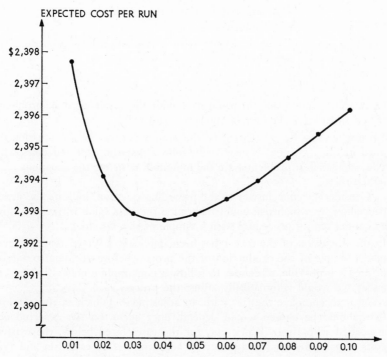

EXPECTED COST PER RUN

approximations, we could approach the correct value. All of these steps would involve repetition of the procedure already illustrated, so we shall not carry them out here. The results of a number of such steps appear in Table 10–2, and Figure 10–3 depicts graphically the behavior of expected cost.

Examination of Table 10–2 indicates that if the testing procedure is carried out with a significance level of $\alpha = 0.04$, the expected cost per run will be about \$2,392.70. This is very nearly the minimum in cost that could be expected, although some slight deviation of α from the value of 0.04 might result in minor improvement. Consequently, if we were to set $\alpha = 0.04$ in a testing procedure employing a two-tail test based on a sample of size $n = 16$, we could be assured that this is the "best" value for α, given the other features of the testing procedure.

Problem Set 10–6

1. It is stated in the text that for a value of $\alpha = 0.05$, the probabilities associated with the six possible circumstances are: $P(1) = 0.34276$, $P(2) = 0.025$, $P(3) = 0.1469$, $P(4) = 0.00724$, $P(5) = 0.475$, and $P(6) = 0.00310$. Perform the calculations to derive these results.

2. Repeat problem 1, using a value of $\alpha = 0.10$.

3. Perform the analysis required to show the result that, at $\alpha = 0.04$, $C = \$2,392.70$, as given in Table 10–2.

4. Find the expected cost associated with a two-tail testing procedure with $n = 16$ and $\alpha = 0.04$, when:
   a) $m(X_s) = 10.2$.
   b) $m(X_s) = 10.0$.

5. Comparing your results in problem 4 with the result cited in problem 3, which situation is the best of the three, and why?

6. Because a value for $\alpha = 0.04$ gave the minimum cost for the situation outlined in the text, does it necessarily follow that the expected costs which you calculated in problem 4 are the minimum costs for the situations represented there?

   Considering your answer to the preceding question, indicate the general procedure by which one could determine the best value for $m(X_s)$, given a two-tail testing procedure with a sample of size $n = 16$.

7. In the discussion of the text it has been implicitly assumed that we should take a sample of the production of the process before deciding to adjust it or not. It is possible, of course, to follow a nonsampling policy. In that case, either we would automatically adjust the process each time, or we would allow it to complete the run with no adjustment. Which of these alternatives should be chosen would depend, once again, on the expected costs associated with them. Work out, for the cases listed below, the expected costs associated with (1) a policy of adjusting before each run and (2) a policy of allowing each run to continue with no adjustment (you will wish to make use of Table 10–1 and the corresponding tables which you constructed in earlier problems). Which is the better alternative in each case?
   a) $m(X_s) = 10.0$.
   b) $m(X_s) = 10.1$.
   c) $m(X_s) = 10.2$.

8. Compare for each of the three values of $m(X_s)$ the expected cost associated with the better decision indicated by your work in problem 7 with the expected cost for the sampling plan ($n = 16$, $\alpha = 0.04$) as worked out in the text and in problem 4. For the three values of $m(X_s)$ considered, is there any case in which the better decision would be not to sample, rather than to proceed with this particular sampling plan?

9. On the basis of the conditional costs which you calculated in the table of problem 2 of Problem Set 10–4, find the expected cost of a sampling plan ($n = 16$, $\alpha = 0.04$), given a tolerance on ($X_s - X_b$) of 0.05 to 0.25 mm. Comparing this result to the expected cost of the best plan to follow among the alternatives considered in problems 7 and 8, what is the value of the loosened tolerance, as reflected in production costs?

The effect of factors other than α on the "best" decision

It is worth reemphasizing that the solution indicated above for the "best" testing procedure comes in the wake of a number of simplifying assumptions. It is obvious that several other factors in the testing procedure are subject to variation. It is quite possible that a solution even better than the one given above can be developed if we allow some of these other factors to take different values. We suggest some of the possibilities here.

We have no basis for thinking, as a first example, that the sample size $n = 16$ is the best possible sample size. It may be that larger samples would improve expected savings through their effect on the probabilities associated with the six circumstances arising from the testing procedure. Or, perhaps smaller samples would be better. Before we could answer the question of the best size sample, of course, we would have to take into account the fact that larger samples are more expensive to collect than smaller samples. In our discussion above, we simplified the problem by disregarding sample size and cost as factors in the problem.

It may also be true that improvement is possible if we were to consider different run sizes. The run size of 1,000 balls selected above was completely arbitrary. It should be evident, however, that expected costs per ball produced could vary significantly with different possible run sizes.

In order to maintain simplicity, we also assumed that the sockets to which the balls must be fitted were produced with a mean of 10.1 millimeters. This value of 10.1 has much to do with the distribution of differences in diameters which we used to arrive at the expected costs associated with each possible mean value for the diameter of the balls. It might be possible to improve on expected cost per run by adjusting the process which produces sockets, so that their mean diameter was above or below the value of 10.1 millimeters.

Finally, we have considered only the results arising from a two-tail test where the value of α is evenly divided between the two tails of the sampling distribution. We did so even though we noted that for the relative costs assumed in the problem, it apparently would be better to perform a one-tail test.

If all of these factors were to be taken into consideration, the problem would become quite complex. Nevertheless, one could arrive at a solution that was at least approximately correct by following much the same sort of trial-and-error procedure illustrated above. It would be very helpful, of course, if this procedure could be carried out with the aid of a computer. Whether or not it would be worth the cost and effort involved in finding a better solution would depend, as always, on the expected savings which might materialize. Many problems would almost certainly not justify the expense required. At the same time, for other problems, a few hours (days, weeks, months) spent on an analysis of this type can pay large dividends in reduced costs. Although the major example developed here related to a production problem, the same general principles are applicable to a wide class of problems. The popcorn stand, for example, represents an elementary marketing problem.

Several factors which could repay attention have been noted in this section. We cannot give them all detailed treatment, but let us look, at least, at the problem of minimizing expected cost when we do not restrict the test to one in which α is evenly divided between the two tails.[8] We could analyze this new problem in the same fashion as above. However, we shall use the problem as a vehicle for introducing a somewhat different statistical approach that has come to be known as Bayesian analysis. Before we attack the main problem, therefore, it will pay us to consider a simple example in the next section, in order to gain an appreciation of the rationale underlying Bayesian analysis.

Bayes' theorem

In our previous discussions, the probability statements with which we have been concerned have usually been of the type, "under a given set of conditions, C, the probability that event A will occur is $P(A|C)$." In an earlier section of this chapter, for example, we considered the probability that a red marble would be drawn from Bag I, which contained nine white and one red marbles, or from Bag II, which contained eight white and two red marbles. The probabilities can be written as $P(R|I) = 0.1$ and $P(R|II) = 0.2$. The type of problems for which Bayesian analysis is appropriate reverse the statement. This type of statement has the form, "given that event A has occurred, the probability that the set of conditions, C, led to A is $P(C|A)$." In terms of the gaming example, the statement might be, given that a red marble has been drawn from one of the two bags, the probability that it was drawn from Bag I is $P(I|R)$.

Our first concern is to see how statements of the second type can be constructed. As a prelude to this task, let us review some elementary probability statements of the first type. Suppose that someone is to draw a marble from one of the two bags described above. The bag from which the draw is to be made will be determined by the flip of a coin. Under these circumstances, we can specify:

The probability of drawing from Bag I, $P(I) = 0.5$.
The probability of drawing from Bag II, $P(II) = 0.5$.
The probability of drawing a red marble from Bag I, $P(R|I) = 0.1$.
The probability of drawing a red marble from Bag II, $P(R|II) = 0.2$.

---

[8] Some aspects of the other factors mentioned are given consideration in the problem sets. Also, for a treatment of the question of how variation in the value of $m(X_s)$ affects the decision problem, see Appendix A at the end of this chapter.

If we wished to determine the unconditional probability that the marble drawn will be red, we can use the "partitioning" rule, Rule P–10, since the "conditions," Bag I and Bag II, partition the sample space of concern. We find that:

$$P(R) = P(I)P(R|I) + P(II)P(R|II)$$
$$= (0.5)(0.1) + (0.5)(0.2)$$
$$= 0.15 .$$

The solution is a straightforward application of the rules that we learned in Chapter 1.

Now, let us consider the second type of problem. Suppose that a draw which has been made under the conditions specified earlier were to result in a red marble being drawn. What is the probability that the marble was drawn from Bag I? In probability notation, we want the value of $P(I|R)$. By Rule P–6, we know that:

$$P(I|R) = \frac{P(I \cdot R)}{P(R)} .$$

And by rule P–7, we also know that $P(I \cdot R)$ can be expressed in two ways:

$$P(I \cdot R) = P(R)P(I|R) ;$$
$$P(I \cdot R) = P(I)P(R|I) .$$

Notice, however, that the first expression for $P(I \cdot R)$ requires us to know $P(I|R)$ before we can evaluate it. But it is $P(I|R)$ that we wish to determine, so we cannot use this expression. Looking at the second expression for $P(I \cdot R)$, we see that it requires values of $P(I)$ and $P(R|I)$. We know both of these, and so we can evaluate this expression.

In order to determine a value for $P(I|R)$, we need the values for $P(I \cdot R)$ and $P(R)$. We have just seen that we can determine the value of $P(I \cdot R) = P(I)P(R|I)$. We saw earlier that we can find the value of $P(R) = P(I)P(R|I) + P(II)P(R|II)$. Therefore, we can find the value of

$$P(I|R) = \frac{P(I)P(R|I)}{P(I)P(R|I) + P(II)P(R|II)} .$$

This last expression is known as Bayes' theorem. It is, as are all the other probability rules which we discussed in Chapter 1, a truism which follows from the axioms and definitions of the probability model. But, as we have found to be the case with the other probability rules, application of this truism can lead to very useful results.

Let us apply the theorem to our problem of the red marble. We wish the probability that the marble has been drawn from Bag I, given that it is a red marble. We find the answer through Bayes' theorem:

$$P(I|R) = \frac{P(I)P(R|I)}{P(I)P(R|I) + P(II)P(R|II)}$$

$$= \frac{(0.5)(0.1)}{(0.5)(0.1) + (0.5)(0.2)}$$

$$= \frac{0.05}{0.05 + 0.10} \simeq 0.33 \ .$$

Notice what Bayes' theorem has done for us. Prior to the draw, we considered draws from the two bags equally probable, $P(I) = P(II) = 0.5$. This was the correct evaluation on the basis of the information available to us at that time. Following the draw, however, we have additional information, namely, the fact that the marble which was drawn is red. On the basis of this additional information, Bayes' theorem allows us to revise the probabilities associated with the two bags. We now assign a probability to Bag I of 0.33. The student can verify through application of Bayes' theorem that $P(II|R) = 0.67$, which is consistent with $P(I|R) = 0.33$, since the two probabilities must sum to a value of 1.0.

Bayes' theorem allows us to revise probabilities on the basis of new information, but it is important to note that it also takes into account information available prior to the new information. Thus, to find the probability that the draw was from Bag I given the additional information that the marble is red, we used values of $P(I)$, $P(R|I)$, $P(II)$, and $P(R|II)$. These four values are all information available to us prior to the draw.

In order to show the influence of the prior information on the revised probability, let us change the circumstances under which the draw is made. Suppose that the draw is made from Bag I if the roll of a die results in an ace (one dot). If the roll results in two through six dots appearing, the draw is made from Bag II. Now we have $P(I) = 1/6$ and $P(II) = 5/6$. If the draw should result in a red marble, the probability that the draw has been from Bag I is:

$$P(I|R) = \frac{P(I)P(R|I)}{P(I)P(R|I) + P(II)P(R|II)}$$

$$= \frac{(1/6)(0.1)}{(1/6)(0.1) + (5/6)(0.2)}$$

$$= \frac{1/60}{1/60 + 10/60} = \frac{1}{11} \ .$$

We find that the revised probability is much less in this case than before. The change is the consequence of the fact that the prior probability of the draw occurring from Bag I is much less than in the earlier case. By suitable examples, we could show that the values $P(R|I)$ and $P(R|II)$ also influence the outcome.

Before we turn to a practical application of Bayes' theorem, it is worthwhile to note a fundamental distinction between the two types of probability statement. In $P(R|I)$, for example, we express the probability that a red marble *will be* drawn, given that the draw will be from Bag I. In $P(I|R)$, however, we express the probability that the marble *has been* drawn from Bag I, given that the marble drawn is red.[9] This distinction relates to the philosophical question noted in Chapter 1 of whether or not probability statements have meaning when they are associated with events or conditions which have already occurred. We shall take the position here, as we did there, that if we are uncertain as to what event or condition has occurred, then such a probability statement can be considered a valid index of that uncertainty.

In the gaming example which has been used to illustrate Bayes' theorem, we made the assumption that we were not able to ascertain from which bag the marble was drawn. This assumption, which was artificial in the gaming situation, becomes real enough in actual situations. In the case of the ball-socket problem which we discussed earlier, for example, it is not evident, even after a sample of the balls has been collected, what state the process is in at the time the sample is collected. We shall consider the ball-socket problem again in the next section. This time, we shall wish to minimize expected costs per run with the restriction removed that the test must be a two-tail test with α equally divided between the two tails. The solution could be reached in the same manner as the earlier solution but we shall introduce Bayesian analysis as a tool, instead. Besides illuminating the usefulness of the Bayesian approach, the illustration should also shed additional light on the concept of a decision as choice among alternative actions.

Problem Set 10–7

1. In the gaming situation described in the text it was determined that $P(I|R)$ $=0.33$. Using the same assumptions given there, find the probability that a marble will have been selected from Bag I if the marble is white.

2. It was shown in the text that modifying the values of $P(I)$ and $P(II)$ leads to a change in the value of $P(I|R)$.
   a) Suppose now that $P(I) = 0.5$ and $P(II) = 0.5$, but $P(R|I) = 0.3$ and $P(R|II) = 0.5$. With these changes in $P(R|I)$ and $P(R|II)$, what is the value of $P(I|R)$?
   b) How do you account for the difference between $P(I|R)$ as you calculated it in (a) and the value in the text of $P(I|R) = 0.33$?

3. In a local bottling plant, the bottles to be filled with a popular soft drink

---

[9] We can, of course, always cast this statement into the future by saying that $P(I|R)$ is the probability that a marble *will have been* drawn from Bag I, given that the marble to be drawn is red. In some applications, however, we are interested in revising probabilities after the event, as indicated in earlier discussion. In those circumstances, the phrase "has been drawn," or an analogous phrase, is required.

are first washed in automatic washers. There are two of these washers. One is operated by Mabel and the other is operated by Martha. Each woman makes a visual check of the bottles as they leave her washer, in an attempt to cull out any bottle that may not have been thoroughly cleaned. Martha's washer is a larger machine and consequently washes bottles at a rate one and one half that of Mabel's machine. A consequence of this is that the probability that Martha will overlook a dirty bottle (0.015) is higher than the probability that Mabel will overlook one (0.01). Suppose that the operator of the machine which fills the bottles coming from Mabel's and Martha's machines finds a dirty bottle in the common conveyor line which leads from their washers. What is the probability that the bottle is from Mabel's washer?

4. Three boys in a family own identical piggy banks. One boy has two nickels in his. The second boy has one nickel and one dime. The third boy has two dimes in his bank. Father, who is short of change, surreptitiously removes a coin from a bank which he picks up at random in the boys' darkened room. The coin, he finds upon entering the lighted hallway, is a dime. What is the probability that the bank from which he borrowed the coin now has a dime in it?

5. Suppose that the father of problem 4 enters a room shared only by the second and third boys. What is the probability that a dime remains in the bank from which he borrowed the dime? Is your answer here the same as in problem 4, or is it different? Why?

6. Your firm buys a certain part from two suppliers, A and B. Of the incoming lots of this part, three tenths are received from A, and seven tenths are from B. Past experience has shown that the sampling plan to which all lots are subjected leads to rejection of five out of every hundred lots received from A. The rejection rate for lots of B is only half that of lots from A. What is the probability that a rejected lot is from supplier A?

Bayesian analysis and the ball-socket problem

In the earlier discussion of the ball-socket problem, the primary focus was on the concept of testing a hypothesis. Let us shift the emphasis somewhat in this section, and look on the problem as one of deciding whether or not to adjust the ball-producing process at the outset of the production run. The two "actions" possible are to adjust and not to adjust. We can decide which of these two actions to take in the same manner that the popcorn stand operator decided on the price to charge for his popcorn. That is, we can evaluate the expected return associated with each action and choose the action with the higher expected return (lower expected cost).

Consider, first, the case where the decision is to be made on the basis of information available to us from past experience. This information is that the process may be in one of three states, B, C, and A, with probabilities $P(B) = 0.35$, $P(C) = 0.50$, and $P(A) = 0.15$. We also know the "returns" associated with these three states are the additional costs to be expected if the process is adjusted or not adjusted. All of this information appears in Table 10–3. We evaluate each action by finding its expected cost, C. For the action, adjust the process,

$$C_a = (\$2{,}484.80)(0.35) + (\$2{,}484.80)(0.50) + (\$2{,}484.80)(0.15)$$
$$= \$2{,}484.80$$

For the action, do not adjust, the expected cost is:

$$C_d = (\$2{,}964.70)(0.35) + (\$2{,}284.80)(0.50) + (\$2{,}381.20)(0.15)$$
$$= \$2{,}537.22$$

The expected cost of adjusting the process is lower, on the basis of prior information, than the expected cost of not adjusting. We should, there-

Table 10–3

State	P(State)	Costs Adjust	Costs Do Not Adjust
B	0.35	$2,484.80	$2,964.70
C	.50	2,484.80	2,284.80
A	.15	2,484.80	2,381.20

fore, adjust the process before each run, if the decision is to be made on the basis of prior information alone.

The role of sample information in the decision

Suppose, now, that we decide to postpone the decision until we have collected a random sample of 16 balls from the production run. With this sample in hand, we can note the mean diameter of the 16 balls and ask if this sample result will lead to a revision of the probabilities which we associate with the three process states. If the sample result does lead to such a revision of the probabilities, we can then ask what are the expected costs of the two actions, given these revised probabilities.

In other words, given a certain value for the sample mean, say, $\bar{x}_0$, we shall determine revised probabilities for the three states, $P(B|\bar{x}_0)$, $P(C|\bar{x}_0)$, and $P(A|\bar{x}_0)$. With these revised probabilities we calculate the expected cost of each action and choose the action with the lower expected cost. In order to determine the probabilities, $P(B|\bar{x}_0)$, $P(C|\bar{x}_0)$, $P(A|\bar{x}_0)$, we shall use Bayes' theorem. Three process states partition the sample space from which $\bar{x}_0$ has come, so we have by Bayes' theorem:

$$P(B|\bar{x}_0) = \frac{P(B)P(\bar{x}_0|B)}{P(B)P(\bar{x}_0|B) + P(C)P(\bar{x}_0|C) + P(A)P(\bar{x}_0|A)} .\qquad (3,a)$$

$$P(C|\bar{x}_0) = \frac{P(C)P(\bar{x}_0|C)}{P(B)P(\bar{x}_0|B) + P(C)P(\bar{x}_0|C) + P(A)P(\bar{x}_0|A)} .\qquad (3,b)$$

$$P(A|\bar{x}_0) = \frac{P(A)P(\bar{x}_0|A)}{P(B)P(\bar{x}_0|B) + P(C)P(\bar{x}_0|C) + P(A)P(\bar{x}_0|A)} .\qquad (3,c)$$

Notice that in these equations we already have the values of $P(B)$, $P(C)$, and $P(A)$. What we require are the values of $P(\bar{x}_0|B)$, $P(\bar{x}_0|C)$, and $P(\bar{x}_0|A)$. These values obviously will depend upon the particular value of $\bar{x}_0$. Given the value of $\bar{x}_0$, however, we can determine the required probabilities, since states B, C, and A correspond to normal distributions.

Revision of probabilities for a given sample result

To see how all of this works out, suppose that the sample collected has a mean diameter of 9.94 millimeters. The first step is to determine the probability that the mean diameter of 16 balls would be 9.94 millimeters if they had been randomly selected from the production stream of a process with a mean of 9.9 millimeters and standard deviation of 0.1 millimeter, that is $P(\bar{x} = 9.94|B)$. We know that the sampling distribution from which the sample mean would have come in these circumstances has a mean of 9.9 millimeters and a standard error of $0.1/\sqrt{16} = 0.025$ millimeter. Even so, however, how can we get a probability for $\bar{x} = 9.94$? The value 9.94 is a point, and we have come to think of probabilities as associated with intervals only. The secret is to recognize that if we say $\bar{x} = 9.94$ we mean that the mean value of a set of 16 *measurements* was 9.94. These measurements are discrete values, however, which we have assumed earlier to be to the nearest hundredth of a millimeter. The values reported for $\bar{x}$, then, will be to the nearest 0.000625 of a millimeter, since $0.01/16 = 0.000625$. In other words, the possible values of $\bar{x}$ will actually be discrete, with an interval of width 0.000625 millimeter. We can, therefore, approximate the probability that $\bar{x}$ will be a given value.

To find the probability that $\bar{x}$ will be 9.94, we act as if that value is the midpoint of an interval with a width of 0.000625 millimeter. The bounds on this interval would be:

$$9.94 - \frac{0.000625}{2} = 9.9396875 ,$$

and

$$9.94 + \frac{0.000625}{2} = 9.9403125 ,$$

If the mean of the sampling distribution is 9.9 and the standard error of the mean is 0.025, we have:

$$P(\bar{x} = 9.94) \simeq P(9.9396875 \leq \bar{x} \leq 9.9403125)$$

$$= P\left(\frac{9.9396875 - 9.9}{0.025} \leq z \leq \frac{9.9403125 - 9.9}{0.025}\right)$$

$$= P(1.5875 \leq z \leq 1.6125)$$

$$\simeq 0.002725 .^{10}$$

Thus, we record that:

$$P(\bar{x} = 9.94|B) = 0.002725 .$$

If the process is in state C, the mean of the distribution will be 10.0 millimeters and the standard error of the mean will be 0.025 once again. In this case,

$$P(\bar{x} = 9.94) \simeq P\left(\frac{9.9396875 - 10.0}{0.025} \leq z \leq \frac{9.9403125 - 10.0}{0.025}\right)$$

$$= P(-2.4125 \leq z \leq -2.3875) \simeq 0.000525 .$$

That is,

$$P(\bar{x} = 9.94|C) = 0.000525 .$$

For the process in state A, the result is:

$$P(\bar{x} = 9.94) \simeq P\left(\frac{9.9396875 - 10.1}{0.025} \leq z \leq \frac{9.9403125 - 10.1}{0.025}\right)$$

$$= P(-6.4125 \leq z \leq -6.3875)$$

$$\simeq 0 .$$

We record:

$$P(\bar{x} = 9.94|A) = 0 .$$

With these three conditional probabilities for $\bar{x} = 9.94$, we have all the information we need to calculate the revised probabilities that the process is in each of the three states. These calculations are to be performed according to equations (3), but it will be useful to construct a table for the calculations.

Table 10–4 summarizes the calculations required. The first and second columns of the table represent the prior probability distribution for the states of the process. The third column records the three conditional probabilities which were calculated above. As its heading indicates, the fourth column contains the products of the entries in the second and third columns. For the first row of the table, therefore, the fourth column contains $P(B)P(\bar{x} = 9.94|B)$. Looking back to equation (3,a), we note that this entry is just the numerator of that equation. In the same way, the second entry of column four in Table 10–4 is the numerator of equation (3,b); and the third entry is the numerator of equation (3,c).

---

[10] Our table for the normal distribution contains values of z only to the nearest hundredth. The probability stated above is based on interpolation between values appearing in the table.

Table 10–4

State	$P(State)$	$P(\bar{x} = 9.94 \mid State)$	$P(State)P(\bar{x} = 9.94 \mid State)$	$P(State \mid \bar{x} = 9.94)$
B	0.35	0.002725	0.00095375	0.7841726
C	.50	.000525	.00026250	.2158274
A	.15	0	0	0
	1.00		0.00121625	1.0000000

It follows, too, that the sum of the entries of column four is the denominator of the equations (3).

Now, we note that equations (3) indicate that the probabilities of the three states, for a given value of $\bar{x}$, can be found by dividing each entry of column four by the total for that column. This is done, and the results are the entries of column five. Thus, the first entry of column five is found as $0.00095375/0.00121625 = 0.7841726$, and is the value of $P(B \mid \bar{x} = 9.94)$. The entries of the fifth column of Table 10–4, then, are the revised probabilities which we required. Note that, with the value of $\bar{x} = 9.94$ as low as it is, this tends to discredit the possibility that the process is in state A, $P(A \mid \bar{x} = 9.94) = 0$, and gives much more weight to the possibility that the process is in state B, $P(B \mid \bar{x} = 9.94) = 0.78$.

Problem Set 10–8

1. Suppose that a sample of size $n = 16$ were to yield a value of $\bar{x} = 9.95$. Determine the revised probabilities, $P(B \mid \bar{x} = 9.95)$, $P(C \mid \bar{x} = 9.95)$, and $P(A \mid \bar{x} = 9.95)$.

Determining the best decision, given the revised probabilities

Having determined the revised probabilities for the three states, we now evaluate the expected costs of the two actions, "adjust" and "do not adjust." For the action "adjust the process," expected cost is still:

$$C_a = (\$2,484.80)(0.7841726) + (\$2,484.80)(0.2158274)$$
$$+ (\$2,484.80)(0) = \$2,484.80$$

The expected cost for the action "do not adjust" is

$$C_d = (\$2,964.70)(0.7841726) + (\$2,284.80)(0.2158274)$$
$$+ (\$2,381.20)(0) \simeq \$2,817.96$$

On the basis of the revised probabilities associated with a sample mean of $\bar{x} = 9.94$, we should adjust the process. The expected cost of adjusting the process is much below that for not adjusting the process.

We had found earlier, on the basis of prior information only, that we ought to adjust the process initially before each production run. We have just learned that, on the basis of a mean of $\bar{x} = 9.94$ for a sample of 16 balls taken from the process stream, again we ought to adjust the process. Did the sample result make no difference? To answer that, compare the expected costs of the two actions in the two different circumstances. In the case of no sample, the expected savings from adjusting the process were $C_d - C_a = \$2,537.22 - \$2,484.80 = \$52.42$. This is a substantial difference, that makes adjusting the process worthwhile. Now compare the difference in the case of the sample result: $\$2,817.96 - \$2,484.80 = \$333.16$. With a mean of $\bar{x} = 9.94$ in hand, the difference in expected costs of the two actions is even greater. Adjustment is more imperative.

The reason for the greater difference in expected costs in the second case is not hard to find. Remember that the sample result gave a much greater weight to state B than to the other states. If we also recall that state B is the state with which the greatest costs are associated, it is easy to see that a high probability of being in state B will lead to a correspondingly imperative need to adjust the process.

A comparison of the two situations indicates that the information contained in a sample can lead to different evaluations of the two actions. If this is the case, there may be some interval of values for the sample mean in which the comparison would lead us to adjust and another interval for which the sample mean would lead us not to adjust the process. Between these two intervals, there should be some value for the sample mean at which we would be indifferent between the two actions. That is, there should be some value of $\bar{x}$ for which the expected cost of adjusting the process will be equal to the expected cost of not adjusting the process. If we can locate this value for $\bar{x}$, it would be the critical value, in the sense we have used the term in testing hypotheses. That is, a sample mean on one side of this critical value would lead us to adjust the process, and a sample mean on the other side would lead us to leave the process alone.

Just as in the test of a hypothesis, too, we must recognize the possibility that there will be two critical values, one critical value of $\bar{x}$ that is too small, and another critical value that is too large. We shall have to consider the two tails of the distribution, in other words. But now we intend to find these critical values, if they exist, by comparing the expected costs of the two actions, given the revised probabilities associated with different values for $\bar{x}$.

Problem Set 10–9

1. In problem 1 of Problem Set 10–8, you determined the revised probabilities of the three process states given $\bar{x} = 9.95$. On the basis of these probabilities, should the process be adjusted or not? Why?
2. Explain the difference in the value of C_d which you calculated in problem 1 and the value of C_d calculated in the preceding section of the text.

Determination of the critical values of the sample mean

Let us concentrate, first, on the lower critical value of $\bar{x}$. We have already found that if $\bar{x} = 9.94$, the action of adjusting the process is much the better alternative. For larger values of $\bar{x}$, closer to the target value of 10.0, there should be a point at which the preferable action would switch from one of adjusting the process to one of not adjusting. If we could find a value for $\bar{x}$ somewhat larger than 9.94, but one for which the preferable action is not to adjust, we would know that the point of indifference lies somewhere between 9.94 and that value. Then, we could interpolate to an approximate value for the point of indifference. This is the plan of action which is illustrated below.

It turns out that if $\bar{x} = 9.96$, the better alternative is not to adjust the process. We show this in the same manner as we analyzed the case for $\bar{x} = 9.94$.

For $\bar{x} = 9.96$, the interval of concern has bounds of:

$$9.96 - \frac{0.000625}{2} \quad \text{and} \quad 9.96 + \frac{0.000625}{2}$$

or

$$9.9596875 \quad \text{and} \quad 9.9603125 \, .$$

We then have the following probabilities for $\bar{x}$ falling in this interval, corresponding to the three states:

$$
\begin{aligned}
P(\bar{x} = 9.96 | B) &\simeq P(9.9596875 \leq \bar{x} \leq 9.9603125) \\
&= P\left(\frac{9.9596875 - 9.9}{0.025} \leq z \leq \frac{9.9603125 - 9.9}{0.025} \right) \\
&= P(2.3875 \leq z \leq 2.4125) \\
&\simeq 0.0005 \, ; \\
P(\bar{x} = 9.96 | C) &\simeq P\left(\frac{9.9596875 - 10.0}{0.025} \leq z \leq \frac{9.9603125 - 10.0}{0.025} \right) \\
&= P(-1.6125 \leq z \leq -1.5875) \\
&\simeq 0.00275 \, ; \\
P(\bar{x} = 9.96 | A) &\simeq P\left(\frac{9.9596875 - 10.1}{0.025} \leq z \leq \frac{9.9603125 - 10.1}{0.025} \right) \\
&= P(-5.6125 \leq z \leq -5.5875 \\
&= 0 \, .
\end{aligned}
$$

These probabilities are placed in Table 10–5, and the revised probabilities of the three states are calculated in the same manner as in Table 10–4.

With the revised probabilities appearing in the fifth column of Table 10–5, we can calculate the expected cost of adjusting the process and of not adjusting it. For adjusting the process, the cost once again is:

Table 10–5

State	P(State)	$P(\bar{x} = 9.96\|State)$	$P(State)P(\bar{x} = 9.96\|State)$	$P(State\|\bar{x} = 9.96)$
B	0.35	0.00050	0.000175	0.11290
C	.50	.00275	.001375	.88710
A	.15	0	0	0
	1.00		0.001550	1.00000

$$C_a = (\$2,484.80)(0.11290) + (\$2,484.80)(0.88710)$$
$$+ (\$2,484.80)(0) = \$2,484.80 .$$

The expected cost if we do not adjust is:

$$C_d = (\$2,964.70)(0.11290) + (\$2,284.80)(0.88710)$$
$$+ (\$2,381.20)(0) \simeq \$2,361.56 .$$

Since the expected cost of adjusting is greater than the expected cost of not adjusting the process, we should not adjust.

We have located two values of $\bar{x}$, one corresponding to a situation in which it is preferable to adjust the process, and the other corresponding to a situation in which it is preferable not to adjust the process. The relevant information for these two values of $\bar{x}$ are summarized in Table 10–6 and Figure 10–4.

Table 10–6

	$\bar{x} = 9.94$	$\bar{x} = 9.96$
C_a	$2,484.80	$2,484.80
C_d	$2,817.96	$2,361.56

The two graphs appearing in Figure 10–4 are linear approximations of the paths that expected costs of the two actions follow in the interval for $\bar{x}$ between 9.94 and 9.96. The line labeled *aa* indicates the path of expected costs arising from adjusting the process. The line labeled *dd* indicates the path of expected costs if we do not adjust the process. The intersection of these two lines is the approximate point at which expected costs of the two actions should be equal. At this point, we should be indifferent between the actions of adjusting or not adjusting the process. For values of $\bar{x}$ to the left of this point, it will pay us to adjust the process, since the expected cost of that action is below the expected cost of not adjusting. For values of $\bar{x}$ to the right of this point (but not so far to the right as to fall in the upper critical region), it will pay us not to adjust the process, since expected cost of this action is below that of adjusting.

Figure 10–4

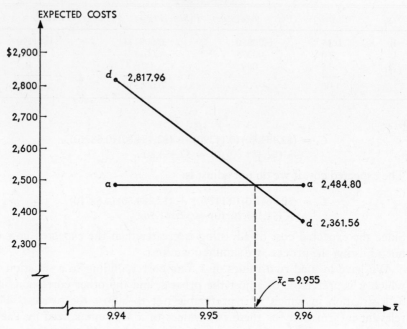

The point on the axis for $\bar{x}$, represented by the symbol $\bar{x}_c$, should, in the light of the comments above, be a good approximation to the lower critical value of $\bar{x}$. In order to find this point, we must specify the equation for C_a, represented by the line aa, and the equation for C_d, represented by the line dd. A solution of these two equations will yield the value of $\bar{x}_c$.

We can express the equation for C_d, using the value of 9.94 as the origin on the axis of $\bar{x}$ and denoting the slope of the line as b_d, as:

$$C_d = \$2{,}817.96 + b_d(\bar{x} - 9.94) .$$

Since the expected cost of adjusting does not vary with the value of $\bar{x}$, the equation for C_a is simply: $C_a = \$2{,}484.80$. We need the value of the slope of the equation for C_d before we can solve for the value of $\bar{x}_c$. The slope of a straight line is the ratio of the vertical change to the horizontal change between any two points on the line. Using the points corresponding to values for $\bar{x}$ of 9.94 and 9.96, we find that:

$$b_d = \frac{2{,}361.56 - 2{,}817.96}{9.96 - 9.94} = -22{,}820 .$$

Substitution of this value in the equation of C_d, and simplifying, leads to:

$$C_d = 229{,}648.76 - 22{,}820(\bar{x}) .$$

Setting this equation equal to $C_a = 2{,}484.80$ and solving for $\bar{x}$ yields the critical value $\bar{x}_c = 9.955$.

Our analysis indicates that if the sample of 16 balls has a mean diameter below 9.955 millimeters, we should adjust the process before continuing the production run. If the mean diameter is above 9.955 millimeters, the production run should be continued without the interruption of the adjustment procedure.

The critical value of $\bar{x}_c$ determined above is just the lower critical value of $\bar{x}$. We still must consider what actions should be taken if the value of $\bar{x}$ should be large; that is, larger than 10.0 millimeters. The analysis will proceed in the same manner as before. To illustrate, suppose we consider a value of $\bar{x} = 10.04$ and ask whether we should adjust or not adjust the process. Leaving detailed comment aside, we calculate the required probabilities:

$$P(\bar{x} = 10.04|B) \simeq P\left(\frac{10.0396875 - 9.9}{0.025} \leq z \leq \frac{10.0403125 - 9.9}{0.025}\right)$$
$$= P(5.5875 \leq z \leq 5.6125) \simeq 0\,;$$

$$P(\bar{x} = 10.04|C) \simeq P\left(\frac{10.0396875 - 10.0}{0.025} \leq z \leq \frac{10.0403125 - 10.0}{0.025}\right)$$
$$= P(1.5875 \leq z \leq 1.6125) \simeq 0.00275\,;$$

$$P(\bar{x} = 10.04|A) \simeq P\left(\frac{10.0396875 - 10.1}{0.025} \leq z \leq \frac{10.0403125 - 10.1}{0.025}\right)$$
$$= P(-2.4125 \leq z \leq -2.3875) \simeq 0.0005\,.$$

We place these values in Table 10–7 and find the revised probabilities of the three states.

Table 10–7

State	P(State)	$P(\bar{x} = 10.04|State)$	$P(State)P(\bar{x} = 10.04|State)$	$P(State|\bar{x} = 10.04)$
B	0.35	0	0	0
C	.50	0.00275	0.001375	0.94828
A	.15	.00050	.000075	.05172
	1.00		0.001450	1.00000

With the revised probabilities in the fifth column of Table 10–7, we calculate the expected costs of the two actions:

$$C_a = (\$2{,}484.80)(0) + (\$2{,}484.80)(0.94828) + (\$2{,}484.80)(0.05172)$$
$$= \$2{,}484.80$$
$$C_d = (\$2{,}964.70)(0) + (\$2{,}284.80)(0.94828) + (\$2{,}381.20)(0.05172)$$
$$\simeq \$2{,}289.79\,.$$

If $\bar{x} = 10.04$, the better action is not to adjust the process.

A bit of reflection makes it clear, moreover, that there is not a value of $\bar{x}$ large enough to lead us to the action of adjusting the process. Let us see why this is so. Notice, first, that as we consider successively larger values of $\bar{x}$, their influence on the revised probabilities for the three states will be to reduce the probabilities of states B and C and to increase the probability of state A. At the limit, the values of $P(B|\bar{x})$ and $P(C|\bar{x})$ approach zero as $\bar{x}$ increases. At the same time, $P(A|\bar{x})$ approaches 1.0.

Now suppose that we used these limiting values in the equations for C_a and C_d. We would have:

$$C_a = (\$2,484.80)(0) + (\$2,484.80)(0) + (\$2,484.80)(1.0)$$
$$= \$2,484.80 ;$$
$$C_d = (\$2,964.70)(0) + (\$2,284.80)(0) + (\$2,381.20)(1.0)$$
$$= \$2,381.20 .$$

Even at the limit, the action of not adjusting the process is expected to be less expensive than the action of adjusting the process. In other words, in the upper region for values of the sample mean, there is no critical value. We should stop the process and adjust it only if the sample mean is less than the lower critical value established earlier. Large values of $\bar{x}$ should not lead us to undertake the expense of adjustment. The possible savings from this procedure will not compensate us for the costs when the process is in state A.

The Bayesian analysis of the testing procedure has led us to decide on a one-tail test of the hypothesis that the process is in control, in state C. We will reject that hypothesis only if the mean of a sample of 16 balls has a value less than 9.955 millimeters. Otherwise, we shall allow the process to continue throughout the run, without adjustment.

Problem Set 10–10

1. Using the values for C_a and C_d associated with a value of $\bar{x} = 9.95$ (see problem 1 of Problem Set 10–9) and the values of C_a and C_d associated with $\bar{x} = 9.96$ (see text), determine the critical value of $\bar{x}$ as in the preceding section.

2. Formulate the decision rule, relative to the testing procedure, that is implied by the critical value of $\bar{x}$ which you calculated in problem 1. Which decision rule do you suppose would be better, the rule indicated in the text based on the analysis there, or the rule which you have just stated? Why?

Determining the value of the testing procedure

We have yet to determine the value to us of a testing procedure based on this one-tail test. It will be recalled that we found that we could expect a minimum cost of approximately $2,392.70, with a two-tail test, if this test was performed with a significance level of $\alpha = 0.04$. Now, let us find the cost to expect under the new procedure. First, we find the value of α to which the critical value, $\bar{x} = 9.955$, corresponds. In the null hypothesis of process control, the value of z associated with the critical value will be $z = (9.955 - 10.0)/0.025 = -1.80$. The value of α is the probability that z will take a value smaller than this; $\alpha = P(z < -1.80) = 0.0359$. Since the significance level in the two-tail test was larger, this indicates that we would have been too quick to reject the hypothesis of control in that test.

We can now evaluate the expected cost of the one-tail test in the same manner that we evaluated the expected cost of the two-tail test earlier. To do this, we need the values of $P(1), \ldots, P(6)$, as before. With $\bar{x} = 9.955$, these are:

$$P(1) = P(B)P(\text{reject}|B) = (0.35)P\left(z < \frac{9.955 - 9.9}{0.025}\right)$$
$$= (0.35)P(z < 2.20) = (0.35)(0.9861)$$
$$= 0.345135 \; ;$$

$$P(2) = P(C)P(\text{reject}|C) = (0.50)P\left(z < \frac{9.955 - 10.0}{0.025}\right)$$
$$= (0.50)P(z < -1.80) = (0.50)(0.0359)$$
$$= 0.01795 \; ;$$

$$P(3) = P(A)P(\text{reject}|A) = (0.15)P\left(z < \frac{9.955 - 10.1}{0.025}\right)$$
$$= (0.15)P(z < -5.80) = (0.15)(0)$$
$$= 0 \; ;$$

$$P(4) = P(B)P(\text{accept}|B) = (0.35)P(z > 2.20) = (0.35)(0.0139)$$
$$= 0.004865 \; ;$$

$$P(5) = P(C)P(\text{accept}|C) = (0.50)P(z > -1.80) = (0.50)(0.9641)$$
$$= 0.48205 \; ;$$

$$P(6) = P(A)P(\text{accept}|A) = (0.15)P(z > -5.80) = (0.15)(1.0)$$
$$= 0.15 \; .$$

With these values, we find the expected cost of the testing procedure to be:

$$C = (\$2,484.80)(0.345135) + (\$2,484.80)(0.01795) + (\$2,484.80)(0)$$
$$+ (\$2,964.70)(0.004865) + (\$2,284.80)(0.48205) + (\$2,381.20)(0.15)$$
$$\simeq \$2,375.18 \; .$$

This cost is somewhat lower than that of the two-tail test procedure, which was $2,392.70 (see Table 10–2).

With the expected costs associated with the testing procedures available to us, we can now determine the value of the testing procedures. Consider first the two-tail test procedure developed in a previous section.

We have noted that the expected cost of the two-tail test procedure is $2,392.70. In order to determine the value of the test procedure, we compare this cost figure with a cost to be expected if no test procedure were instituted.

Remember that in the analysis of Table 10–3, we found that the better action was to adjust the process each time if we must act on the basis of prior information alone. We came to this conclusion by noting that the expected cost of not adjusting the process, $2,537.22, is larger than the expected costs of adjusting the process each time, which was $2,484.80. We could thus expect the cost per run under a policy in which no test of the state of the process is made to be $2,484.80. If we were to institute the two-tail test procedure, however, we have noted that the expected cost would be $2,392.70. The difference in the costs associated with these two policies evidently represents the value to us of the test procedure. That is to say, the two-tail test procedure would have a value to us of $2,484.80 − $2,392.70 = $92.10 per run.

In the same manner, we can find the value of the one-tail test procedure developed in the preceding section. With this test procedure we have found that the expected cost per run is only $2,375.18. It follows that the value to us of the one-tail test procedure would be $2,484.80 − $2,375.18 = $109.62 per run. This amount is the value to us of the additional information that we get from the sampling plan used with the test procedure.

This completes the discussion of decision theory and of Bayesian analysis. There are many more points of importance in these topics that we are forced to neglect here. Much emphasis was placed on the production example as a vehicle for developing the concepts. It should go without saying that the concepts and techniques explained in that context have wide application to other areas of business operation.

Problem Set 10–11

1. Determine the value of α implied by the critical value for $\bar{x}$ which you calculated in problem 1 of Problem Set 10–10.
2. What is the expected (additional) costs associated with the one-tail testing procedure using samples of size $n = 16$ and α equal to the value you determined in problem 1 above?
3. What is the value of the sampling plan indicated in problem 2? Is it better than the plan discussed in the text?

Appendix A

It was noted in the text that several factors would have an important effect on the expected costs of production of the ball-socket assemblies. In the interest of simplification, however, only the value of α was considered there. In this appendix, we give some consideration to another factor, the value of $m(X_s)$, in order to achieve some additional insight into the total problem.

It will be recalled that the value of $m(X_s)$ entered the analysis of the chapter at the early stage when the appropriate target value of $m(X_b)$ was selected. We found the expected (additional) costs associated with $m(X_b) = 9.9$, 10.0, and 10.1, on the assumption that $m(X_s)$ was stable at a value of 10.1. These cost figures then became the entries of Table 10–1, which depicted the six possible circumstances that could arise in the use of a testing procedure to determine if the ball-producing process should be adjusted or not. Needless to say, these cost figures played an influential role in the final determination of the testing procedure to be used and the expected cost of that procedure.

We found that for $m(X_s) = 10.1$ the target level of $m(X_b)$ should be $m(X_b) = 10.0$, since the value of $C_C = \$2.2848$ was smaller than either $C_B = \$2.9647$ or $C_A = \$2.3812$. We now wish to see what influence varying $m(X_s)$ will have on these costs. Looking at the target state, C, we have, when $m(X_s) = 10.1$,

$$C_C = \$3(0.3264) + \$0(0.3472) + \$4(0.3264) = \$2.2848 .$$

It will be recalled that the probability of 0.3264 associated with the figure of \$3 in this equation is the probability of reworking a ball-socket assembly. The probability of 0.3264 associated with the figure of \$4 is, of course, the probability of scrapping an assembly. It is obvious from an examination of the equation that, if we could manipulate $m(X_s)$ so that the probability of scrapping was reduced and the probability of reworking was increased, a reduction of C_C could be achieved.

One difficulty in the scheme of lowering $P(\text{scrap})$ to increase $P(\text{rework})$ is that, because of the nonlinear nature of the normal distribution, continued lowering of $P(\text{scrap})$ will be accomplished only at the expense of increasing increases in $P(\text{rework})$. The question becomes, then, how far can $m(X_s)$ be shifted from the value of 10.1 before the reduction in expected scrapping costs is more than compensated by the increase in expected reworking cost?

The answer to this question can be given by setting up an equation relating the change in expected cost arising from an increase in $P(\text{rework})$ to the change in expected cost arising from a reduction of $P(\text{scrap})$. Letting $\Delta P(\text{rework})$ denote a change in $P(\text{rework})$ and $\Delta P(\text{scrap})$ denote a change in $P(\text{scrap})$, we wish a positive value for the former, $\Delta P(\text{rework}) > 0$, and a negative value for the latter, $\Delta P(\text{scrap}) < 0$.

Now, since we want to decrease the value of C_C, we will shift $m(X_s)$ downward, thereby increasing $P(\text{rework})$ and reducing $P(\text{scrap})$, as long as

$$\$3(\Delta P(\text{rework})) < -\$4(\Delta P(\text{scrap})) \,.$$

If this condition is met, we reduce expected costs due to scrapping at a faster rate than we increase expected costs due to reworking, thus reducing, on balance, the value of C_C. When we come to the point where

$$\$3(\Delta P(\text{rework})) = -\$4(\Delta P(\text{scrap})) \,,$$

we have reached the "break-even" point. Any further shifting of $m(X_s)$ will increase C_C. Thus, the condition for minimizing C_C is to shift $m(X_s)$ to the point where

$$\$3(\Delta P(\text{rework})) = -\$4(\Delta P(\text{scrap})) \,,$$

or,

$$\Delta P(\text{rework}) = -(4/3)\Delta P(\text{scrap}) \,.$$

The last expression tells us that we should increase $P(\text{rework})$ by lowering $m(X_s)$ until the point is reached where the increase in $P(\text{rework})$ due to the last shift in $m(X_s)$ equals one and one third times the

Figure 10–5

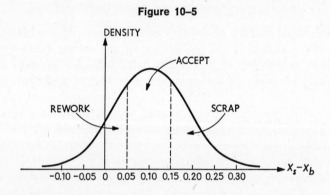

decrease in $P(\text{scrap})$. We can find this point by using Table C for the probability distribution of z. Let us see how this can be done.

We recall that, with $m(X_s) = 10.1$ and $m(X_b) = 10.0$, the distribution of the random variable $(X_s - X_b)$ is centered at a mean value of $m(X_s - X_b) = 0.1$. Figure 10–1(b) of the text is redrawn here as Figure 10–5 to remind the student of the situation.

It happens that in the situation depicted the value $m(X_s - X_b)$ falls exactly in the center of the interval representing acceptable values of $(X_s - X_b)$, 0.05 to 0.15. The value of the standardized normal variate associated with the lower limit of this interval is $z = (0.05 - 0.1)/0.1118 \cong -0.45$. This leads to $P(\text{rework}) = P(z < -0.45) = 0.3264$. By symmetry, $P(\text{scrap}) = P(z > +0.45) = 0.3264$, also.

Note, now, what will happen as we reduce $m(X_s)$. This will lead to a corresponding reduction in $m(X_s - X_b)$. Graphically, the curve of Figure 10–5 will shift to the left, with $m(X_s - X_b)$ approaching the lower limit of 0.05 in the interval of acceptable values for $(X_s - X_b)$. At the same time, the distance between the upper limit of the acceptable interval and $m(X_s - X_b)$ would increase by the same amount that the distance on the left has decreased. This, in turn, will increase $P(\text{rework})$ and decrease $P(\text{scrap})$. It is evident from examination of the curve, however, that $P(\text{rework})$ will increase at a faster rate than $P(\text{scrap})$ will decrease, as the shift to the left is continued. Moreover, the *rate of*

Table 10–A–1

	Left Tail			Right Tail	
z	$P(rework)$	$\Delta P(rework)$	z	$P(scrap)$	$\Delta P(scrap)$
−0.45	0.3264		0.45	0.3264	
−0.44	0.3300	+0.0036	0.46	0.3228	−0.0036
.	.		.	.	
.	.		.	.	
.	.		.	.	
−0.35	0.3632		0.55	0.2912	
−0.34	0.3669	+0.0037	0.56	0.2877	−0.0035
.	.		.	.	
.	.		.	.	
−0.25	0.4013		0.65	0.2578	
−0.24	0.4052	+0.0039	0.66	0.2546	−0.0032
.	.		.	.	
.	.		.	.	
−0.15	0.4404		0.75	0.2266	
−0.14	0.4443	+0.0039	0.76	0.2236	−0.0030
−0.13	0.4483	+0.0040	0.77	0.2206	−0.0030

increase in $P(\text{rework})$ will, itself, increase as the *rate of decrease* in $P(\text{scrap})$ will fall. We must keep track of these changes in probabilities, in order to find the point where $\Delta P(\text{rework}) = -(4/3)\Delta P(\text{scrap})$.

Table 10–A–1 is constructed in a manner to allow us to keep track of these changes. The table has two general sections. The section on the left records successive values of z for the left tail as we shift the distribution of $(X_s - X_b)$ to the left toward the lower limit of 0.05. It also has a column indicating the value of $P(\text{rework})$ corresponding to each successive value of z. Finally, a third column records the change in $P(\text{rework})$ which occurs between successive values of z. The right section of the table includes three columns, also, which record the same information relative to the right tail of the distribution of $(X_s - X_b)$.

Let us look at the first row of Table 10–A–1. This row describes the situation as depicted in Figure 10–5. For the left tail, $z = -0.45$ and $P(\text{rework}) = 0.3264$. There is no entry in the third column, since we have not yet shifted the curve. The entries of the first row in the right section pertain to the right tail of the distribution.

If we examine the second row of the table, we find that the value of z for the left tail has been changed to $z = -0.44$, reflecting a shift to the left of the curve. At the same time, the value of z in the right tail has been increased to $z = 0.46$ to reflect this shift. The entries in the second columns of each section have been changed accordingly, to give the new values of $P(\text{rework})$ and $P(\text{scrap})$ following this shift. Finally, the third columns record the fact that the change in $P(\text{rework})$ resulting from this shift has been an increase of 0.0036, while $P(\text{scrap})$ has decreased by 0.0036. Since we wish to continue shifting the curve until the increase in $P(\text{rework})$ is one and one third the decrease in $P(\text{scrap})$, it is evident that a much greater shift is required.

The next two rows which appear in Table 10–A–1 are those representing the situation if we had already shifted to the left to the point where z for the left tail is $z = -0.35$ and for the right tail is $z = 0.55$. Considering a shift of one more step to the left from this point, we find that $P(\text{rework})$ will increase by 0.0037 and $P(\text{scrap})$ will decrease by 0.0035. We still have not reached the point where $\Delta P(\text{rework}) = -(4/3)\Delta P(\text{scrap})$.

The next two rows included in the table indicate a value of $\Delta P(\text{rework}) = +0.0039$ associated with a change of z in the left tail from -0.25 to -0.24. This value is not one and one third the decrease of 0.0032 in $P(\text{scrap})$, so we continue the leftward shift. At that point where $z = -0.15$ for the left tail and $z = +0.75$ for the right tail, we find that the condition we seek is nearly achieved. A shift to $z = -0.14$ and $z = +0.76$ leads to $\Delta P(\text{rework}) = +0.0039$ and $\Delta P(\text{scrap}) = -0.0030$. These values nearly satisfy the condition

$$\Delta P(\text{rework}) = -(4/3)\Delta P(\text{scrap}) .$$

Shifting one more step to the left, to $z = -0.13$ and $z = +0.77$, yields $\Delta P(\text{rework}) = +0.0040$ and $\Delta P(\text{scrap}) = -0.0030$. At this point the condition is satisfied:

$$\Delta P(\text{rework}) = -(4/3)\Delta P(\text{scrap}) ,$$
$$+0.0040 = -(4/3)(-0.0030) ,$$
$$+0.0040 = +0.0040 .$$

We have found that in order to minimize the value of C_0, we must shift $m(X_s)$ to the point where z for the left tail of the distribution of $(X_s - X_b)$, beyond the lower limit of acceptable values of $(X_s - X_b)$, has a value of $z = -0.13$. The corresponding value of z for the upper limit of acceptable values is $z = +0.77$.

We now find this minimizing value of $m(X_s)$ by solution of an appropriate equation. The value of $z = +0.77$ indicated above is the distance of the upper limit of acceptable values for $(X_s - X_b)$, 0.15, from the shifted value of $m(X_s - X_b)$, in standard units. That is,

$$z = \frac{0.15 - m(X_s - X_b)}{0.1118} = +0.77 .$$

Solution of this equation yields

$$m(X_s - X_b) \simeq +0.064 .$$

Since we are considering state C, where $X_b = 10.0$, this leads to the required value of

$$m(X_s) = 10.064 .$$

Our analysis indicates that the value of C_C will be minimized if we set the socket-producing process so as to produce sockets with a mean diameter of $m(X_s) = 10.064$. We now wish to determine the expected (additional) costs associated with each of the three states of the ball-producing process, given that $m(X_s) = 10.064$. We accomplish this in the same manner as in Chapter 10. With $m(X_s) = 10.064$, the values of $m(X_s - X_b)$ are as given in the table below:

Process State	$m(X_b)$	$m(X_s - X_b)$ $= m(X_s) - m(X_b)$
B	9.9	0.164
C	10.0	0.064
A	10.1	−0.036

For each of the three possible situations, we need the probability that an assembly must be reworked, $P(\text{rework})$; the probability that an assembly will be acceptable, $P(\text{accept})$; and the probability that an assembly will be scrapped, $P(\text{scrap})$. For state B:

$$P(\text{rework}) = P\left(z < \frac{0.05 - 0.164}{0.1118}\right) \simeq P(z < -1.02) = 0.1539 ;$$

$$P(\text{accept}) = P\left(\frac{0.05 - 0.164}{0.1118} \leq z \leq \frac{0.15 - 0.164}{0.1118}\right)$$
$$\simeq P(-1.02 \leq z \leq -0.13) = 0.2944 ;$$

$$P(\text{scrap}) = P\left(z > \frac{0.15 - 0.164}{0.1118}\right) \simeq P(z > -0.13) = 0.5517 .$$

For state C:

$$P(\text{rework}) = P\left(z < \frac{0.05 - 0.064}{0.1118}\right) \simeq P(z < -0.13) = 0.4483 \ ;$$

$$P(\text{accept}) = P\left(\frac{0.05 - 0.064}{0.1118} \leq z \leq \frac{0.15 - 0.064}{0.1118}\right)$$
$$\simeq P(-0.13 \leq z \leq +0.77) = 0.3311 \ ;$$

$$P(\text{scrap}) = P\left(z > \frac{0.15 - 0.064}{0.1118}\right) \simeq P(z > +0.77) = 0.2206 \ .$$

For state A:

$$P(\text{rework}) = P\left(z < \frac{0.05 - [-0.036]}{0.1118}\right) \simeq P(z < +0.77) = 0.7794 \ ;$$

$$P(\text{accept}) = P\left(\frac{0.05 - [-0.036]}{0.1118} \leq z \leq \frac{0.15 - [-0.036]}{0.1118}\right)$$
$$\simeq P(+0.77 \leq z \leq +1.66) = 0.1721 \ ;$$

$$P(\text{scrap}) = P\left(z > \frac{0.15 - [-0.036]}{0.1118}\right) \simeq P(z > 1.66) = 0.0485 \ .$$

We now calculate the expected cost for each of the three states:

$$C_B = \$3(0.1539) + \$0(0.2944) + \$4(0.5517) \simeq \$2.6685 \ ;$$
$$C_C = \$3(0.4483) + \$0(0.3311) + \$4(0.2206) \simeq \$2.2273 \ ;$$
$$C_A = \$3(0.7794) + \$0(0.1721) + \$4(0.0485) \simeq \$2.5322 \ .$$

These costs are considerably below those we determined in the text for $m(X_s) = 10.1$: $C_B = \$2.9647$, $C_C = \$2.2848$, and $C_A = \$2.3812$. It is evident that shifting the value of $m(X_s)$ will lead to substantial savings.

In order to get some idea of these savings, we now evaluate the testing procedure outlined at the close of Chapter 10: $n = 16$, $a = 0.0359$, one-tail test. The conditional costs associated with the six possible circumstances are now as they appear in the table below.

	Real Situation		
Decision	B	C	A
Reject	(1) $2,427.30	(2) $2,427.30	(3) $2,427.30
Accept	(4) $2,668.50	(5) $2,227.30	(6) $2,532.20

The values of $P(1), P(2), \ldots, P(6)$ are those developed in the last section of Chapter 10, that is:

$$P(1) = 0.345135 \,,$$
$$P(2) = 0.01795 \,,$$
$$P(3) = 0 \,,$$
$$P(4) = 0.004865 \,,$$
$$P(5) = 0.48205 \,,$$
$$P(6) = 0.15 \,.$$

With the new conditional costs and the probabilities associated with these costs, we find that the expected (additional) cost is:

$$C = \$2,427.30(0.345135) + \$2,427.30(0.01795)$$
$$+ \$2,427.30(0) + \$2,668.50(0.004865)$$
$$+ \$2,227.30(0.48205) + \$2,532.20(0.15)$$
$$\simeq \$2,347.80 \,.$$

The cost figure just calculated is considerably below the value of $2,375.18 associated with a value of $m(X_s) = 10.1$, as developed in the text. As we supposed earlier, therefore, the setting of the socket-producing process is a highly important factor in the total decision problem.

Looking back, now, at the conditional costs for the six circumstances, given a value of $m(X_s) = 10.064$, we notice that a two-tail test is called for in this situation. This is the case because, in both state B and state A, the costs of accepting the hypothesis of control are greater than the costs of rejecting the hypothesis. Evidently, then, the cost figure of $2,347.80 can be further improved! We leave the problem at this point, however. Suitable use of the techniques already illustrated could lead to such an improvement.

Statistical
analysis and
the computer

Introduction

This appendix is devoted to introducing the student to the digital computer as a tool for statistical analysis. The introduction must necessarily be a slight one. However, the appendix should provide the student with enough understanding of computer programming to enable him to do simple programming on his own. Certainly, it is intended to provide an initial taste of programming that should serve to overcome an awe-inspired reluctance on the part of many students even to consider using a computer to solve problems. Hopefully, many students will be encouraged to learn more about the computer, either by enrolling in a course devoted wholly to the subject or by self-instruction with the help of one of many good books now available on the subject.

What is a program?

A useful definition of a computer program is that it is a series of instructions telling the computer:

1. What operations to perform.
2. On what type of data these operations are to be performed.
3. From what input device (card reader, magnetic tape, paper tape, typewriter) this data is to become accessible to the computer.
4. Which results of the operations performed on the data are to be made available as output.
5. In what form to make these results available.

Some embellishment of this definition would include more precise detail in how operations are accomplished, and so forth, but such embellishment would add little to the definition. In our later discussion, much of this detail will be provided.

A program is a series of instructions. An important question is, What form must these instructions take? It is important for the student to realize at the outset that a digital computer is capable of processing instructions only if they are in numeric form. The language of the computer is a language of numbers. In "the good old days" this meant that any one who wished to communicate with a computer was required to learn the numeric language that the particular computer used. With a rapidly rising computer technology, this is no longer true. Means have been developed whereby the programmer is able to write out his program of instructions in a language very nearly like his own. This program in his language must then be translated into a program in the numeric language of the computer. The process of translation is accomplished by a specially written program, made available by the manufacturer of the computer to be used. These special translating programs are called *compilers*.

Several different programming languages are available to the programmer. To mention only two, there are COBOL and FORTRAN. The word COBOL is an acronym composed from the description of the language: COmmon Business Oriented Language. As the description implies, it has been designed chiefly to serve the needs of business, particularly as this relates to the data processing requirements of a business in accounting, billing, and so forth. The word FORTRAN is an acronym composed from the two words, FORmula TRANslation. Its greatest usefulness is in programming analytical problems involving mathematical expressions, or formulas. In statistical analysis, much use is made of mathematical formulas. We therefore direct our attention throughout the appendix to FORTRAN programming.

The FORTRAN language

FORTRAN is described as a problem-oriented language. This means that the series of FORTRAN statements which make up the program will parallel rather closely the actual operations which one would perform with pencil and paper in finding a solution to the problem. This is an important feature because it means that if one can formulate the problem for solution with pencil and paper, then he has gone a long way toward programming the problem. This is especially important for us, because we will use the problems discussed and formulated in several chapters throughout the book as points of departure for discussion of programming. The procedure that we shall follow will be to present a program which accomplishes the task of solving a particular problem discussed in that chapter. Through an ensuing discussion of the program, the student will become aware of various programming techniques. Having been introduced in this manner to several different programs, the student will have learned many of the details of programming by the end of the appendix. One important caution that should be introduced at the outset is that the appendix does not constitute a full course in FORTRAN programming. There will be many very useful and powerful features of FORTRAN that the student will not know.[1] He is urged to become familiar with these features through subsequent study, as suggested earlier.

The format of a FORTRAN program

FORTRAN being a special language, it follows that statements in this language must observe certain elements of form. These elements relate to questions of the meanings of different specified words, the manner in which names can be formed, the meanings of special symbols, and the format which must be observed in writing statements. Our first concern will be with the latter.

The program may be written initially on a FORTRAN program sheet, if one is available, or on an ordinary sheet of paper. In either case, it is helpful to think of spaces on the paper as relating to the columns appearing on the familiar 80-punch card. These cards have 80 columns in which punches corresponding to letters, numbers, and special characters (, % #, etc.) may be placed. All statements in the program must be confined to the first 72 columns of the card and, therefore, of the program sheet. The remaining eight columns may be used for comments, for example, or for serially numbering the cards to preserve their order.

The 72 columns available for the program have varying functions. The first five columns may be used to number the statement which begins with that card. Also, a letter "C" punched in the first column of the card (written on the program sheet) serves to identify the statement on that card as a COMMENT. A COMMENT serves no function in the program itself, but is placed in the program write-up by the writer of the program to indicate some feature of the program he feels it useful for the program user to know.

The sixth column is used to indicate that the statement appearing on the card is a continuation of a statement initiated on a previous card. Some statements may run through several cards, and these cards must

---

[1] As a mattter of fact, some liberties will be taken with the flexibility of the language in order to simplify the presentation. That is, although the statements and procedures used in the programs will be correct, little will be said concerning alternative ways of accomplishing the same thing through varying construction of statements or different procedures.

follow one another in their proper sequence. A continuation card is indicated by punching a number in the sixth column. A useful procedure is to number these continuation cards serially, 1 up to 9. There can be no more than nine continuation cards.

The remaining available columns of the card, 7 through 72, are used to write the statements which constitute the instructions to the computer. The statement appearing on any one card may be shorter than is required to extend to column 72, but any portion of a statement written beyond that column will be lost to the FORTRAN compiler. The computer will, therefore, not be able to process the statement correctly.

Most of these points can be shown with respect to the program which appears in Figure A–1. As the first two statements in the program indi-

Figure A–1

```
C       A PROGRAM TO CALCULATE THE MEAN, VARIANCE, STANDARD DEVIATION, AND
C       COEFFICIENT OF SKEWNESS FOR A DISCRETE PROBABILITY DISTRIBUTION
     1  FORMAT (F4.0, F4.4)
     7  SUMX = 0.0
        SUMX2 = 0.0
        SUMX3 = 0.0
     5  READ 1, X, PX
        IF (PX − 0.9999) 2, 3, 2
     2  SUMX = SUMX + X*PX
        SUMX2 = SUMX2 + (X**2)*PX
        SUMX3 = SUMX3 + (X**3)*PX
        GO TO 5
     3  XMEAN = SUMX
        VARX = SUMX2 − XMEAN**2
        STDEVX = SQRTF(VARX)
        SK1 = SUMX3
        SK2 = (XMEAN*SUMX2)
        SK3 = XMEAN**3
        SKX = (SK1 − 3.0*SK2 + 2.0*SK3)/STDEVX**3
        PRINT 6, XMEAN, VARX, STDEVX, SKX
     6  FORMAT (3F11.4, F9.4)
        PAUSE
        GO TO 7
        END
```

cate, this is a program to calculate certain characteristics of a probability distribution. Notice that the letter "C" appears to the left on each of these two lines, in the position corresponding to column 1. This indicates that the statement is a COMMENT. Following these two lines is the series of statements which constitute the program. Notice, next, that all of these statements begin in the same place, at the position corresponding to column 7. Finally, notice that several of these statements are preceded by a number which appears in a position corresponding to column 5. These numbers serve to identify the accompanying statements so that reference can be made to them within other statements of the program. It is not necessary that the statement numbers be written serially. They may be of any size up to some limit which differs from one type of computer to the next. We shall be content with numbers not over three digits in length. No two statements in the same program may have the same number.

A program written to meet the specifications outlined above will satisfy the format requirements of the FORTRAN compiler. Our next concern is with the form and meaning of the various statements that comprise the program. To proceed to an understanding of these questions, we shall first relate different portions of the program to the steps we should have to take if we were to calculate the required characteristics of a probability distribution with pencil and paper. To that end, Table A–1 is provided in which the required calculations are performed for the

Table A–1

r	$P(r)$	$rP(r)$	$r^2P(r)$	$r^3P(r)$
0	0.24	0.00	0.00	0.00
1	.40	.40	0.40	0.40
2	˙26	.52	1.04	2.08
3	.09	.27	0.81	2.43
4	.01	.04	0.16	0.64
5	.00	.00	0.00	0.00
	1.00	1.23	2.41	5.55

$$\bar{r} = \Sigma r P(r) = 1.23$$
$$\mathrm{var}(r) = \Sigma r^2 P(r) - (\bar{r})^2 = 2.41 - (1.23)^2 = 0.8971$$
$$\sigma = +\sqrt{\mathrm{var}(r)} = +\sqrt{0.8971} \simeq 0.9471$$
$$\mathrm{sk}(r) = \frac{\Sigma r^3 P(r) - 3\bar{r}\Sigma r^2 P(r) + 2(\bar{r})^3}{\sigma^3}$$
$$= \frac{5.55 - 3(1.23)(2.41) + 2(1.23)^3}{(0.9471)^3}$$
$$= +0.4459$$

distribution of r. It repeats Table 3–5. Following that discussion, we shall once again approach a description of the program and what it accomplishes through a flow diagram. Some repetition at this early stage will prove helpful.

Making data available to the computer

Although we would not usually think of it in this way, before we could calculate the values appearing at the bottom of Table A–1, we had to make the data available to ourselves by setting up the probability distribution of r. The computer must also have access to the data in order to perform the calculations required of it by the program. Two statements of the program in Figure A–1 indicate to the computer where it is to find the data, and what form the data will have. These two statements are numbered 1 and 5 in the program. We consider the latter statement first: 5 READ 1, X, PX. This statement tells the computer that the data is to be entered through the card reader (READ indicates that the card reader is to be used). It indicates, further, that the contents of the card which is read are to be interpreted according to the FORMAT statement numbered 1 (this is the function of the digit 1, following READ). Finally, the first set of data on the card (the sets of data are distinguished by the FORMAT statement, as we shall see) is to be stored in a computer *location* which is to be called X, and the second set of data is to be stored in a computer *location* to be called PX.

The interpretation of the word READ and the digit 1 is just a matter of grammar. They should cause the student no trouble. The use of the symbols X and PX is a different matter, however. Notice that the word "location" was italicized in the explanation above. X and PX are *names* which will, for this program, refer to two locations in the computer's storage component in which two values read from a card are to be stored. The programmer need not concern himself with the question of just exactly *where* these values are stored. He contents himself with the knowledge that *somewhere* in the storage component, there are locations reserved for these two values and that he can always refer the computer to them by using their names, X and PX. Note, also, that if he had chosen to call the data by the names Y and PROBY, this would have been all right with the computer. So long as he used the names Y and PROBY later in the program, he would be referring to the proper values. There are some rules regarding the assigning of names which we shall discuss a bit later. At this point we can note that a name must begin with an alphabetic character, must not exceed six characters in length, and may include numeric characters (but no special characters).

The READ statement referred to a FORMAT statement according to which the contents of the card are to be interpreted. We consider that statement now: 1 FORMAT (F4.0, F4.4). The word FORMAT indicates that what follows it in parentheses is a set of specifications which indicate what columns of the card have relevant data, and what form this data is to take. Notice that the specification, F4.0, has the digit 4 appearing to the left of the decimal point. This digit indicates that the specification is for four columns of the card, and since this is the first specification, it will be the first four columns of the card. The number appearing to the left of the decimal point in the second specification is also 4, indicating that this specification is for the second set of four columns, columns 5–8.

Both specifications begin with the letter F. This indicates that the numbers appearing in the corresponding sets of columns are to be treated as *floating-point* numbers. Floating-point numbers are numbers which the computer is to treat as mixed numbers, that is, as possibly having a fractional value. Thus, the number 67.45 should be specified as a floating-point number if we want the computer to keep track of the fractional part of the value. We shall not attempt an explanation of how the computer "keeps track" of the fractional value, but it will do so if we ask it. Supposing that we punched the digits 6745 in the first four columns of a card and we wished the computer to treat this as the value 67.45, we would need a statement, FORMAT (F4.2).

Before considering additional features of floating-point numbers, and other alternative forms of numbers, let us first dispose of the last element in the specifications—the digit appearing to the right of the decimal point. In the FORMAT statement of the program, the first specification has the digit 0, following the decimal point. This indicates that none of the digits in the first four columns of the card are to the right of the decimal point in that number. If the first four columns contained the digits 6745, for example, the specification F4.0 would tell the computer to treat them as the value 6745. If the specification had been F4.2, as suggested in the preceding paragraph, the computer would treat these digits as the value 67.45. Looking, now at the second specification of the FORMAT statement in the program, F4.4 indicates that the four digits in these columns are to be considered as falling to the right of the decimal point. A card with the digits 6745 in the columns 5–8 would be read, according to the FORMAT statement, as if the value in these columns was .6745.

There are other forms in which the data of a problem may be specified. We shall consider only one of these, since it and floating point will serve our needs. This second form of data is called *fixed-point* data. If data is specified as fixed-point data, the computer will treat the digits involved as if they formed an integer, that is, a nonfractional whole number. We specify a set of data as fixed-point data by the letter I appearing in place of the F. Since there will be no decimal point to associate with the value, the specification is completed by placing a number after the I. This number indicates the number of columns allotted to the fixed-point value. Thus if the first four columns of a card contained the digits 6745 and they were to be read as an integer, the proper FORMAT statement would be FORMAT (I4).

There will usually be some limits on the number of digits that can be interpreted as one floating-point number or fixed-point number. These limits relate to the capacity of the computer and will, therefore, vary. We shall assume that a fixed-point number cannot contain more than four digits and that a floating-point number cannot contain more than eight digits. We should also note that if a number to be read by the computer has a negative sign, the leftmost of the columns indicated in the specification must be allotted to that sign. In the absence of a sign, the number is automatically treated as positive.

To summarize, a READ statement is an instruction to the computer to accept data which is in the form of a punched card. A READ statement must always refer to a FORMAT statement, which will indicate to the computer which columns of the card contain different items of data, and what the form of these data will be, fixed or floating point. The remainder of the READ statement lists the names of computer locations in which these data items are to be stored. Subsequent reference to these names in other program statements will be associated with the values stored in those computer locations at the time the reference is made.

In order to see how we can make use of this *input* procedure for the problem of computing characteristics of a probability distribution, let us look at the first two columns of Table A–1. These two columns contain the values for r, the random variable of interest, and $P(r)$, the probability associated with each corresponding value of r. There are six pairs of r and $P(r)$ in the distribution, and we must make this data available to the computer if it is to perform the computations we wish it to perform. Suppose, then, that we were to punch one card for each of these pairs of values. The first card, for example, would be punched with four zeros in the first four columns and the digits 2400 in the columns 5 through 8. The second card would be punched with 0001 in the columns 1 through 4 and 4000 in the columns 5 through 8. All other cards would be punched in the same manner, with the last card having 0005 in the first four columns and 0000 in the next four columns.

Now, the actual procedure for "reading" a card consists of two steps. First, the card must be entered into a card-reading device which is separate from, but connected through wiring to, the computer. The card-reading device will "hold" the data it has read from the card until the computer initiates a transfer of that data to its own storage area. The computer will make this transfer when, in the process of executing a program, it comes upon a READ statement. Suppose, then, that we have entered the contents of the first card into the card reader, and the computer comes upon the statement, 5 READ 1, X, PX. By reference to the FORMAT statement numbered 1, the computer will execute this statement by transferring the data of the first four columns of the card (which will be the digits 0000) to a location in its storage, and it will establish the name "X" to refer to this location. It also will transfer the data of the next four columns of the card (which will be the digits 2400) to another storage location and give this location the name "PX." Moreover, the data in the location X will be treated as a floating-point number with the decimal point to the right of the fourth digit (0000.) and the data in the location PX will be treated as a floating-point number with the decimal point to the left of the first digit (.2400). In this manner, the first pair of values of r and $P(r)$ in Table A–1 will have been made available to the computer for subsequent use in computation.

The student may ask at this point, why were four columns of a card allotted to each of the values r and $P(r)$ when the first are only one-digit numbers and the second are only two-digit numbers? The answer is that the program has been written so that it can be used on probability distributions with larger numbers than the ones occurring in the present example. We could have specified a larger or smaller number of digits for each of these variables, in which case the manner in which we punched the cards would have to change accordingly.

Computing the sums of $rP(r)$, $r^2P(r)$, and $r^3P(r)$

Following the first execution of the READ statement, the data on the first card will have been transferred to the computer's storage area. Although we have referred to these values as r and $P(r)$ in Table A–1, the computer will refer to them as X and PX. The next step is to begin the process of generating the values for $rP(r)$, $r^2P(r)$, and $r^3P(r)$, or in terms of the names assigned by the computer, $X \cdot PX$, $X^2 \cdot PX$, and $X^3 \cdot PX$. These sums are necessary for us to find the values of the mean, variance, standard deviation, and skewness of the probability distribution.

We must digress for a moment to consider the arithmetic operations which we can ask the computer to perform through the FORTRAN language. There are five of these. We can ask the computer to perform directly through the FORTRAN language the following operations: addition, subtraction, multiplication, division, and exponentiation. Addition of two values is specified by inserting the plus sign between the names for the two values. Thus, the expression $X + Y$ would indicate to the computer that it is to form the sum of the values in the locations named X and Y. Subtraction is indicated by the minus sign. The computer will interpret the expresson $X - Y$ to mean that it is to compute the difference between X and Y. The operation of multiplication is signified by the asterisk, so that $X * Y$ means to form the product of X and Y. The slash specifies division: X/Y tells the computer to divide the value located in X by the value located in Y. Finally, we can ask the computer to raise some value to a given power (the operation of exponentiation) by using two asterisks. For example, $X ** 3$ indicates to the computer that the third power of the value in location X is desired. We can combine several of these operations in one expression, $X - Y ** 2$, for example.[2]

If we ask the computer to perform an arithmetic operation, or series of operations, of the type illustrated in the last paragraph, we must also specify a name for the location in which it is to store the result of these operations. We can name a location which has already been specified earlier in the program, or we can name a new location, depending on our needs. The specification of the location at which the result is to be

---

[2] There are certain rules about the order of precedence in which the operations are carried out in such combined expressions. We defer consideration of these rules until later.

stored is accomplished through the use of a statement with an equality (=) sign. Consider, for example, the following three statements in the program of Figure A–1:

$$
\begin{aligned}
2 \quad \text{SUMX} &= \text{SUMX} + \text{X*PX} \\
\text{SUMX2} &= \text{SUMX2} + (\text{X**2})\text{*PX} \\
\text{SUMX3} &= \text{SUMX3} + (\text{X**3})\text{*PX}
\end{aligned}
$$

In each of these statements, a name appears alone on the left of the equality sign, and an expression appears on the right of the equality sign. In each case, the statement is interpreted by the computer as meaning, "replace the value which is currently stored in the location named to the left of the equality sign with the result of the operations specified in the expression to the right of the equality sign."

To be more specific, the statement SUMX = SUMX + X * PX (we ignore the statement number, 2, of this statement) tells the computer to multiply the value stored in location X by the value stored in location PX and add to this product the value currently stored in location SUMX. Having performed these operations, the result is to be stored in location SUMX (the value previously stored in SUMX is replaced by this new result). A good question at this point is, What will the computer be multiplying and adding when it executes this statement? Well, we have just seen a little earlier that, as a result of execution of the READ statement, the locations X and PX will contain the values of the first data card, 0000. and .2400. But what about the location SUMX?

We have not asked the computer to read data from a card into a location named SUMX. Notice, however, that the first statement in the program following the FORMAT statement is SUMX = 0.0. The computer will have executed this statement prior to any other statements of the program. Consequently, the location SUMX will currently contain a value of zero. This is necessary because, if we had not done this, the location SUMX might contain just about anything, depending on what was left there from the last program run on the computer. Notice, too, that the locations SUMX2 and SUMX3 have also been "zeroed" at the very start of the program, before any computations involving them occur.

At the point in time when statement number 2 is first executed, then, the location SUMX contains a zero, the location X contains a zero, and the location PX contains the value .2400. The result of executing the statement will be to replace the current value of SUMX (zero) with the value of SUMX + X · PX (= 0000. + (0000.) (.2400) = 0.0000).[3] That is, on the basis of the computations involving the data on the first card, the value stored in SUMX will remain unchanged at zero. For similar reasons,

---

[3] The value of 0.0000 shown here is not meant to indicate, necessarily, the full number of zero digits that will have been stored in SUMX. Throughout our discussion, no attempt will be made to keep track of superfluous high- and low-order zeroes which do not alter the numeric value of the result.

it should be clear that execution of the two statements following statement number 2 will also result in SUMX2 and SUMX3 containing values of zero. Because the first value of the random variable, r, (or X, from the computer's point of view) is zero, it adds nothing to $\Sigma r P(r)$, $\Sigma r^2 P(r)$, and $\Sigma r^3 P(r)$ (or SUMX, SUMX2, and SUMX3, from the computer's point of view).

Having executed the three instructions just discussed, with the data of the first data card, the computer will come upon the statement GO TO 5. This statement has a straightforward interpretation: It asks the computer to proceed to the statement in the program numbered 5. But statement number 5 is just the READ statement once again. In other words, the program contains what is called a *loop*. Having processed the data of the first card, the computer is asked to return to the READ statement and read in a second card. It will do so if, in the meantime, a second data card has been entered in the card-reading unit. The process of reading successive cards in the card-reading unit is done automatically. The cards are stacked in a hopper on the card reader, so that they will be fed into the card reader in successive order. As the computer executes the READ statement for each card, the data of the next card following it are "read" by the card reader.[4]

The second of our data cards contains a value for r which the computer will store in the location named X as 0001., and a value for $P(r)$ which the computer will store in the location named PX as .4000. The values which were stored there from the first card will be replaced by these new values. Let us ignore the statement beginning with IF, once again, and proceed directly to statement number 2. This statement asks the computer, it will be recalled, to replace the current value of SUMX with the result of adding the product X · PX to the current value of SUMX. As a result of the first card, SUMX still contains a value of zero. The locations X and PX, however, now contain the values 0001. and .4000. Thus, the value in SUMX (0.0000) will be replaced by the result, $0.0000 + (0001.)(.4000) = 0.4000$. Following this, execution of the statement SUMX2 = SUMX2 + (X ** 2)PX replaces the current value of SUMX2 (also still 0.0000) by the result, $0.0000 + (0001.)^2(.4000) = 0.4000$. And the next statement changes the contents of SUMX3 from zero to the value, $0.0000 + (0001.)^3(.4000) = 0.4000$. Having completed these statements, the computer will again be asked to GO TO 5, where it will read the third data card.

It is time, now, to stand back a bit and see what is happening. Looking

---

[4] It may often be the case that the computer can perform the statements in the program *loop* faster than the card reader can "read" another card. In that case, the computer will wait on the card reader and transfer the data of the next card as soon as the card reader makes it available. In such a circumstance, the computer is said to be *input bound*, since its speed of operation is bound by the speed of operation of the input device.

at Table A–1, we can see that the third data card should contain a value for X of 0002. and a value for PX of .2600. We also see that, for this card, $rP(r) = X * PX = 0.5200$. With the execution of statement number 2 for this card, a value of 0.5200 will be added to the current value of SUMX, which is 0.4000. The new value in SUMX will be 0.9200. Also, as a result of the statement following statement number 2, the value of SUMX2 will be increased by the amount of $r^2P(r) = (X ** 2) * PX = 1.0400$, to a value of 1.4400. Finally, the third statement will result in an increase of SUMX3 by 2.0800, to 2.4800.

It should be apparent, from the considerations of the last paragraph, just what purpose the three statements we have been considering were designed to accomplish. With each new data card, the statements instruct the computer to increase the values currently in SUMX, SUMX2, and SUMX3 by the appropriate values of $X * PX$, $(X ** 2) * PX$ and $(X ** 3) * PX$. That is, as the computer continues to "loop" back and read in each new data card, it also generates a cumulating sum for these three values. By the time the sixth card, containing a value for X of 0005. and a value for PX of .0000, has been processed by these statements, the location SUMX will contain a value of 1.23—the sum of $rP(r)$, as shown at the bottom of the third column in Table A–1. Likewise, the location SUMX2 will contain a value of 2.41—the sum shown in the fourth column in Table A–1, and the location SUMX3 will contain a value of 5.55. This *loop* of the program was designed to calculate the sums which are required to calculate the mean, variance, standard deviation, and coefficient of skewness of the probability distribution, as indicated in the lower portion of Table A–1.[5]

---

[5] The student may be perplexed as to why the complication of a *loop* was necessary in this program. He may be asking himself if the same thing could have been accomplished by reading in the six data cards consecutively by placing six READ statements in succession in the program, and then performing the required calculations with all of the data available in computer storage at the same time. The answer is yes, this could have been done. There are two reasons why this was not done, however. First, such a procedure would have resulted in a much larger program, since the effect would have been to "string out" six sequences of READ statements and the required computational statements just discussed above. In each sequence, however, exactly the same steps must be performed, and so we can save programming effort by using the loop. A second very cogent reason for using the loop relates to what has been said in an earlier footnote concerning the possibility of the computer being *input bound*. If we were to write the program so that all six data cards were read in prior to any computations being performed, the computer would be able to proceed in working out the problem only as fast as the card reader could feed in six successive data cards. This would slow down the process considerably, since the card reader operates at a much slower speed than the computer. By contrast, with the loop as written in the program, the computer is able to perform the calculations on each successive card as the card reader is going through the cycle of reading in the next card. There is a substantial saving of time, because the computer will not have to wait on the card reader for as long a total period of time.

Leaving the loop: The IF statement

We have seen that the loop designed in the program of Figure A–1 has the purpose of generating the sums which are needed before the values of the mean and other characteristics of the probability distribution can be computed. With the instructions of that loop performed by the computer on the data of the sixth card, this task will have been accomplished. Now the question becomes, How do we get the computer to leave this loop? The answer lies in the instruction following the READ statement, which we have ignored to this point: IF (PX − 0.9999) 2, 3, 2. This instruction to the computer is rather complex. It can be translated as follows: "If the value resulting from the computations in parentheses —that is, PX − 0.9999—is negative, proceed to statement number 2 for the next instruction; if it is equal to zero, proceed to statement number 3 for the next instruction; and if it is positive, proceed to statement number 2 for the next instruction."

The function of an IF statement is to provide a way of allowing the computer to *branch* out of one sequence of instructions and proceed to another sequence of instructions. In the absence of such a branching procedure, the computer will continue through a sequence of instructions serially, performing each instruction successively as it appears in the program. The IF statement provides a switch by which it can *branch* to another part of the program.[6] The elements of the IF statement, in addition to the word "IF" itself, are an expression in parentheses which must be evaluated and the sequence of three numbers designating statements within the program to which the computer is to branch. The expression in parentheses can be more complex than the one of our program, or it may consist of one variable alone. In either case, the computer notes if the value within the parentheses is negative, zero, or positive in value. If the value is negative, the computer will branch to the statement in the program whose number appears as the leftmost number in the sequence of three numbers. If the value is zero, the computer branches to the statement whose number is in the center of the sequence of three numbers. If the value is positive, finally, the computer branches to the statement with the rightmost number in the sequence.

---

[6] There are other statements available which provide for branching, but we shall not consider them in this appendix. Another type of branching operation procedure that is very useful, for example, allows the computer to branch to another part of the program if a specified switch among a set of switches on the computer console is turned "on" or "off." The GO TO statement which we considered earlier also provides a means for allowing the computer to branch. This statement provides an *unconditional* branch. That is, the computer must branch to the statement whose number follows the words GO TO, with no alternative possibilities. The IF statement provides for a *conditional* branch. Thus, in the case discussed here, the computer may proceed to statement 2 or statement 3, depending on the value in parentheses. This point is made clear in subsequent discussion of the text.

In the program of Figure A–1, the sequence of numbers in the IF statement is 2, 3, 2. This directs the computer to go to statement number 2 of the program if the expression in parentheses has a negative or a positive value (that is, if the value is nonzero). If the value in parentheses is zero, however, the computer is to branch to statement number 3. Noting that statement number 2 of our program falls within the loop which we have discussed, we see that if the value in parentheses is non-zero, the computer will continue in the loop. This, in turn, means that the computer will process the data on the card which it has just read in the manner explained earlier. If the value in parentheses is zero, however, the computer will not continue in the loop and will not, therefore, process the data of the card. Instead, it will branch out of the loop, to statement number 3, which begins the sequence of instructions in which the characteristics of the probability distribution are computed.

With the IF statement written as in the program of Figure A–1, we can signal to the computer that it has processed all of the data cards by following these data cards with another card. This final card will have no punches in the first four columns, and it will contain the value 9999 in the second set of four columns. When this card is read by the computer, a value of zero will be placed in location X, and a value of .9999 will be placed in location PX. Following execution of the READ instruction, the computer will come upon the IF statement. When it evaluates the expression in parentheses, it will find that $PX - 0.9999 = 0.9999 - 0.9999 = 0$. Since the value in parentheses is zero, the computer will branch to statement number 3 immediately, thereby bypassing the remainder of the loop.

In order for this procedure to work properly, it is, of course, necessary that none of the data cards preceding this final card will have a value for PX of .9999. If one of the data cards did have such a value, the computer would be led to branch out of the loop before it had processed all of the data, and the resulting values computed for the characteristics of the distribution would be incorrect. The use of a value with all nines, however, will usually assure us that a premature branch of this type will not occur. If a set of data to be processed does happen to contain that same value, we should have to rewrite the program in order to provide a "signal value" which was not included in the data, or we should have to modify the value in the data slightly. In the latter case, for example, if the value of $P(r)$ for a particular value of r had been 0.9999. we might have entered it on a data card as 0.9998. The changes which this would make in the computed values of the characteristics of the distribution would be very minor.

Before continuing the discussion of the program following the branch by the computer to statement 3, it should be pointed out that the IF statement is very flexible. It is used in other ways than just to provide a method for leaving a program loop. Other uses of the IF statement are illustrated in programs presented later in this appendix.

Computation of the characteristics of the distribution

When the computer branches from the loop, it comes upon statement number 3, which begins a sequence of instructions designed to use the sums generated in the loop to arrive at the values for the characteristics of the distribution. There are four of these characteristics which are computed: the mean, the variance, the standard deviation, and the coefficient of skewness.

Statement number 3 is a statement in which a name only, rather than a more extensive expression, appears to the right of the equality sign. The effect of the statement is to instruct the computer to provide a location called XMEAN and to duplicate in that location the value contained in the location named SUMX. Since the mean of a random variable is the sum of the products of the values taken by the variable times their respective probabilities, and since this is exactly the value contained in SUMX as a result of the loop which the computer has just left, nothing more than this is required.[7] With the execution of the statement, XMEAN = SUMX, these two locations now both contain the same value.

The variance of any random variable, x, can be calculated with the formula, $\mathrm{var}(x) = \Sigma x^2 P(x) - (\bar{x})^2$. Comparison of this formula with the statement VARX = SUMX2 − XMEAN ** 2 suggests the meaning of the description of FORTRAN as "formula translation." The value contained in SUMX2 is just the sum of the products of the squares of the values taken by the random variable, times their respective probabilities. The second term in the expression leads the computer to compute the square of the mean. Subtraction of the latter value from the former yields the variance of the distribution, and this value is then placed in a location referred to as VARX.

The standard deviation of a random variable is, of course, the positive square root of its variance. This value is provided by the computer when it executes the statement, STDEVX = SQRTF(VARX). Upon "reading" the expression to the right of the equality sign, the computer translates it as follows: "Branch to the *subroutine* by which the square root of a value is computed, and use that *subroutine* to compute the

---

[7] As a matter of fact, not even this statement is actually required. The value contained in SUMX is the mean of the distribution. All we really needed to do was to write the name SUMX wherever we wished to refer to the mean in the program, and the results would have been correct. Statement number 3 is included so that we can refer to this value by a name closer in form to the value to which we have reference.

It is important to note that the statement, XMEAN = SUMX, places a value in XMEAN equal to the value in SUMX, *but does not modify the contents of SUMX*.

square root of the value contained in the location VARX." Having computed the square root of VARX as instructed, the computer will place that value in a location called STDEVX.

A *subroutine* is just a special-purpose program which can be branched to from any point in the main program, if the proper statement is provided. Most computers now available on the market will be accompanied by a library of such subroutines, to provide the programmer automatically with programs required to compute certain values that recur often in programming problems. The square root subroutine is one of these. These subroutines are provided with names that end with the letter F, and these names indicate rather clearly the purpose of the subroutines. The format for statements calling on these subroutines follows that indicated above: the name of the subroutine follows the equality sign; the name of the variable for which the function is to be performed follows this name immediately, in parentheses; and to the left of the equality sign appears the name of the location in which the result is to be stored. Because of the special nature of these subroutines, the programmer must not duplicate the name of such a subroutine in a name which he assigns to a variable within the main program. Usually he may duplicate all but the last two letters in the subroutine name.[8]

The next value required is the coefficient of skewness. This value is provided by a set of four statements in sequence. Let us look, first, at the formula for the coefficient of skewness of a probability distribution, before we consider these four statements. The formula is:

$$\text{sk}(x) = \frac{\Sigma x^3 P(x) - 3\bar{x}\Sigma x^2 P(x) + 2(\bar{x})^3}{\sigma^3}.$$

The expression in the numerator of the formula contains three terms in values of x or $\bar{x}$ which could be represented by, say, sk1, sk2, and sk3. If this substitution is made, the formula becomes

$$\text{sk}(x) = \frac{\text{sk}1 - 3 \cdot \text{sk}2 + 2 \cdot \text{sk}3}{\sigma^3},$$

where $\text{sk}1 = \Sigma x^3 P(x)$, $\text{sk}2 = \bar{x}\Sigma x^2 P(x)$, and $\text{sk}3 = (\bar{x})^3$.

Examination of the second formula above indicates the manner in which the four statements of the program lead to the value of the coefficient of skewness. The first statement, SK1 = SUMX3, provides the value of sk1. The second statement, SK2 = (XMEAN * SUMX2), provides the value of sk2. The third statement, SK3 = XMEAN ** 3, provides the value of sk3. The fourth statement, SKX = (SK1 − 3.0 * SK2 +

---

[8] A person who is involved extensively in programming may find it convenient to write subroutines, or subprograms, of his own to meet his particular needs. In later discussion, we shall consider this possibility.

2.0 $*$ SK3)/STDEVX $**$ 3, computes the numerator of the formula and divides the value of the numerator by the cube of the standard deviation. The resulting value of the coefficient of skewness is stored in the location SKX.

There are several programming points that can be usefully illustrated by reference to the statements we have just considered for computing the characteristics of a distribution. Before considering these, however, let us continue through the remainder of the program.

Specifying the output of the program

Following execution of the statement in which the coefficient of skewness is computed, the computer will have computed all of the values which we require. In so doing, of course, the computer will have computed several preliminary results, such as SUMX2 and SK2, which we do not require. The values which we wish the computer to provide as output are specified in the statement, PRINT 6, XMEAN, VARX, STDEVX, SKX. The student will note that this statement is much like the READ statement considered earlier. The only true distinction is the use of the word "PRINT," where before the word "READ" appeared. The number 6 following PRINT refers to the FORMAT statement numbered 6. The list of names following this number specifies the values to be printed and the order in which they are to be printed. The use of the word "PRINT" indicates to the computer that output is to be on a printing device connected electrically to the computer. Substitution of the word "PUNCH" would have instructed the computer that the output was to be punched in cards on a card punching unit connected to the computer.

The FORMAT statement number 6 performs the same function in conjunction with the PRINT statement that statement number 1 performed with the READ statement. It instructs the computer how many spaces (in the case of the printer) or columns (in the case of the card punch) are to be allotted to each variable named in the PRINT (or PUNCH) statement. It also indicates the number of digits which are to appear to the right of the decimal point, in the same manner as the earlier FORMAT statement. Notice, however, that only two entries appear within the parentheses of the statement, whereas there are four values named in the PRINT statement. The reason for this is that it was decided to give the first three values the same configuration, and this is indicated by preceding the specification of that configuration by the number 3. In other words, the values for XMEAN, VARX, and STDEVX are to be printed with 11 spaces allotted to each, with four digits following the decimal point. The last of the four values, SKX, is to be printed with nine spaces allotted to it and four decimal places. All four values are to be printed as floating-point numbers. Such collection of similar specifications for values can be done in any FORMAT statement, be it associated with an input or an output statement.

There is one major difference between specifications in output FORMAT statements and input FORMAT statements. This is due to the fact that in floating-point output, the programmer must provide one space (or column) for a decimal point and one more space (column) for a possible sign which may require printing. This contrasts with the input FORMAT statement, in which the decimal point need not actually be punched in the card and in which the sign need be punched only if it is negative. The result of this requirement is that the programmer must specify at least two more spaces (columns) than he expects the numeric digits for the values generated by the program to occupy. If he should like several blank spaces to appear between successive values in the printout, he may do so by making the specifications for a correspondingly larger number of spaces. If the programmer does not specify enough spaces to accommodate the generated value, a part of this value will be lost, since the computer will truncate it so as to fit the spaces allotted for it.

The PAUSE statement and the STOP statement

Following the FORMAT statement number 6, the single word "PAUSE" appears in the program. The function of this statement is, as one might anticipate, to instruct the computer to suspend execution of the program—to pause. Upon encountering this statement, the computer will discontinue operation until the programmer reactivates it by depressing the START button on the computer console. When this button is depressed, the computer will continue to the next statement following the PAUSE statement and execute it in the normal fashion. Thus, in the present program, the computer will discontinue operation after coming upon the PAUSE statement. When the START button is depressed on the console, the computer will continue to the next instruction and then branch to statement number 7 as indicated there: GO TO 7.

The purpose of the PAUSE statement is usually to help the programmer in the initial validation of the program he has written. Several PAUSE statements may be inserted in the program, at strategic places, so that the programmer can check results of the program up to those points. If he is satisfied that everything is working properly up to the point at which the computer pauses, he depresses the START button. The computer continues with the program until it comes upon the next PAUSE statement.

Following the last executable instruction in a program, the programmer will often insert the statement, STOP. As the statement implies, when the computer reaches this statement it stops execution unconditionally. The program is finished and no further execution will occur.

Instructing the computer to return to the beginning of the program: A second loop

The statement, GO TO 7, which follows the PAUSE statement will send the computer back to the beginning of the program. There, it will once again zero the contents of SUMX, SUMX2, and SUMX3 in preparation for another set of data for another probability distribution. With this second loop designed into the program, the programmer can have the computer process as many probability distributions as he may desire.

The several sets of data cards corresponding to these different probability distributions can be stacked in the hopper of the card reader, in one stack. It is only necessary for the programmer to be sure that each separate set of data cards is followed by the special card that indicates that all of the data cards for that set of data has been processed—that is, the card with nines in columns 5 through 8. As the results for each set of data are computed, they will be printed (punched) on a separate line (card). The PAUSE statement will allow the programmer to check the results for each set of data before continuing to the next set of data, if he should choose to do so.

The END statement

The last statement to appear in all FORTRAN programs must be the END statement. This statement is not executable. That is, the statement does not instruct the computer to do anything as the program is being executed. The function of the END statement is merely to indicate to the compiler (the program which provides a translation of the FOR-TRAN program) that all of the program which is to be translated has been processed by it prior to this statement.

With the END statement considered, we have finished a consideration of the entire program. We noted earlier, however, that there were some points of interest that we should wish to return to later. We take these up in the next two sections.

Names and constants in fixed- and floating-point modes

It was pointed out earlier that variables can be specified to be fixed-point variables or floating-point variables. The same is true of any constants which may appear in the program. In the program of Figure A–1, several constants appear in the various statements. In each of the first three statements, following the COMMENT statements, the number 0.0

appearing to the right of the equality sign is a constant. Other illustrations are the constant 0.9999 which appears in the IF statement and the 2 and the 3 that appear in (X ** 2) and (X ** 3). Of these, the first two—0.0 and 0.9999—are floating-point constants, and the last two—2 and 3—are fixed-point constants. The two types of constant are distinguished from each other by the fact that the floating-point constants contain a decimal point and the fixed-point constants do not.[9]

In the case of a constant appearing in the program, a specific value is written for the constant. We have just indicated that whether the constant is floating point or fixed point is indicated by the presence or absence, respectively, of a decimal point in the value. In the case of a variable, however, a name is provided for it in the program, since the value of the variable will be determined during the execution of the program. Thus, the value of SUMX in the program changes as each successive data card is processed, in the present program. Some method is required to distinguish floating-point variables from fixed-point variables. This has been done in FORTRAN programming by adoption of the rule that the names of fixed-point variables must begin with one of the letters I, J, K, L, M, or N. The name of a floating-point variable must begin with one of the letters of the alphabet other than I, J, K, L, M, or N. All of the variables of the program in Figure A–1 are treated as floating-point variables. As a consequence, the names for all of them begin with letters other than I, J, K, L, M, or N.[10] Note, in particular, that in statement number 3, the location in which the value of the mean of the random variable is to be stored is named XMEAN, rather than MEANX. The latter name seems a bit more natural, perhaps; but since this name begins with the letter M, it would have designated to the computer that the mean of the random variable be stored as a fixed-point number. We shall consider the consequences of this below.

A rule that must be followed in FORTRAN programming is that all variables and constants appearing in an expression to the right of the equality sign of a statement must be in the same *mode*, either fixed-point mode or floating-point mode. The one exception to this rule is the case of exponents. An exponent may be written in either fixed-point or floating-point mode. Thus, in the statement, SUMX2 = SUMX2 + (X ** 2) * PX, the exponent 2 in X ** 2 is a fixed-point constant, although the remainder of the expression to the right of the equality sign is made

---

[9] Actually, the floating-point constant 0.0 could have been written as 0., and the floating-point constant 0.9999 could have been written as .9999. The additional zero written in each case was put there by the author as a mental device to help emphasize the floating-point nature of these constants.

[10] A mental trick that helps the author remember these letters is to think of the name I. J. KuhLMaN, who is a man of very *fixed* habits.

up of floating-point variables.[11] The statement could as well have been written using X ** 2.0.

Although all variables and constants in an expression must be in the same mode, with the exception noted above, it is not necessary that the mode of the variable named to the left of the equality sign be the same as the mode of the expression to the right of the equality sign. In the present program it happens to be the case that all variables to the left of the equality sign are in floating-point mode, as are all the expressions to the right of the equality sign. This was dictated by the needs of the program, not by any requirement of the FORTRAN language. If, as was suggested above, statement number 3 had been written MEANX = SUMX, this would have been acceptable from the standpoint of the requirements of FORTRAN. The statement would not have been acceptable from the standpoint of the program, however.

There are two reasons why this is so. First, the computer would interpret the statement MEANX = SUMX to mean "convert the value in the location SUMX from floating point to fixed point and store the fixed-point value in location MEANX." As we have seen earlier, at the point in time when this statement is executed, the value stored in SUMX is 1.23. In converting this value to a fixed-point value, the computer will truncate all of the digits to the right of the decimal point and store a value of 1 as the value of MEANX. This, of course, is not the true value of the mean of the random variable, but only a rather gross approximation. We would rather have the more exact value of 1.23.

A second problem arises when we consider statements in the program which follow statement number 3. In those statements, wherever the name XMEAN appears, we would have to change it to MEANX. In the case of the statement, SK2 = (MEANX * SUMX2), we would have an improper statement. The expression to the right of the equality sign now contains a fixed-point variable and a floating-point variable. The expression is in *mixed mode*, and the compiler would not translate it in this condition. The translation of the FORTRAN program would stop until the programmer had corrected this error.

Whenever a statement contains a variable of different mode to the left of the equality sign, there is a standard procedure which the computer follows. The expression to the right of the equality sign is evaluated in its mode. The value which results from this computation is then converted to the corresponding value as it would be represented in the other mode, and the converted value is stored in the location named to the left of the equality sign. This fact is a useful feature of the language, which is used in programs to be discussed later.

---

[11] Note that the number 2 which appears in SUMX2 is a part of the name of that variable and is, therefore, not subject to the rule we are discussing.

Hierarchy of arithmetic operations

In the absence of some convention to follow in the processing of arithmetic expressions in a FORTRAN program, a great deal of confusion and ambiguity could ensue. The point is easily made by consideration of the expression, $X - Y ** 2$. This expression might be interpreted in two different ways. One possibility is to suppose that the expression is equivalent to squaring the value of $X - Y$, that is, $(X - Y)^2$. A second possibility is to interpret the expression as equivalent to finding the difference between X and the square of Y, that is, $X - Y^2$. It is in this latter sense that the computer will interpret the expression above.

One can look upon the process by which the computer interprets arithmetic expressions in FORTRAN as involving a scanning of the expression from left to right, in a series of successive scans. In the first scan of the expression, all terms to be exponentiated are raised to the proper powers. In the second scan, all operations of multiplication and division that appear in the expression will be performed. In a third scan, all operations of addition and subtraction are performed. This plan indicates the *hierarchy* of arithmetic operations: first, exponentiation; second, multiplication and division; and third, addition and subtraction. At all levels, the operations are performed as they appear in the expression, moving from left to right. Given this plan of interpretation, we see, for example, that the expression $X/Y * Z$ would be interpreted as $\left(\frac{X}{Y}\right)Z$, rather than as $\frac{X}{Y \cdot Z}$. If we wished to write an expression which would accomplish the second result, we would have at least two choices. One possibility is to write the expression as $X/Y/Z$, which by the algebraic characteristics of division is equivalent to $\frac{X}{Y \cdot Z}$.

Probably a better choice would be to make use of parentheses, writing the expression as $X/(Y * Z)$. The use of parentheses in FORTRAN expressions serves the same purpose as in the usual algebraic expression. They reduce the ambiguity that may arise in certain expressions and, in programming, they serve as a means of assurance that the computer will perform the operations as intended by the programmer. In the scanning process described above, we can think of the computer as evaluating all expressions which are enclosed in parentheses before using the values of these expressions to perform further operations which appear outside the parentheses. If one expression in parentheses is itself part of a larger expression also enclosed in parentheses, the expression within the inner parentheses is evaluated first. Thus, in the expression $((X - Y) * Z) ** 2$, the value of $X - Y$ will first be computed, this value will be multiplied by Z, and the resulting product will be raised to the second power. Because of the critical importance of parentheses in an expression, the programmer must always make sure that each opening parenthesis is matched by a closing parenthesis.

Some of these points can be emphasized by reference to various statements in the program of Figure A–1. Consider, for example, the use of parentheses in the statements, SUMX2 = SUMX2 + (X ** 2) * PX and SUMX3 = SUMX3 + (X ** 3) * PX. These parentheses are not required for the computer to evaluate the expressions in the correct manner. If the parentheses were absent, the computer would first exponentiate the value of X in each expression. Then it would multiply this exponentiated value by PX. In this manner, the computer will have generated the proper value. In this case, the parentheses were included as a matter of clarification for the programmer and subsequent readers of the program.

By way of comparison, we consider the parentheses appearing in the statement, SK2 = (XMEAN * SUMX2). These parentheses are superfluous from any point of view. They are not required in order to make certain that the computer performs the operations in the proper order. Neither are they necessary in order to reduce ambiguity in subsequent reading of the program.

By contrast, the parentheses which appear in the statement, SKX = (SK1 − 3.0 * SK2 + 2.0 * SK3)/STDEVX ** 3, are essential to proper reading and execution of the program. We wish the expression in parentheses to be evaluated as the numerator which is to be divided by the cube of the standard deviation. The parentheses indicate to the computer that this full expression must be evaluated prior to the division operation, which assures us of the proper result. Without the parentheses, the computer would have evaluated the expression as $\mathrm{sk1} - 3 \cdot \mathrm{sk2} + 2 \cdot \mathrm{sk3}$.
$$\frac{}{\sigma^3}$$

Through consideration of the first program, we have been able to present most of the basic rules of the FORTRAN language. In the remainder of the appendix, we shall consider several other programs. These include two programs to analyze a set of data, a program to compute the coefficients desired in a simple linear correlation, a program to generate quasi-random numbers, programs to generate a random normal variate, and a program to simulate the production process which was described in Chapter 9. As we proceed to a discussion of these programs, some additional features of FORTRAN programming will be presented and discussed.

A program to analyze grouped data

The program presented in Figure A–2 is designed to provide the values of the mean, variance, standard deviation, and coefficient of skewness of a set of grouped data, as well as the number of items in the set of data. The reference to grouped data means that the values of the items constituting the data have been organized into a frequency distribution prior to punching the information in data cards. With the data so organized, the relevant information to punch in data cards are the midpoint value for each class of the frequency distribution and the number of items which fall in that class. There will, therefore, be one punched card for each class in the distribution, and these data cards will be followed by a card to signal that the last data card has been processed.

In the discussion of the frequency distribution in an earlier chapter, it was noted that the frequency distribution and the probability distribution were quite similar. The major difference in the two types of distribution is that whereas a probability is associated with each value of the random variable in a probability distribution, there is an integer associated with each midpoint in a frequency distribution—the number of items in that class. This is an inconsequential difference in the formal appearances of the two types of distribution, but it does require some difference in the calculation of the various characteristics. Therefore, it also necessitates some differences in the programs designed to provide these characteristics.

The first of these differences that must be provided for in the program of Figure A–2 is the fact that we must have the computer sum up the class frequencies as they are provided on each data card. The name which designates these frequencies in the program is FX, as is apparent from examination of the READ statement. In the third statement following statement number 3, $EN = EN + FX$, the computer is instructed to generate the cumulative sum of FX as each data card is processed. As with the other statements in this loop, there is a statement at the first of the program to set the value in the location EN to zero prior to processing the first data card: $6\ EN = 0.0$.

In other respects, the loop of this program which generates the sums required for subsequent computations is formally similar to the loop which we discussed in the first program. The READ statement which initiates the loop is followed by an IF statement whose purpose is to detect the signal that all data cards have been processed, and thereupon to leave the loop. In this instance, however, the value on the data card corresponding to X is used as the signal. Following the last data card, we place a card with nines appearing in the first seven columns. When the computer reads this card and proceeds to the IF statement, it will find the expression $X - 99999.99$ is equal to zero. Consequently, the computer will branch out of the loop and proceed to statement number 4.

In the FORMAT statement number 1, seven columns have been allowed for the values of X, which are the midpoints of the classes. Two decimal places are specified. The class frequencies, FX, have four columns allotted to them. Note that, although these frequencies are integers by their nature, we instruct the computer to treat them as floating-point numbers with no decimal digits. This allows us later to instruct the computer to use these values in floating-point operations.

The statements of the program by which the computer is instructed to compute the various characteristics of the distribution are all designed to duplicate the corresponding formulas presented for these characteristics in the earlier discussion of frequency distributions. Note, for example, that the formula for the variance of a frequency distribution, $\text{var}(x) = \dfrac{\Sigma f \cdot x^2}{n - 1} - \dfrac{(\Sigma f \cdot x)^2}{n(n - 1)}$, is reflected in the statement, $\text{VARX} = \text{SUMXSQ}/(\text{EN} - 1.0) - \text{SUMX} ** 2/\text{EN}/(\text{EN} - 1.0)$. The location SUMXSQ contains the value of $\Sigma f \cdot x^2$ and the location SUMX contains the value

Figure A–2

```
C          A PROGRAM TO CALCULATE THE MEAN, VARIANCE, STANDARD DEVIATION, AND
C          COEFFICIENT OF SKEWNESS FOR GROUPED DATA
     1     FORMAT (F7.2, F4.0)
     6     EN = 0.0
           SUMX = 0.0
           SUMXSQ = 0.0
           SUMXCU = 0.0
     2     READ 1, X, FX
           IF (X — 99999.99) 3, 4, 3
     3     SUMX = SUMX + X*FX
           SUMXSQ = SUMXSQ + X**2*FX
           SUMXCU = SUMXCU + X**3*FX
           EN = EN + FX
           GO TO 2
     4     XMEAN = SUMX/EN
           VARX = SUMXSQ/(EN — 1.0) — SUMX**2/EN/(EN — 1.0)
           STDVX = SQRTF(VARX)
           SKWX =  (SUMXCU/(EN  —  1.0)  —  3.0*XMEAN*(SUMXSQ/(EN  —  1.0))  +  2.0*XM
          1EAN**2*(SUMX/(EN — 1.0)))/STDVX**3
           PRINT 5, XMEAN, VARX, STDVX, SKWX, EN
     5     FORMAT (2XF9.2, 2XF9.2, 1XF10.3, F6.2, F8.0)
           PAUSE
           GO TO 6
           END
```

of $\Sigma f \cdot x$, as a result of the looping process by which the data cards were processed. In that earlier loop, also, the location EN will have come to contain the cumulated sum of frequencies, that is, the value for number of items in the distribution, n.

The statement for the computation of SKWX (the coefficient of skewness) illustrates several points. First, it indicates that the programmer is not required to break down computations into smaller parts, as was done in the first program considered. Rather than compute the several terms of the numerator separately, and then combining them to compute the coefficient of skewness, the present program develops the numerator and divides it by the denominator, all in one statement.

As a consequence of performing all these operations in one statement, this statement is rather long. The statement is long enough that it must be continued on a second line. Notice that this continuation occurs in the middle of a location name, XMEAN. The letters of the name are extended on the first line until the letter M has been punched in column 72. On the continuing line, a digit 1 punched in column 6 indicates that what follows is a continuation of the previous line. The next letter of the name, E, follows immediately, in column 7.

A third point illustrated by this statement is the use of parentheses. The major portion of this statement is required to generate the numerator of the coefficient of skewness. The opening parenthesis that appears before SUMXCU and the closing parenthesis that appears just to the left of the slash prior to STDVX**3 serve to indicate to the computer that everything within these parentheses must be evaluated prior to division by STDVX**3. The other parentheses which appear within the numeraator are required in order to assure that each value in the expression is evaluated in its proper order before it is used in conjunction with other values.[12]

There is one final point illustrated in the program of Figure A–2 that we should mention. Notice that in FORMAT statement number 5, the first three specifications are written with a beginning digit, followed by the letter X. Beyond that, the specifications have the form already discussed for floating-point specifications. The function of the 2 and the letter X in the first specification, 2XF9.2, illustrates the use of this form. This specification is for the form in which the value of XMEAN is to be printed. It indicates that two blank spaces (2X) are to be allowed to the left of the printed value, which must be limited to nine spaces, including spaces for the sign, the decimal point, and two decimal digits. This form of specification assures the programmer that even if all nine spaces allotted to the value of XMEAN are used to record the value, there will be two blank spaces to the left of this value in the print-out. The same thing is true of the print-out of VARX, since its format specification also is 2XF9.2. In the print-out of STDVX, one blank space is assured between it and the print-out of VARX to its left: the specification is 1XF10.3. By contrast, if the values of SKWX and EN are large enough to fill six (F6.2) and eight (F8.0) spaces, respectively, the print-outs for these values will be run together with the values to their left. As usual, the

----

[12] In actuality, the expression for the numerator in this statement does not follow exactly the expression for the numerator as it appears in the formula presented earlier for the coefficient of skewness. The reason for this is that when a statement written exactly in that form was used in the program, the computer generated an underflow (that is, in attempting to generate the numerator, the computer was forced to compute values that were smaller than the allowable range for that particular computer). As a consequence, an algebraically equivalent expression was used, as indicated in the equation:

$$\frac{\Sigma f \cdot x^3}{n-1} - 3\frac{\Sigma f \cdot x \cdot \Sigma f \cdot x^2}{n(n-1)} + 2\frac{(\Sigma f \cdot x)^3}{n^2(n-1)} = \frac{\Sigma f \cdot x^3}{n-1} - 3 \cdot \bar{x} \cdot \frac{\Sigma f \cdot x^2}{n-1} + 2 \cdot (\bar{x})^2 \cdot \frac{\Sigma f \cdot x}{n-1}.$$

programmer must allow enough spaces in his FORMAT specifications to accommodate the values which the program will generate. Otherwise, the values will be truncated to fit the allotted spaces, and part of these values will be lost.

A program to analyze ungrouped data

In the analysis of a set of data with a computer, it does not represent a great saving of time for the data to be grouped in a frequency distribution prior to the computations. As a matter of fact, the cost of the analyst's time spent in making this grouping may be greater than the slightly greater length of time the computer may need to spend in processing ungrouped data. When that is the case, the better plan is to present the computer with the ungrouped data. We shall suppose that the data are recorded on punched cards, with one value appearing in the first seven columns of each card. There will then be as many data cards as there are items in the set of data. The program of Figure A–3 is designed to process data presented to the computer in this form.

Figure A–3

```
C        A PROGRAM TO COMPUTE VALUES FOR THE MEAN, STANDARD DEVIATION, COEF
C        FICIENT OF SKEWNESS FOR UNGROUPED DATA
    1    FORMAT (F7.2)
         EN = 0.0
         SUMX = 0.0
         SUMX2 = 0.0
         SUMX3 = 0.0
   10    READ 1, X
         IF (X — 99999.99) 2, 3, 2
    2    SUMX = SUMX + X
         SUMX2 = SUMX2 + X**2
         SUMX3 = SUMX3 + X**3
         EN = EN + 1.0
         GO TO 10
    3    XMEAN = SUMX/EN
         VARX = SUMX2/(EN — 1.0) — SUMX**2/(EN*(EN — 1.0))
         STDVX = SQRTF(VARX)
         SKW1 = SUMX3/(EN — 1.0)
         SKW2 = (SUMX*SUMX2)/(EN*(EN — 1.0))
         SKW3 = SUMX**3/(EN**2*(EN — 1.0))
         SKWX = (SKW1 — 3.0*SKW2 + 2.0*SKW3)/STDVX**3
         PRINT 4, XMEAN, STDVX, SKWX, EN
    4    FORMAT(2XF9.2, 2XF9.2, 2XF6.3, 2XF6.0)
         STOP
         END
```

The changes required in this program are obvious ones. First, since each card contains only one value, the FORMAT statement number 1 includes only one specification. Second, in order to generate the total frequency for the set of data, the statement EN = EN + 1.0 increases the value in the location EN by one as each data card is processed. Following the processing of n data cards in the set of data, the location EN contains the value of n. These are the only changes required in the program. There are other differences, however, which have been incorporated to emphasize points in programming techniques.

A comparison of the statements in the two programs by which the variance of the data is computed, $VARX = SUMX2/(EN - 1.0) - SUMX ** 2/EN/(EN - 1.0)$ in Figure A–2 and $VARX = SUMX2/(EN - 1.0) - SUMX ** 2/(EN * (EN - 1.0))$ in Figure A–3, points up the two methods indicated earlier by which one can write an expression involving a product in the denominator. Each form of the expression yields the proper result. Notice, also, that the program of Figure A–3 reverts to a procedure of computing the coefficient of skewness in a series of statements, rather than in one long statement. This seems the better procedure to follow, especially for novice programmers. The chance of confusion and error is reduced considerably if long computations are performed in stages.

A program to perform a simple linear correlation

The next program we consider is designed to compute the important coefficients related to simple linear regression and correlation, as specified in the COMMENT statements. The program appears as Figure A–4. In addition to the program, formulas representing the functions of certain statements in the program are set to the right of these statements. This will facilitate the student's interpretation of these statements, and will also reduce the need for detailed explanation of these statements in the following discussion.

Let us consider, first, the fact that two READ statements appear in this program: 5 READ 1, N, and the eighth statement following, READ 2, X, Y. The two FORMAT statements, 1 FORMAT (I4) and 2 FORMAT (2F6.2), are associated with the two READ statements as indicated by the digits 1 and 2 appearing in the READ statements. The second READ statement falls within a series of statements which forms a DO loop. We shall, consequently, defer consideration of that statement for a while.

The first READ statement, 5 READ 1, N, is designed to read an initial card on which will be punched the number of observations (X, Y pairs) contained in the data for which we wish the correlation. The associated FORMAT statement number 1 indicates that the number is to occupy the first four columns of the card, and it is to be stored as a fixed-point number. Actually, the number of observations is required in this program for two different reasons. In one use, it is needed in conjunction with the DO loop (to be explained below), and in this connection it must be a fixed-point number. In a second use, it is required in subsequent computations of the various coefficients in the correlation, and in that use it must be a floating-point number.

Figure   A–4

```
C     A PROGRAM TO CALCULATE THE COEFFICIENTS OF A SIMPLE LINEAR REGRESS
C     ION, STANDARD ERROR OF ESTIMATE, COEFFICIENT OF CORRELATION, COEFF
C     ICIENT OF DETERMINATION, AND STUDENTS T FOR TEST OF SIGNIFICANCE
    1 FORMAT(I4)
    2 FORMAT(2F6.2)
    5 READ 1, N
      SUMX = 0.0
      SUMY = 0.0
      SUMXY = 0.0
      SUMX2 = 0.0
      SUMY2 = 0.0
      EN = N
      DO 3 I = 1, N
      READ 2, X, Y
      SUMX = SUMX + X
      SUMY = SUMY + Y
      SUMXY = SUMXY + X*Y
      SUMX2 = SUMX2 + X*X
    3 SUMY2 = SUMY2 + Y*Y
      XMEAN = SUMX/EN
      YMEAN = SUMY/EN
      SUMSXY = SUMXY − EN*XMEAN*YMEAN
      SUMSX2 = SUMX2 − EN*XMEAN**2
      B = SUMSXY/SUMSX2
      A = YMEAN − B*XMEAN
      SUMSY2 = SUMY2 − EN*YMEAN**2
      SUME2 = SUMSY2 − B*SUMSXY
      STERES = SQRTF(SUME2/(EN − 2.0))
      RTSX2 = SQRTF(SUMSX2)
      RTSY2 = SQRTF(SUMSY2)
      R = SUMSXY/(RTSX2*RTSY2)
      R2 = R*R
      RTDEGF = SQRTF(EN − 2.0)
      RT1MIN = SQRTF(1.0 − R2)
      T = R*RTDEGF/RT1MIN
      PRINT 6, SUMX, SUMY, SUMXY, SUMX2, SUMY2
      PRINT 4, A, B, STERES, R, R2, T
    4 FORMAT(2XF10.2, 2XF10.3, 2XF10.2, 2XF6.3, 2XF6.3, 2XF10.4)
    6 FORMAT(5F12.4)
      GO TO 5
      END
```

(See the discussion of the text)

$\bar{X} = \Sigma X/n$

$\bar{Y} = \Sigma Y/n$

$\Sigma xy = \Sigma XY - n \cdot \bar{X} \cdot \bar{Y}$

$\Sigma x^2 = \Sigma X^2 - n \cdot (\bar{X})^2$

$b = \Sigma xy/x^2$

$a = \bar{Y} - b \cdot \bar{X}$

$\Sigma y^2 = \Sigma Y^2 - n \cdot (\bar{Y})^2$

$\Sigma e^2 = \Sigma y^2 - b\Sigma xy$

$\sigma'\epsilon = \sqrt{\Sigma e^2/n - 2}$

$\sqrt{\Sigma x^2}$

$\sqrt{\Sigma y^2}$

$r = \Sigma xy/(\sqrt{\Sigma x^2} \cdot \sqrt{\Sigma y^2})$

$r^2 = r \cdot r$

$t = r \cdot \sqrt{n - 2}/\sqrt{1 - r^2}$

The program is designed to provide the number of observations in both of the required modes. It is made available to the computer in fixed-point mode by the initial READ statement, as indicated in the last paragraph. Subsequently, in the sixth statement following this READ statement, EN = N, it is converted to a floating-point value, and the floating-point number is stored in location EN.[13] The intervening statements of the program have the familiar function of zeroing certain locations prior to performance of computations in which these locations will be required.

We come, now, to the DO statement, DO 3 I = 1, N. This statement has the function of instructing the computer to treat a sequence of statements as a loop, automatically, with the loop to be performed (in this particular case) N times before the loop is left, again automatically. The manner in which this is specified by the statement can be illustrated by

---

[13] We repeat that the contents of locations whose names appear to the right of the equality sign are not changed. Thus, the location N will still contain the fixed-point value of n.

interpreting portions of the statement separately. The first portion, DO 3, indicates to the computer that it is to include all statements *following* the DO statement, up to and *including* statement number 3, in the loop. Thus, the last statement included in a DO loop must be numbered, and this number is referred to immediately following the word DO in the DO statement.

The second portion of the DO statement, I = 1, N, is interpreted by the computer in a manner which has the effect of instructing it to perform the series of statements specified by the first portion N times. In detail, the computer is instructed to place a value of 1 (a fixed-point value) in a location named I (a name for a fixed-point variable), and then to perform the loop one time. Having completed the loop one time, the computer is then to increase the value contained in I by one[14] and perform the loop once more. This process of increasing the value of I by one and performing the loop is to be continued until the value in I is equal to N (also a fixed-point value). When the value in I is equal to N, the computer is to perform the loop for the last time and then to continue to the next statement following statement number 3.

An examination of the statements included within the DO loop indicates that they perform the familiar task of generating certain sums which are required in later computations. As the cards are read by the computer, the values of X and Y punched on the cards are processed to yield ΣX, ΣY, ΣXY, ΣX^2, and ΣY^2. When the last X, Y pair has been processed, the computer leaves the loop and proceeds to the statement, XMEAN = SUMX/EN. This and the following arithmetic statements compute the various coefficients desired, as indicated by the formulas appearing to the right in Figure A–4.

Following these arithmetic statements, two PRINT statements appear. Each PRINT statement has associated with it a FORMAT statement as indicated by the digit following the word PRINT. The first PRINT statement causes the computer to print on one line of the printer the various sums generated earlier. The second PRINT statement provides a print-out, on a second line, of the required regression and correlation coefficients.

---

[14] The fact that the value in I is to be increased by one each time is implied by the absence of a third value following the equality sign in this portion of the statement. If we had wished the computer to increase the value by two each time, for example, we would have written this portion of the DO statement as I = 1, N, 2. This would not have served our purpose here, of course. The flexibility of the DO statement is greater than we have indicated above, but we shall not concern ourselves with some features of this flexibility. One feature which we shall make use of later is the fact that the current value in I at the time a loop is being performed can be used within the loop as an indexing value (subscript). It should also be noted, perhaps, that we could have used any appropriate fixed-point name in place of I in the statement. The values following the equality sign may be constants or variables. In the statement above, we have used one of each type.

Since the analyst may wish to process more than one set of data in one visit to the computer, the GO TO 5 statement instructs the computer to return to the first of the program. If a second set of data does follow the first in the hopper of the card reader, the computer will begin immediately to process this data. Successive sets of data will be processed so long as they are made available to the card reader.

Simulation (Monte Carlo methods) with the computer: Outline of the problem

In Chapter 9, the procedure of simulation by use of Monte Carlo methods was illustrated by using an example in which a process for producing steel balls was simulated. In that chapter, several trials of the simulation were achieved by paper-and-pencil techniques. We noted there that in order to arrive at a good estimate of the proportion of balls that would be defective, we should have to proceed through a large number of trials of the simulation. This was prohibitive in terms of the paper-and-pencil technique because of the cost in time and effort. The results of 100 trials of the simulation, achieved with the use of the computer, were cited in that chapter to indicate the better quality of estimates based on a larger number of trials. Our final task in this appendix will be to present the program which produced this simulation, and to explain its components. It will pay us if we approach this discussion by considering different segments of the ultimate program separately. In this way, we shall arrive at a better understanding of the final program. We shall also have an opportunity to illustrate some alternatives in programming techniques which do not all appear in the final program. Before we proceed to these separate aspects of the program, however, we should consider the main requirements which the final program must meet.

The main ingredient in the simulation of the production process consisted of a set of random numbers. These random numbers were used in two ways in the simulation. First, they were used to determine which state the production process was in, for each trial. Second, the state of the process having been determined for a given trial, random numbers were used to determine the exact diameter to associate with the ball whose production was simulated in that trial. This was done by converting a four-digit sequence of random digits to the standardized normal variate, and converting this variate, in turn, into a particular diameter by noting the values of the mean and standard deviation associated with the given state of the process for that trial. Having determined a particular value for the diameter of the steel ball in that trial, it was finally noted whether or not the ball was defective by comparing this diameter against the lower and upper limits set for a nondefective ball.

The program which we design to perform the simulation must include these four elements. It must provide sequences of random digits. It must provide a method for converting sequences of random digits to the states of the process. It must provide a method for converting sequences of random digits to a normal random variable with a particular mean and standard deviation. And, finally, it must compare the resulting value for a diameter to the limits for a nondefective ball and note if the particular trial resulted in a ball that was nondefective or defective.

In Chapter 9, we made use of a table of random numbers to provide the random digit sequences we required. In the computer simulation, we wish the computer to make such sequences available internally, as they are required. We have already learned that the computer cannot provide anything for us unless we instruct it how it is to do so through a list of statements called a program. It is, therefore, up to the programmer to make a program available to the computer that will generate random numbers. This means that he must first decide upon a method which he believes will actually produce random numbers, and then he must write a program which instructs the computer in the steps required to follow this method.

There are many methods which have been suggested for producing random numbers. Some of these are much better than others. To be able to evaluate these different methods, one needs a high level of sophistication in mathematics. Moreover, we should like to choose a method which is relatively simple to understand and use. As a consequence of these two considerations, we shall illustrate generation of random numbers by a process known as the middle-digit rule. By this rule, one selects an initial number consisting of, say, four digits and squares this number. The result of the squaring process is an eight-digit number. For example, if the initial number is 7653 the square is 58568409. For some initial numbers, the square will contain several so-called high-order zeros in order to include eight digits. For example, the square of 1234 is 01522756, where the first digit is a high-order zero. Having squared the initial number, the middle four digits are considered to be a four-digit sequence of random digits. If the initial number had been 7653, as above, the square would be 58568409 and the middle four digits, 5684, would be chosen as a four-digit sequence of random digits. The next step is to square, in turn, this four-digit sequence and to select the middle four digits of that square as a second four-digit random number. Thus, the square of 5684 is 32307856, which yields a second four-digit sequence of 3078. Continuation of this procedure yields successive four-digit sequences which we treat as random sequences.

The middle-digit rule provides an easy method of generating four-digit sequences. It suffers from the deficiency that, eventually, this procedure will return to its starting place, if it does not in the meantime degenerate to a situation where it produces successive sequences containing nothing but zeros. It is easy to see that once a sequence containing nothing but zeros occurs, all following sequences must also be zeros. It is also rather obvious, intuitively, that if the procedure does not produce zeros, it will finally come back to the initial sequence of four digits from which the process started.

With these two defects, it is hard to accept the proposition that numbers generated by such a process can be truly random. One can, by proper selection of the initial four-digit sequence, improve on the process. That is, some initial values will provide a longer list of four-digit sequences before it is overcome by one or the other of these defects than will other initial values. In that sense, certain initial values provide sequences that are "more random" than others. Usually, also, if larger sequences of digits are used, say eight-digit sequences instead of four-digit sequences, for example, the procedure will provide a longer series of numbers. Since, in any case, the deficiencies noted are present, we shall refer to this procedure as one which generates quasi-random numbers. It will serve our purposes in illustrating the simulation process and in illustrating certain additional programming techniques.[15]

Once we have a procedure for generating random numbers, we must develop methods for converting these numbers into the states of the production process and into the normally distributed ball diameters associated with these states. Conversion of random numbers into the state of the production process will be accomplished in a manner analogous to the method used in Chapter 9. That is, the random sequence of digits will be compared to the cumulative probabilities we have learned to associate with each of the states of the production process. If the random sequence falls in a certain interval of these cumulative probabilities, the state corresponding to that interval will be assigned for the given trial of the simulation. We defer further consideration of this procedure until we come to a consideration of the final program.

The procedure used in the program for converting random numbers to a specific value of the normal random variable required will differ from the procedure of Chapter 9. There, we made use of the probability table for the standardized normal variate. We could do much the same thing with the computer. However, this would require that we first store such a probability distribution in the storage of the computer. We then would have to write a series of instructions which would lead the computer to search this table, in much the same way that we were required to search the probability table in the book, in order to find the value for z to asso-

---

[15] Any good computer installation will, of course, have available programs which generate random numbers, based upon more sophisticated procedures than the one we outlined above. Strictly, however, these procedures will also suffer from one or the other of the deficiencies noted above, unless special effort has been made to overcome them. In other words, the "randomness" of generated random numbers is a question of degree.

ciate with the particular random sequence. This involves rather difficult programming, so we choose an alternative. It has been shown[16] that if one has available a series of random digit sequences in decimal (fractional) form, one can generate a value with the characteristics of a standardized normal variate by using these fractional numbers, two at a time, in the following equation:

$$z = (-2 \cdot \log(R_1))^{\frac{1}{2}} \cdot \cos(6.283 \cdot R_2) \,,$$

where R_1 is one fractional sequence of random digits and R_2 is another.

We need not concern ourselves with the mystery of why the equation above will provide us with values of z that approximate the standardized normal variate. We need only note that, in order to make use of it, we must have access to a series of random digit sequences, in the form of decimal fractions which we can plug into the equation in pairs.[17] If the equation will provide us with a value for the standardized normal variate, z, it is still necessary for us to convert this value to a ball diameter from a normal distribution with mean value μ and standard deviation σ which will depend on the state of the production process. This can be accomplished by the computer in the same manner that it was done in Chapter 9. That is, the required diameter, x, corresponding to a given value of z is $x = z \cdot \sigma + \mu$.

The final function of the program, to determine if the ball simulated in a given trial is defective or not, can easily be accomplished by having the computer compare the diameter of the ball with the two limits on a nondefective ball. We defer consideration of this function until later.

Generation of quasi-random numbers

Having considered an outline of the full problem involved in writing a simulation program for the production process, we turn now to a consideration of the first element in the problem: providing quasi-random numbers. The program presented in Figure A–5 generates such numbers by use of the middle-digit rule (slightly modified in ways and for reasons which will be explained subsequently). The random sequences are then printed, 15 to a line. The program is written so as to provide 50 lines, for a total of $50(15) = 750$ four-digit sequences. Each of these four-digit sequences is expressed as a decimal fraction, with the decimal point falling immediately to the left of the four digits.

---

[16] In Box and Muller, "A Note on the Generation of Normal Deviates," *Annals of Mathematical Statistics*, Vol. XXIX (1958), pp. 610–11.

[17] The computer installation should have available standard subroutines to compute the values of LOGF(X) and COSF(X) which this equation requires. These subroutines are activated in the same fashion as SQRTF(X), as we shall note later.

Figure A–5

```
C        A PROGRAM TO PROVIDE QUASI-RANDOM FOUR DIGIT SEQUENCES BY A
C        MODIFICATION OF THE MIDDLE DIGIT RULE
         DIMENSION RAN (15)
     1   FORMAT (F4.4)
         READ 1, X
         DO 101 J = 1, 50
         DO 100 I = 1, 15
         X2 = X*X
         INITL2 = X2*100.0
         FLINL2 = INITL2
         DECIN2 = FLINL2/100.0
         XLAST6 = X2 − DECIN2
         X = XLAST6*100.0
   100   RAN(I) = X
   101   PRINT 2, (RAN(I), I = 1, 15)
     2   FORMAT (15F7.4)
         END
```

In order to see how the program accomplishes its purpose, let us look first at the sequence of instructions:

$$X2 = X*X$$
$$INITL2 = X2*100.0$$
$$FLINL2 = INITL2$$
$$DECIN2 = FLINL2/100.0$$
$$XLAST6 = X2 - DECIN2$$
$$X = XLAST6*100.0$$

This sequence of instructions falls within a loop specified by the statement, DO 100, $I = 1$, 15, and ending with the statement, 100 RAN(I) = X. At this point in the discussion, however, we wish to concentrate our attention only on the sequence listed above.

We have seen in the earlier discussion of the middle-digit rule that an initial value of four digits is required before the procedure can be started. Suppose that such an initial value has been stored in the location X prior to our consideration of the sequence of instructions given above. As a matter of fact, the statements 1 FORMAT (F4.4) and READ 1, X, are designed to provide such an initial value in four-digit decimal form.

With the initial value provided, the first statement in the sequence squares this value and stores the result in location X2. The value stored in X2 will, therefore, be an eight-digit sequence with a decimal point located to the left of the eight digits. If, for example, the initial value read into X had been .5555, X2 would contain the square of this value, or .30858025.

The second statement in the sequence, $INITL2 = X2 * 100.0$, multiplies the value in X2 by 100 and stores the result in the location INITL2. Note, however, that INITL2 is the name for a fixed-point variable, since it begins with the letter I. Consequently, the computer will truncate the decimal portion of the product generated in the expression to the right of the equality sign, and store only the nondecimal portion in INITL2. We see that the expression to the right of the equality sign will generate the product, $(.30858025)(100.0) = 30.858025$. Only the nondecimal portion of this value, 30, will be stored in INITL2 and it will be a fixed-point number. The effect of this statement, then, has been to isolate the upper two digits in the squared value. This was accomplished by making use of the fact that only the nondecimal portion of a floating-point value is stored in a location named for a fixed-point variable.

Although the second statement has isolated the upper two digits in the squared value for us, we will wish to use these digits later as a floating-point number. Consequently, the third statement, FLINL2 = INITL2 has the sole function of converting the fixed-point value of 30 back to a floating-point value of 30.0.

With the upper two digits isolated and again in floating-point form, this value is again converted to appropriate decimal form by the statement, DECIN2 = FLINL2/100.0. The result is to store the value of the quotient, $30.0/100.0 = .30$, in location DECIN2.

These first two decimal digits in the squared value are then subtracted in the statement, XLAST6 = X2 − DECIN2. The result is to place the value, $.30858025 - .30 = .00858025$, in location XLAST6.

Finally the statement, X = XLAST6 * 100.0, stores the product, $(.00858025)(100.0) = .858025$, in X. We see that the effect of the sequence of instructions is to square whatever value is in X at the beginning of the sequence and to convert the last six digits of the square of this value to a decimal fraction with the decimal point immediately to the left of these six digits. The six-digit decimal fraction is then stored back in the location X, replacing the initial value. The first four of these six digits are, of course, the middle four digits of the square of the value originally in X.

At this point, we have a six-digit sequence stored in location X, the first four digits of which are the four-digit sequence that we desire. We could have the computer print these four decimal digits by a PRINT and FORMAT statement such as PRINT 2, X and 2 FORMAT (F7.4). Given these two statements, the computer would reserve seven spaces on the printer line for a floating-point value, and these seven spaces would include room for four decimal digits, as well as a space for a sign, a space for the decimal point, and one extra space which would be printed as a blank. Thus, with the value .858025 stored in X, the computer would print out the value .8580, which is the desired four-digit sequence.

Although it is possible for us to get a print-out of each successive four-digit sequence as it is generated, in the manner indicated above, this would be wasteful of the computer's time and of the paper on which the print-out is made. We would be activating the printer each time to print one four-digit sequence per line, whereas the line of the printer sheet can hold many such numbers. The program in Figure A–5 was designed to print 15 such sequences at a time. In order to do this, however, it was necessary to store each successive set of six digits generated in the sequence of instructions explained above in a separate storage location until a full set of 15 such sequences were available to print. This was accomplished through the use of the variable I associated with this DO loop.

If we consider, now, the two statements in the DO loop that we have so far neglected, we shall see how the set of 15 sequences is generated and stored until all 15 can be printed at once. The statement, DO 100 I = 1, 15, instructs the computer to set the value of location I at 1 for the initial loop through and including statement number 100, and to loop through these statements a total of 15 times, increasing I by one each time. We have considered all of the statements in this loop, except statement number 100. In that statement, 100 RAN(I) = X, the computer will replace the I in parentheses with the value contained in the location I at the time that it comes upon the statement. In other words, the computer will read this statement, in the first loop when the value in I is one, as 100 RAN(1) = X. The function of the letter I appearing in this statement, then, is to serve as a subscripting index. The computer has been instructed to place the value currently in X, which we have seen will be .858025, in a location named RAN(1). When the computer continues through the second loop, the value of I will be two and the statement will then be interpreted as 100 RAN(2) = X. Accordingly, the computer will place the second generated value, which is now in location X, in a location specified as RAN(2). By the time that the computer has looped through this sequence of statements 15 times, it will have generated 15 six-digit values and stored these values in an *array* consisting of 15 separate locations. Notice that, at the beginning of each new loop, the value of X generated in the previous loop becomes the initial value which is used in the new loop.

We have indicated that the function of the term RAN(I) is to designate not one, but several different locations. In this case, since the value of I ranges from 1 through 15, there must be available 15 separate locations for storing these values. Moreover, the computer must have been instructed to reserve these locations prior to the point in the program where they actually must be used. In this program, the computer was asked to make available 15 locations for an *array*, which is to be referred to in the program by the name RAN, in the statement, DIMENSION RAN (15), appearing just above statement number 1. The name, RAN, refers to the total *array* of 15 locations. Any one of these locations can be referred to, as we did in the loop, by using the name RAN in conjunction with a subscript, RAN(I). The value of this subscript, at the time it is used in this manner, must be a value between 1 and 15, since only that number of locations are specified in the DIMENSION statement. The DIMENSION statement can be used to reserve locations for more than one array at a time, and these arrays must be subscripted with more than one subscript. We shall not endeavor, here, to explain the full use of the DIMENSION statement. We should mention that a DIMENSION statement may appear anywhere in the program, except as the first statement in a DO loop,[18] and that it must appear prior to the point in the program in which the array to which it pertains is used.

To summarize, the DO loop in the program which terminates in statement number 100 is designed to generate in succession 15 six-digit values and to store these values in separate locations of an array named RAN.

Having performed this DO loop 15 times, the computer will be ready to continue to the next statement, 101 PRINT 2, (RAN(I), I = 1, 15). This statement, in conjunction with the statement, 2 FORMAT (15F7.4), instructs the computer to print out, on one line, the 15 values stored in the array, RAN. Since the FORMAT statement allows only four decimal digits, however, the numbers printed will include only the required four-digit decimal sequences. Note, once again, that the subscript, I in RAN(I), in conjunction with the specification that I = 1, 15, serves to notify the computer that all 15 values are to be printed at once. The outer parentheses that enclose this designation are required for just that reason, to notify the computer that everything within constitutes one specification.

If our purpose had been to generate only 15 four-digit sequences, we would have been finished at this point. The program would have been complete. However, our purpose was to generate 50 lines of 15 such sequences. In order to return the computer to the task of generating another line of sequences, we insert another DO statement prior to the one which we have analyzed. The statement, DO 101 J = 1, 50, specifies a loop which contains within it all of the loop which we have just analyzed. When the computer comes upon the statement DO 101 J = 1, 50 for the first time, it sets a value in the location J equal to one and continues to the next statement. The next statement is, of course, DO 100 I = 1, 15. Accordingly, it sets a value of one in the location I and continues to the next statement. At this point, it has entered the loop which we have analyzed and which leads to the generation and storage of 15 six-digit sequences. Since this entire loop is contained within the loop specified by the DO 101 statement, this loop must be performed the full 15 times before the computer continues to the statement following this loop, 101 PRINT 2, (RAN(I), I = 1, 15). At this point, the first line of 15 four-digit values is printed, as described earlier.

With the performance of statement 101, the computer will have run through the loop associated with the DO 101 statement one time. It will then return to the first of this loop, set the value in J equal to two, and

---

[18] This is so because the first statement in a DO loop must be an executable instruction, and a DIMENSION statement is nonexecutable. That is, the computer does not execute any operation upon coming to a DIMENSION statement.

again start through the loop. Once again, it comes immediately to the second DO loop, which requires it to generate and store a second set of 15 six-digit sequences. Having completed the requirements for this loop a second time, it continues to the PRINT statement, which yields a second line of 15 four-digit values. The computer repeats this pattern 50 times, until on the last time through the two loops, J contains a value of 50. By this time, 50 lines of 15 values will have been printed, and the program will have been completely executed. Our purpose will have been accomplished.

When an arrangement of DO loops appears as in the program of Figure A–5, we refer to the loops as being *nested*. The ability to combine DO loops in this fashion allows great flexibility and power in programming. We cannot describe fully here the scope and features of DO statements. One point that should be mentioned is that if one DO loop begins within another DO loop, it must not extend beyond the range of that loop. Two DO loops may end with the same statement, however.

Before ending the discussion of this program, the modification of the middle-digit rule must be explained. In the strict middle-digit rule, only the four middle digits are squared each time, to arrive at the next value from which the middle four digits will again be taken. In our program, however, six digits remained in location X at the end of each loop. These six digits were then squared as the computer returned once again to the first of the loop, in the statement $X2 = X*X$. This means that in reality the computer generated successive squares by using all six digits in each loop, not just four digits. Each time, however, the first two digits were truncated, and the next four were then printed in the print-out. The reason for doing this is that if we had used only four digits each time to get a new squared term, the series of sequences would have returned to the initial value of the series, or degenerated to zero, much too quickly. Carrying along the extra digits served to lengthen the series of sequences we could get before one of these conditions occurred.

Even with the program written in this fashion, the longest series of sequences that it provided, for different initial values to start the series, consisted of about 140 sequences. Some other initial values might have improved on this performance. As it is, however, in order to use this program as a random number generator through a large series of operations in the simulation program, that program was designed, as we shall see, to begin a second series based on another initial value, so as to avoid the possibility of these conditions occurring part way through the execution of the program. With a more sophisticated random number generator, this would not be required.

With a program available which will generate quasi-random numbers in decimal form, the next step is to incorporate this program in a larger one which will convert these random numbers to a standardized normal variate, using the equation presented earlier. This can be done in several ways. As a vehicle for presenting additional features of the FORTRAN language to the student, we choose to present two alternatives which illustrate the use of subprograms.

It was indicated earlier that a computer installation will usually have available a library of subroutines which have been designed to perform certain functions that commonly are used in many different programs. The subroutine which is called into use by SQRTF(X), and which computes the square root of the value stored in X, is an example. It was also noted that an individual programmer might find that he required some function to be performed in several different problems which he had programmed. If that is the case, the programmer may wish to design a program which he can test to make sure it performs this function adequately, and then incorporate this program as a subprogram in the other programs where it is to be used. There are two types of subprogram which we consider. Their FORTRAN names are FUNCTION and SUBROUTINE, and they have slightly different features, which we shall point out. We consider the FUNCTION subprogram first.

Generating a random normal variate: Use of function illustrated

We wish to write a program which will generate a random normal variate. The program which we write to accomplish this must make use of random digits in decimal form. We already have a program available which provides six-digit sequences of random numbers in decimal form, so we wish to use it as a FUNCTION subprogram in the program which generates the normal variate. The program presented in Figure A–6 accomplishes this.

In actuality, the program of Figure A–6 consists of two programs, a

Figure A–6

```
C        A PROGRAM TO GENERATE A RANDOM NORMAL VARIATE. USE OF FUNCTION
C        ILLUSTRATED
     1   FORMAT (2F4.1, F4.4)
         READ 1, STADEV, XMEAN, RANX
         DO 100 J = 1, 50
         RAN1 = RAND(RANX)
         RAN2 = RAND(RAN1)
         RANX = RAN2
         STDNOR = (−2.0*LOGF(RAN1))**0.5*COSF(6.283*RAN2)
         VNORM = STDNOR*STADEV + XMEAN
   100   PRINT 2, VNORM, STDNOR
     2   FORMAT (F10.0, F7.3)
         END
         FUNCTION RAND(X)
         XSQ = X*X
         INITL2 = XSQ*100.0
         FLINL2 = INITL2
         DECIN2 = FLINL2/100.0
         XLAST6 = XSQ − DECIN2
         RAND = XLAST6*100.0
         RETURN
         END
```

main program and a FUNCTION subprogram. An END statement appears after each of them, indicating to the computer where the main program ends and the subprogram begins and ends.

Let us look, first, at the subprogram. The beginning statement, FUNCTION RAND(X), indicates to the computer that this is a FUNCTION subprogram, that its name is RAND, and that the function it performs is to be performed using a value in a location which will be referred to, in the subprogram, as X. Looking beyond this first statement, we see that the remaining statements duplicate the sequence of statements which we had occasion to give first consideration in the discussion of the program of Figure A–5. In other words, these statements make use of the value stored in the location X to generate a six-digit sequence which can be considered a sequence of random numbers, with the decimal point located immediately to the left of the sequence. The only differences between the earlier sequence of statements and this one is that the name X2 which appeared in the earlier one is replaced by XSQ here, and the name X which began the last statement in the earlier sequence of statements is here replaced with RAND. The first change is not required; we could as easily have used the name X2 again. The second change is required, because we must refer to the location in which the final result of the FUNCTION subprogram named RAND is stored by that same name, RAND.

To summarize, the FUNCTION subprogram named RAND is designed to take the value appearing in a location which it refers to as X, to generate a six-digit random sequence in decimal form using this value in X, and to store that six-digit sequence in a location named RAND. Having accomplished this, the computer will come upon the statement, RETURN, which indicates it is to return to the main program.

We began our consideration of this program with the subprogram. The computer, however, will start its execution of the statements in the main program. Our next task, therefore, is to see how the computer is instructed to go to the subprogram from the main program. The first statement in the main program which instructs the computer to go to the subprogram is RAN1 = RAND(RANX). This statement follows the general form of such statements as we have discussed them before. That is, it indicates to the computer that a value is to be arrived at according to the expression on the right of the equality sign, and this value is to be stored in the location specified on the left of the equality sign. Our concern, therefore, is to interpret the expression on the right of the equality sign.

The expression, RAND(RANX), can be usefully examined in two parts. The first part is the name, RAND. This part informs the computer that it is to go to the FUNCTION subprogram named RAND and perform the operations required in that subprogram before continuing with the main program. The second part of the expression, (RANX), indicates to the computer that wherever it comes upon the name X in the subprogram, it is to substitute the name RANX. This substitution feature means that when a value is stored in RANX, in the main program, it is this value which will be used, in the subprogram, wherever a statement of the subprogram refers to X.

This point bears repeating, from another approach. Let us compare the first statement in the subprogram with the statement of the main program that we have just interpreted. They are:

$$\text{FUNCTION RAND}(X)$$

and

$$\text{RAN1} = \text{RAND}(\text{RANX}) .$$

Notice that the name RAND appears in both of them. Notice, also, that in the first statement the name X appears in parentheses, and in the second statement the name RANX appears in parentheses. The computer notes this parallel and is thus instructed to use the value in RANX, as generated in the main program, wherever the name X is used in the subprogram. The reason for this substitution feature is that it allows the subprogram to be used in conjunction with any appropriate main program, regardless of what names have been used in the main program. It is not necessary that the names of the main program and those of the subprogram match.

Bearing in mind that the subprogram RAND performs the function of generating a six-digit random sequence from an initial value, and noting that this initial value will be equated with the value in a location named RANX in the main program, we see that the location RAN1 will come to contain a six-digit decimal value which will have been generated from the value in RANX.

The next statement of the main program, RAN2 = RAND(RAN1), performs in the same fashion as the one just discussed. In this case, however, the value now stored in RAN1 as a result of the previous statement is to be used in the subprogram to generate a new six-digit sequence. This new six-digit sequence is then to be stored in a location named RAN2. The next statement in the main program, RANX = RAN2, serves the purpose of storing the latest generated six-digit sequence in RANX. This is done so that when the computer again goes through the DO loop in the main program, there will be a new value waiting in RANX with which it can continue to generate the series of random numbers.

At this point in the loop, two random digit sequences are available, in decimal form, in the locations RAN1 and RAN2. These values are used in the statement, STDNOR $= (-2.0 * \text{LOGF}(\text{RAN1})) ** 0.5 * \text{COSF}$ (6.283 * RAN2), to generate a value for z, the standardized normal variate. This statement, of course, is just the FORTRAN equivalent of the equation presented earlier. The terms LOGF(RAN1) and COSF(6.283 * RAN2) make use of standard subroutines available in the computer's library of subroutines. They are used in much the same way as the subprogram we have described. With a value of z stored in the location STDNOR, the computer is asked to convert this to a particular normal variate with given values for σ and μ, through the relation $x = z \cdot \sigma + \mu$. The statement, VNORM = STDNOR * STADEV + XMEAN, accomplishes this conversion and stores the result in the location VNORM.

Finally, the PRINT statement instructs the computer to print out the values of the particular normal variate and the standardized normal variate according to the FORMAT statement number 2.

As is usually the case, certain values must be made available at the start of the program. In this case, values were needed for the standard deviation and mean of the particular normal distribution and for an initial value to begin the series of random numbers. These are provided on a data card which is read by the computer according to the first two statements in the main program.

One or two additional comments should be made concerning the FUNCTION subprogram. One point to note is that the FUNCTION subprogram can be used with more than one argument (that is, more than one value to be used in evaluating the function). In our program, only one argument was required, the value of X (which became, in turn, RANX and RAN1 as the FUNCTION subprogram was used in conjunction with the main program). The function which generates random digit sequences requires only a single value, X, to accomplish this. Many functions require more than one argument, however, and a FUNCTION subprogram written to perform such a function would list, in the parentheses following the name of the function, all of these arguments. The names of the separate arguments would be separated by commas. Suppose, for example, that a FUNCTION subprogram was to be written which would compute the area of a rectangle. This function requires two arguments: the lengths of the two sides. Suppose that the names of these lengths are specified in the subprogram as S1 and S2. Then the first statement in the subprogram, which will name the subprogram and specify the arguments, could be written as:

FUNCTION AREA (S1, S2) .

If, in the main program, the two sides were designated by the names SIDE1 and SIDE2, a statement in that program would refer to the FUNCTION subprogram by an expression to the right of the equality sign: AREA(SIDE1, SIDE2). Then the computer would equate the names S1 and S2 with the names SIDE1 and SIDE2, respectively.

To summarize, although the FUNCTION subprogram can provide only one value as the result of the function which it performs (for example, the value AREA for a rectangle), it may use more than one argument in arriving at that value (for example, S1 and S2).

Another point that must be made concerning the FUNCTION subprogram is with regard to the name assigned to it. This name must observe the rule stated earlier concerning fixed-point names and floating-point names. That is, if the value yielded by the function is to be a fixed-point value, the name of the FUNCTION subprogram must begin with one of the letters, I, J, K, L, M, or N. If it is to be a floating-point value, one of the other letters of the alphabet must be used as the first letter of the name. One further general rule that it is useful to observe is not to end the FUNCTION name with the letter F. This will avoid any possibility of the computer confusing the programmer's specially written subprogram with one of the subroutines that are available to it as a part of the standard library of subroutines.

Once again, we must serve notice that the description of the FUNCTION subprogram given above does not exhaust all the features of this type of program. The student may gain greater familiarity with its uses through study of material devoted more especially to programming.

Generating a random normal variate: Use of subroutine illustrated

We wish to turn our attention at this point to a second type of subprogram, the SUBROUTINE. Since it is also a subprogram, the SUBROUTINE has many of the features of the FUNCTION subprogram. It varies only with respect to the rules for naming it, the manner in which it is referred to in the main program, and the fact that it can be used to generate more than one value which is to be used in the main program. It is this third difference which makes the SUBROUTINE a useful alternative to the FUNCTION subprogram.

In a SUBROUTINE subprogram, several different values may be generated, using several different arguments. The values generated in the SUBROUTINE may be either fixed point or floating point, or may consist of both types. Consequently, the name of the SUBROUTINE need not start with a letter which reflects either of these two modes. This is the only difference in the rules for naming SUBROUTINE and FUNCTION subprograms.

The manner in which the SUBROUTINE is used, and the differences between it and the FUNCTION subprogram, can best be illustrated by reference to a program in which one is used. The program of Figure A–7 is designed to accomplish the same purpose as the program of Figure A–6, to generate a random normal variate. In Figure A–7, however, this is accomplished with a SUBROUTINE subprogram.

Let us look, first, at the subprogram to see what it accomplishes. We note that the first statement in the subprogram identifies it as a SUB-

ROUTINE with the name RAND and that there are two variables specified in the parentheses, RANDX and X. The first of these, RANDX, is actually the name of an array. In the subprogram, we wish to generate two random digit sequences and store these to be used later in the main program. Consequently, we designate a name for this array. The second statement in the subprogram, DIMENSION RANDX(2), then indicates to the computer that this name is associated with an array which is to contain two separate locations. The second variable, X, in the parentheses of the SUBROUTINE statement is the name which will refer, in the subprogram, to the value from which a random digit sequence is to be generated by the middle-digit rule (as modified for our use).

Figure A–7

```
C       A PROGRAM TO GENERATE A RANDOM NORMAL VARIATE. USE OF SUBROUTINE
C       ILLUSTRATED
     1  FORMAT (2F4.1, F4.4)
        READ 1, STADEV, XMEAN, RANX
        DIMENSION RAN(2)
        DO 100 J = 1, 50
        CALL RAND(RAN, RANX)
        RANX = RAN(2)
        STDNOR = (−2.0*LOGF(RAN(1)))**0.5*COSF(6.283*RAN(2))
        VNORM = STDNOR*STADEV + XMEAN
   100  PRINT 2, VNORM, STDNOR
     2  FORMAT (F10.1, F7.3)
        END
        SUBROUTINE RAND (RANDX, X)
        DIMENSION RANDX (2)
        DO 1 I = 1, 2
        XSQ = X*X
        INITL2 = XSQ*100.0
        FLINL2 = INITL2
        DECIN2 = FLINL2/100.0
        XLAST6 = XSQ − DECIN2
        RANDX(I) = XLAST6*100.0
     1  X = RANDX(I)
        RETURN
        END
```

Looking, now, beyond the DIMENSION statement, we note that the subprogram consists of a DO loop which is very much like the loop of Figure A–5 which was used to generate 15 successive random digit sequences to be printed in one line on the printer. As a matter of fact, the only substantive difference between these two loops is that the one of Figure A–7 is designed to generate and store only two random digit sequences at a time. The reason for this is, of course, that in the main program these sequences will be used only two at a time in the equation that generates the standardized normal variate. These two random digit sequences will be stored in locations referred to, in the subprogram, as RANDX(1) and RANDX(2). The last statement of the loop, 1 X = RANDX(I), is placed there to make certain that a value will be available, the next time the loop is performed, to be used in generating the next random digit sequence. When the DO statement of the subprogram has been satisfied, that is, when two random digit sequences have been generated and stored as indicated, the computer will come upon the RE-TURN statement which sends it back to the main program.

We have only to see, now, the manner in which the main program and the SUBROUTINE are linked together. The computer will come upon the statement, CALL RAND(RAN, RANX), in the main program. This is its signal to branch to the SUBROUTINE subprogram named RAND. In addition, it is instructed by the names in parentheses that the name RAN in the main program is to substitute for the name RANDX in the subprogram and that the name RANX of the main program is to substitute for the name X in the subprogram. It makes these substitutions, as in the case of the FUNCTION subprogram, by noting the order of occurrence of the two sets of names in their respective designations. The names RAN and RANDX, then, refer to the same thing. We have noted, however, that RANDX is an array containing two locations. It is necessary, therefore, to specify in the main program that RAN is an array with two locations. This is done by the statement, DIMENSION RAN(2), just prior to the DO 100 statement.

Comparison of the function and subroutine subprograms

The SUBROUTINE of Figure A–7 serves the same purpose as the FUNCTION of Figure A–6. It will be profitable to compare the two and note the difference in the manner this is accomplished. Note, first, that in the FUNCTION subprogram only one value is generated, the value of RAND in the final statement, RAND = XLAST6 * 100.0. By contrast, the SUBROUTINE generates two values, RANDX(1) and RANDX(2), through the performance of the DO loop it contains. The important distinction is not that the SUBROUTINE contains a DO loop and the FUNCTION does not. A FUNCTION subprogram could be written with a DO loop also. The important point is that the SUBROUTINE has the flexibility to generate more than one value at a time, whereas the FUNCTION can generate only one.

A consequence of this difference in the two subprograms is that, while a FUNCTION can be referred to within an arithmetic statement as if it were a variable, a SUBROUTINE cannot. Thus, a separate CALL statement is required for the SUBROUTINE. By contrast, in Figure A–6, the FUNCTION subprogram is referred to within a statement, such as RAN1 = RAND(RANX). Note, however, that the main program of Figure A–6 required two such statements to generate the two random digit sequences, whereas the main program of Figure A–7 required only one CALL statement. Since only two values are required in the main programs, there is not much to choose between the two types of subprogram. If we had required a large number of these sequences to be used within the main program, however, it should be obvious that the SUB-ROUTINE would take on a decided advantage.

With the discussion of subprograms, we complete the catalog of programming techniques which can be presented within the scope of this book. To emphasize again, the points made here are the bare fundamentals of the FORTRAN language. With these techniques, the student can accomplish many programming tasks. The full range of power and flexibility of the FORTRAN language is not revealed in the short space that we have allotted to it, however. The student with a continuing interest in computer analysis should avail himself of other sources of information on programming, in order to develop a wider and firmer knowledge of the field.

Meanwhile, we turn our attention to the simulation program which has been our ultimate goal. No programming devices are required there that we have not already used. We will need to consider some of the detail of the program, however.

Computer simulation of a production process

It was noted earlier in this chapter that a computer simulation of the production process described in Chapter 9 requires four elements. The first of these is a method to generate random digit sequences. The second is a method of converting these random digit sequences to a normal variate with specified mean and standard deviation. The third element is a method of determining, with the use of random digit sequences, the state of the production process (that is, the mean diameter of the steel balls being produced by the process). The fourth element required is a method of distinguishing defective from nondefective balls by comparing the simulated diameter to the lower and upper limits of a satisfactory diameter. We have gone to great lengths to develop a method of generating random digits and converting these into a random normal variate with specified mean and standard deviation. Either of the programs in Figure A–6 and Figure A–7 will accomplish this purpose. Either can easily be incorporated in a larger program to perform the total simulation. The other elements are also easily provided by techniques which we have discussed earlier. The program in Figure A–8 combines all of these elements.[19]

Notice, first of all, that this program makes use of the FUNCTION subprogram discussed earlier. It uses this subprogram in three separate statements of the main program. It is used, first, in the statement RAN1 = RAND(RANX), which is the second statement following statement number 1. It is used for the second and third time in statement number 6 and

---

[19] We must discuss the program in segments. The student may find it helpful to refer to the flow diagram of Figure A–9, page 425, from time to time.

the statement immediately following. If the student will follow the main program from statement number 6 to statement number 30, he will note that this segment of the program just performs the familiar function of converting two random digit sequences to a normal variate with given mean, U, and standard deviation, S, and then printing the value of this

Figure A–8

```
C        A PROGRAM TO SIMULATE A PROCESS THAT MANUFACTURES A PART. THE DIM
C        ENSION OF THE PART IS N (U,S). THE VALUE OF S IS STABLE. THE VAL
C        UE OF U VARIES ACCORDING TO A DISCRETE PROBABILITY DISTRIBUTION.
C        P(U = B) = PB, P(U = C) = PC, P(U = A) = PA. IF DIMENSION OF
C        PART IS LESS THAN 9.8 OR MORE THAN 10.2 THE PART IS DEFECTIVE.
     10  FORMAT (3(F5.1, F4.4), F7.3)
         READ 10, B, PB, C, PC, A, PA, S
     20  FORMAT (F4.4)
         NA = 0
         NB = 0
      1  READ 20, RANX
         DO 40 I = 1, 50
         RAN1 = RAND(RANX)
         RANX = RAN1
         IF (PB − RAN1) 3, 3, 2
      3  IF (PB + PC − RAN1) 5, 5, 4
      2  U = B
         GO TO 6
      4  U = C
         GO TO 6
      5  U = A
      6  RAN1 = RAND(RANX)
         RAN2 = RAND(RAN1)
         RANX = RAN2
         STDNOR = (−2.0*LOGF(RAN1))**0.5*COSF(6.283*RAN2)
         VNORM = STDNOR*S + U
         PRINT 30, VNORM
     30  FORMAT (F10.3)
         IF (10.2 − VNORM) 50, 40, 60
     60  IF (9.8 − VNORM) 40, 40, 70
     50  NA = NA + 1
         GO TO 40
     70  NB = NB + 1
     40  CONTINUE
         PRINT 80, NA, NB
     80  FORMAT (2I4)
         GO TO 1
         END
         FUNCTION RAND(X)
         XSQ = X*X
         INITL2 = XSQ*100.0
         FLINL2 = INITL2
         DECIN2 = FLINL2/100.0
         XLAST6 = XSQ − DECIN2
         RAND = XLAST*6100.0
         RETURN
         END
```

variate. Thus, this segment of the program provides one of the four required elements of the simulation.

The second and third uses of the FUNCTION subprogram occur in connection with the generation of a simulated value for the diameter of the steel ball, given a particular value of the mean and the standard deviation for the production process. The standard deviation of the process was, it will be remembered, assumed to be stable, so that a value for this parameter can be provided once and for all at the first of the program in a READ statement. In the case of the mean of the process, however, there were three possible values of this parameter, and the particular state of the process must be determined randomly according to the probability distribution of these states.

It is in this connection that the random digit sequence generated in the first use of the FUNCTION subprogram is employed. To understand how this is done, we need to recall the manner in which it was decided, in Chapter 9, if the process was in state B, C, or A on each trial of the simulation. An examination of Figure 9–2 (page 303) will refresh the student's memory on this point. There, we note that the rule was: If the sequence of random digits selected is less than .35, the process is in state B; if the sequence is between .35 and .84 inclusive, the process is in state C; and if the sequence is between .85 and .99 inclusive, the process is in state A. For the process to be in one of these states corresponded to the mean diameter of the steel balls being equal to 9.9 mm., 10.0 mm., or 10.1 mm., respectively.

In order for the computer to simulate these three states, therefore, it must have available the mean values associated with the three states and the probabilities associated with these three states. If these are available, the computer can then compare a sequence of decimal random digits to cumulated sums of the probabilities for the states and select the proper value for the mean of the process according to the rule stated above. A sequence of decimal random digits is provided, of course, by use of the FUNCTION subprogram, RAND.

The values of the three means and their probabilities are provided through a data card which is read in the format specified by the FOR-MAT statement number 10, in response to the second statement of the program, READ 10, B, PB, C, PC, A, PA, S. This data card also contains the value of the standard deviation, S, relevant in all three states of the process. The contents of the data card, and their interpretation according to the FORMAT statement, are given below:

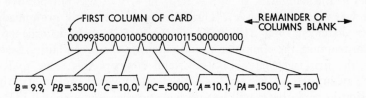

Notice that the data card contains three pairs of values corresponding to the three values of the mean and the associated probabilities. These pairs have the same configuration, F5.1, F4.4. The FORMAT statement number 10 takes advantage of this similarity in the specification 3(F5.1, F4.4). The second specification, of course, is for the value of the standard deviation, indicating a total of seven columns allotted to that value, with three decimal digits.

A second READ statement, statement number 1 of the program, is used to make a beginning value available in location RANX to "start" the random number generation when the FUNCTION subprogram is used the first time.

Following this READ statement, the computer immediately enters a DO loop which provides simulated diameters for the steel balls, notes whether each is defective or not, and keeps separate count of the number of defective balls which are too large and those which are too small. These two counts are generated in locations NA and NB, respectively. Prior to entering the DO loop, therefore, the two locations are given zero values by the two statements, NA = 0 and NB = 0.

Immediately following entry of the DO loop, the computer comes upon the portion of the program designed to determine the state of the process. The first step is to generate a decimal random digit sequence, and this is provided by use of the FUNCTION. This random decimal is then first compared to PB, in the statement IF (PB − RAN1) 3, 3, 2. If RAN1 is smaller than PB, the expression in parentheses will have a positive value, and the computer will accordingly branch to statement number 2. In the case, when the random decimal is smaller than the value in PB, of course, the process is to be in the state with the mean diameter equal to the value in location B, 9.9. Consequently, statement number 2 places this mean value in the location U, and the computer branches to statement number 6 according to the instruction, GO TO 6, which immediately follows statement number 2. We have already seen that statement number 6 and those following generate and print a normal variate with mean equal to the value in U and a standard deviation equal to the value in S. Thus, if this sequence of statements is followed, a random diameter for a steel ball produced in state B is provided.

Suppose, now, that the computer found that the expression in parentheses in the statement, IF (PB − RAN1) 3, 3, 2, was not positive (that is, it was zero, or negative). Then the computer would go immediately to the statement, 3 IF (PB + PC − RAN1) 5, 5, 4. In accordance with this instruction, the computer would cumulate the probabilities associated with the first two states, PB + PC, and compare this value to RAN1. Once again, if RAN1 is smaller than this cumulated probability, the expression in parentheses will be positive, and the computer will branch to statement number 4. At this point, it has been determined that RAN1 is not smaller than PB, but it is smaller than PB + PC. It must, therefore, be the case that the correct mean value for the process is the value in location C, 10.0. Consequently, statement number 4 causes the computer to store this value in location U, and the computer once again branches to the portion of the program in which a random diameter is determined. This time, however, the mean of the process will be simulated as equal to 10.0 mm.

Finally, suppose that the value in parentheses in the statement, 3 IF (PB + PC − RAN1) 5, 5, 4, is not positive. Then, since the mean values of 9.9 and 10.0 will have been eliminated, the mean value must be 10.1. The computer branches to statement number 5, where it stores the value 10.1 in U and goes immediately to statement number 6. In this case, the random diameter generated will be for the process in the state with mean diameter of 10.1 mm. Thus, the two IF statements just discussed provide a basis of determining the mean of the process, and subsequent execution of statement number 6 and following statements generates the random diameter associated with that state.

A final task of the program is to keep a count of the defective balls that are too large and too small. This is accomplished by the two IF statements following statement number 30. The first of these, IF (10.2 − VNORM) 50, 40, 60, determines if the simulated diameter, VNORM, is larger than, equal to, or smaller than, the upper limit, 10.2 mm. If it is larger, the ball is defective on the high side, and the computer is directed to statement number 50. There, it adds a value of one to the current contents of NA and continues to statement number 40. If the simulated value is equal to the upper limit, the computer is directed to statement number 40, with no count made, since the ball is not defective in this case. If the simulated value is smaller than the upper limit, it still must be determined if it is also smaller than the lower limit. This is accomplished by the statement, 60 IF (9.8 − VNORM) 40, 40, 70. Only in the case where the expression in parentheses is positive will the ball be defective (that is, too small). Accordingly, the computer goes directly to statement number 40 if the expression is negative or zero, and it goes to statement number 70 if it is positive. In statement 70, a value of one is added to the count of balls which are too small.

Notice that the pair of IF statements in which it is determined if the simulated diameter is too large, too small, or satisfactory serve to branch the computer to different statements, depending upon the condition found to exist. They operate in the same fashion as the pair of IF statements which are used to determine the state of the process. In each case, it is necessary for the computer to be directed back into the main flow of the program, once the relevant condition (state of the process in the one case, defective or nondefective in the other case) has been determined. In the case of the state of the process, it will be noted that once the state has been determined, the computer is directed to statement number 6, which begins the simulation of a particular diameter. In the case of determining if the diameter is too large, too small, or satisfactory, once this determination has been made, and the appropriate count made if needed, the computer is directed to the statement 40 CONTINUE. This statement is placed in the program to provide a common ending place for the DO loop which the computer entered at the first of the program. It is not an executable instruction but serves only to indicate to the computer that the loop has been satisfied and it should therefore return to the first of the loop until it has satisfied the loop the full number of times specified. The CONTINUE statement is required in other circumstances which we shall not mention here.

The loop that terminates in statement number 40 must be performed 50 times before the computer will leave the loop. This is the case since the initiating DO statement is DO 40 I = 1, 50. Upon leaving the loop, the computer will have generated and printed 50 simulated diameters for steel balls, it will have noted in each case if the diameter was satisfactory or not, and in the cases in which the diameter was unsatisfactory it will have kept count of how many were too large and how many were too small. The first statement following the loop, PRINT 80, NA, NB, causes the computer to print the fixed-point values contained in these two locations, which are just the number of diameters among the 50 which were too large and the number which were too small.

The computer was limited to 50 times through the loop because of the fact we noted earlier that the quasi-random digit generator which we have used will degenerate rather quickly. In the course of 50 loops, the computer will be required to generate 150 sequences of random digits. This may be close to the full number of such sequences the quasi-random digit generator will provide before it degenerates, depending on the starting value used. Because of this, the computer is instructed, following the print-out of the numbers of balls that were too large and too small, to GO TO 1, where it can then read a new starting value. With a second starting value available, it then enters the DO loop for a second time and generates 50 more simulated diameters.

This process can be continued with additional starting values, to give a number of simulation trials equal to a large multiple of 50. One must be careful, of course, to select a set of starting values which are known to provide at least 150 quasi-random digit sequences before degenerating. We emphasize, again, that our simulation program incorporates this particular quasi-random digit generator because it afforded us the opportunity to work through all aspects of the simulation. In an actual simulation, the programmer would wish to make use of a more sophisticated random digit generator which will provide a virtually inexhaustible supply of random digit sequences.

The simulation program of Figure A–8 is not large, but it is somewhat complex. As an aid in gaining an understanding of the manner in which it performs the simulation, a flow diagram is provided as Figure A–9.

Figure A–9

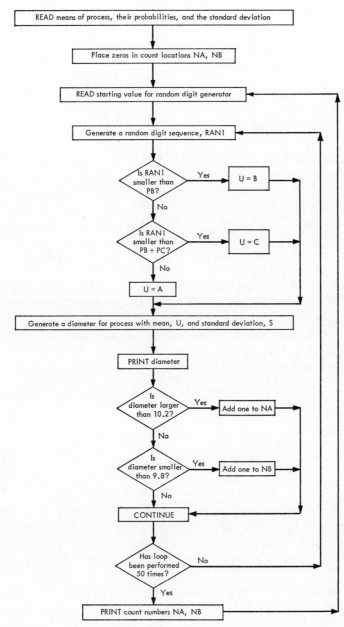

Tables

Table A

SELECTED VALUES OF WILCOXON'S (UNPAIRED) DISTRIBUTION

$(W_s - \text{Min } W_s)$ or $(\text{Max } W_l - W_l)$

s	l	Min W_s	Max W_l	0	1	2	3	4	5	6	7	8	9	10	11	12	13	14	15	16	17	18	19	20
2	2	3	7																					
	3	3	12	.100																				
	4	3	18	.067	.133	.190																		
	5	3	25	.048	.095	.190																		
	6	3	33	.036	.071	.143																		
	7	3	42	.028	.056	.111																		
	8	3	52	.022	.044	.089	.133																	
3	2	6	9	.100																				
	3	6	15	.050	.100																			
	4	6	22	.029	.057	.114																		
	5	6	30	.018	.036	.071	.125																	
	6	6	39	.012	.024	.048	.083	.131																
	7	6	49	.008	.017	.033	.058	.092	.133															
	8	6	60	.006	.012	.024	.042	.067	.097	.139														
4	2	10	11	.067	*																			
	3	10	18	.029	.057	.114																		
	4	10	26	.014	.029	.057	.100	*																
	5	10	35	.008	.016	.032	.056	.095	.143															
	6	10	45	.005	.010	.019	.033	.057	.086	.129														
	7	10	56	.003	.006	.012	.021	.036	.055	.082	.115													
	8	10	68	.002	.004	.008	.014	.024	.036	.055	.077	.107												
5	3	15	21	.018	.036	.071	.125	*																
	4	15	30	.008	.016	.032	.056	.095	.143															
	5	15	40	.004	.008	.016	.028	.048	.075	.111														
	6	15	51	.002	.004	.009	.015	.026	.041	.063	.089	.123												
	7	15	63	.001	.003	.005	.009	.015	.024	.037	.053	.074	.101											
	8	15	76	.001	.002	.003	.005	.009	.015	.023	.033	.047	.064	.085	.111									

Table A (Continued)

$(W_s - \text{Min } W_s)$ or $(\text{Max } W_l - W_l)$

s	l	$\text{Min } W_s$	$\text{Max } W_l$	0	1	2	3	4	5	6	7	8	9	10	11	12	13	14	15	16	17	18	19	20
6	3	21	24	.012	.024	*																		
	4	21	34	.005	.010	.019	.033	.057	.086	.129	*													
	5	21	45	.002	.004	.009	.015	.026	.041	.063	.089	.123												
	6	21	57	.001	.002	.004	.008	.013	.021	.032	.047	.066	.090	.120										
	7	21	70	.001	.001	.002	.004	.007	.011	.017	.026	.037	.051	.069	.090	.117								
	8	21	84	.000	.001	.001	.002	.004	.006	.010	.015	.021	.030	.041	.054	.071	.091	.114						
7	4	28	38	.003	.006	.012	.021	.036	.055	*														
	5	28	50	.001	.003	.005	.009	.015	.024	.037	.053	.074	.101											
	6	28	63	.001	.001	.002	.004	.007	.011	.017	.026	.037	.051	.069	.090	.117								
	7	28	77	.000	.001	.001	.002	.003	.006	.009	.013	.019	.027	.036	.049	.064	.082	.104						
	8	28	92	.000	.000	.001	.001	.002	.003	.005	.007	.010	.014	.020	.027	.036	.047	.060	.076	.095	.116			
8	4	36	42	.002	.004	.008	.014	*																
	5	36	55	.001	.002	.003	.005	.009	.015	.023	.033	.047	.064	*										
	6	36	69	.000	.001	.001	.002	.004	.006	.010	.015	.021	.030	.041	.054	.071	.091	.114						
	7	36	84	.000	.000	.001	.001	.002	.003	.005	.007	.010	.014	.020	.027	.036	.047	.060	.076	.095	.116			
	8	36	100	.000	.000	.000	.001	.001	.001	.002	.003	.005	.007	.010	.014	.019	.025	.032	.041	.052	.065	.080	.097	.117

* Indicates that the value at head of this column (and those values that are larger) are not possible for the given values of s and l in this row.

Table B

BINOMIAL DISTRIBUTIONS: $P(r \leqslant r_0|n,p)$

n	r_0	.10	.25	.40	.50	n	r_0	.10	.25	.40	.50
1	0	.9000	.7500	.6000	.5000	20	0	.1216	.0032	.0000	.0000
	1	1.0000	1.0000	1.0000	1.0000		1	.3917	.0243	.0005	.0000
							2	.6768	.0912	.0036	.0002
5	0	.5905	.2373	.0778	.0313		3	.8669	.2251	.0159	.0013
	1	.9185	.6328	.3370	.1875		4	.9567	.4148	.0509	.0059
	2	.9914	.8965	.6826	.5000		5	.9886	.6171	.1255	.0207
	3	.9995	.9844	.9130	.8125		6	.9975	.7857	.2499	.0577
	4	.9999	.9990	.9898	.9687		7	.9995	.8981	.4158	.1316
	5	1.0000	1.0000	1.0000	1.0000		8	.9999	.9590	.5955	.2517
							9	1.0000	.9861	.7552	.4119
10	0	.3487	.0563	.0060	.0010		10	1.0000	.9960	.8723	.5881
	1	.7361	.2440	.0463	.0108		11	1.0000	.9990	.9433	.7483
	2	.9298	.5256	.1672	.0547		12	1.0000	.9998	.9788	.8684
	3	.9872	.7759	.3822	.1719		13	1.0000	1.0000	.9934	.9423
	4	.9984	.9219	.6330	.3770		14	1.0000	1.0000	.9983	.9793
	5	.9999	.9803	.8337	.6230		15	1.0000	1.0000	.9996	.9941
	6	1.0000	.9965	.9452	.8281		16	1.0000	1.0000	1.0000	.9987
	7	1.0000	.9996	.9877	.9453		17	1.0000	1.0000	1.0000	.9998
	8	1.0000	1.0000	.9983	.9892		18	1.0000	1.0000	1.0000	1.0000
	9	1.0000	1.0000	.9999	.9990		19	1.0000	1.0000	1.0000	1.0000
	10	1.0000	1.0000	1.0000	1.0000		20	1.0000	1.0000	1.0000	1.0000

This table is adapted from *Tables of the Binomial Probability Distribution*, National Bureau of Standards, Applied Mathematics Series, 6, U.S. Department of Commerce, 1952.

Table C. AREAS UNDER THE NORMAL CURVE

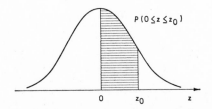

$P(0 \leq z \leq z_0)$

z_0	.00	.01	.02	.03	.04	.05	.06	.07	.08	.09
0.0	.0000	.0040	.0080	.0120	.0160	.0199	.0239	.0279	.0319	.0359
0.1	.0398	.0438	.0478	.0517	.0557	.0596	.0636	.0675	.0714	.0753
0.2	.0793	.0832	.0871	.0910	.0948	.0987	.1026	.1064	.1103	.1141
0.3	.1179	.1217	.1255	.1293	.1331	.1368	.1406	.1443	.1480	.1517
0.4	.1554	.1591	.1628	.1664	.1700	.1736	.1772	.1808	.1844	.1879
0.5	.1915	.1950	.1985	.2019	.2054	.2088	.2123	.2157	.2190	.2224
0.6	.2257	.2291	.2324	.2357	.2389	.2422	.2454	.2486	.2518	.2549
0.7	.2580	.2612	.2642	.2673	.2704	.2734	.2764	.2794	.2823	.2852
0.8	.2881	.2910	.2939	.2967	.2995	.3023	.3051	.3078	.3106	.3133
0.9	.3159	.3186	.3212	.3238	.3264	.3289	.3315	.3340	.3365	.3389
1.0	.3413	.3438	.3461	.3485	.3508	.3531	.3554	.3577	.3599	.3621
1.1	.3643	.3665	.3686	.3708	.3729	.3749	.3770	.3790	.3810	.3830
1.2	.3849	.3869	.3888	.3907	.3925	.3944	.3962	.3980	.3997	.4015
1.3	.4032	.4049	.4066	.4082	.4099	.4115	.4131	.4147	.4162	.4177
1.4	.4192	.4207	.4222	.4236	.4251	.4265	.4279	.4292	.4306	.4319
1.5	.4332	.4345	.4357	.4370	.4382	.4394	.4406	.4418	.4429	.4441
1.6	.4452	.4463	.4474	.4484	.4495	.4505	.4515	.4525	.4535	.4545
1.7	.4554	.4564	.4573	.4582	.4591	.4599	.4608	.4616	.4625	.4633
1.8	.4641	.4649	.4656	.4664	.4671	.4678	.4686	.4693	.4699	.4706
1.9	.4713	.4719	.4726	.4732	.4738	.4744	.4750	.4756	.4761	.4767
2.0	.4772	.4778	.4783	.4788	.4793	.4798	.4803	.4808	.4812	.4817
2.1	.4821	.4826	.4830	.4834	.4838	.4842	.4846	.4850	.4854	.4857
2.2	.4861	.4864	.4868	.4871	.4875	.4878	.4881	.4884	.4887	.4890
2.3	.4893	.4896	.4898	.4901	.4904	.4906	.4909	.4911	.4913	.4916
2.4	.4918	.4920	.4922	.4925	.4927	.4929	.4931	.4932	.4934	.4936
2.5	.4938	.4940	.4941	.4943	.4945	.4946	.4948	.4949	.4951	.4952
2.6	.4953	.4955	.4956	.4957	.4959	.4960	.4961	.4962	.4963	.4964
2.7	.4965	.4966	.4967	.4968	.4969	.4970	.4971	.4972	.4973	.4974
2.8	.4974	.4975	.4976	.4977	.4977	.4978	.4979	.4979	.4980	.4981
2.9	.4981	.4982	.4982	.4983	.4984	.4984	.4985	.4985	.4986	.4986
3.0	.49865	.4987	.4987	.4988	.4988	.4989	.4989	.4989	.4990	.4990
3.1	.49903	.4991	.4991	.4991	.4992	.4992	.4992	.4992	.4993	.4993
3.2	.4993129	.4993	.4994	.4994	.4994	.4994	.4994	.4995	.4995	.4995
3.3	.4995166	.4995	.4995	.4996	.4996	.4996	.4996	.4996	.4996	.4997
3.4	.4996631	.4997	.4997	.4997	.4997	.4997	.4997	.4997	.4998	.4998
3.5	.4997674	.4998	.4998	.4998	.4998	.4998	.4998	.4998	.4998	.4998
3.6	.4998409	.4998	.4999	.4999	.4999	.4999	.4999	.4999	.4999	.4999
3.7	.4998922	.4999	.4999	.4999	.4999	.4999	.4999	.4999	.4999	.4999
3.8	.4999277	.4999	.4999	.4999	.4999	.4999	.4999	.5000	.5000	.5000
3.9	.4999519	.5000	.5000	.5000	.5000	.5000	.5000	.5000	.5000	.5000
4.0	.4999683									
4.5	.4999966									
5.0	.4999997133									

Source for table: Frederick E. Croxton and Dudley J. Cowden, *Practical Business Statistics*, 2nd ed., © 1948 Prentice-Hall, Inc., Englewood Cliffs, New Jersey, p. 511.

Table D

RANDOM DIGITS

53	13	40	94	73	42	30	40	40	69	35	21	26	16	72
50	81	48	91	37	91	22	75	76	92	43	48	69	08	26
58	49	59	81	47	76	18	39	85	25	98	31	92	00	26
12	74	51	28	44	49	62	20	36	77	04	70	10	09	79
99	00	26	76	48	89	62	43	29	04	41	18	73	40	12
01	70	13	69	66	89	70	19	67	53	91	76	49	87	97
59	62	26	99	42	73	62	41	30	83	61	33	69	25	69
08	80	97	28	68	58	22	55	48	39	35	54	25	47	94
81	79	45	81	98	13	73	07	38	26	03	35	35	86	03
03	66	93	28	34	58	55	14	04	94	58	19	54	76	65
97	95	21	59	59	19	55	60	72	98	07	71	32	76	69
91	62	64	30	49	70	04	88	19	75	18	32	48	19	59
66	58	34	09	99	02	61	52	61	56	74	13	24	80	25
55	33	82	62	06	59	14	95	35	19	04	10	59	06	41
97	71	73	24	27	31	09	75	48	03	62	23	10	09	92
14	28	57	15	15	35	46	94	19	08	33	98	08	79	26
62	56	62	15	90	36	11	14	70	36	22	58	22	88	68
07	23	41	36	29	20	58	57	92	88	53	39	37	72	40
64	81	85	81	82	48	61	69	09	33	66	11	35	53	74
88	60	06	32	39	51	62	36	40	74	01	23	01	02	35

Source: Output of the computer program, Figure 5 of the Appendix: Statistical Analysis and the Computer.

Table E

CRITICAL VALUES OF STUDENT'S t FOR SPECIFIED DEGREES OF FREEDOM

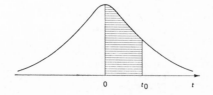

$P(0 \leq t \leq t_0)$: The left-most entries in the rows are the number of degrees of freedom; the entries at the heads of the columns are the probabilities indicated by the shaded area; the entries in the body of the table are the values of t_0 associated with the degrees of freedom and probability for the respective cells.

Degrees of Freedom $\backslash$ P	.45	.475	.495
1	6.314	12.706	63.657
2	2.920	4.303	9.925
3	2.353	3.182	5.841
4	2.132	2.776	4.604
5	2.015	2.571	4.032
6	1.943	2.447	3.707
7	1.895	2.365	3.499
8	1.860	2.306	3.355
9	1.833	2.262	3.250
10	1.812	2.228	3.169
11	1.796	2.201	3.106
12	1.782	2.179	3.055
13	1.771	2.160	3.012
14	1.761	2.145	2.977
15	1.753	2.131	2.947
16	1.746	2.210	2.921
17	1.740	2.110	2.898
18	1.734	2.101	2.878
19	1.729	2.093	2.861
20	1.725	2.086	2.845
21	1.721	2.080	2.831
22	1.717	2.074	2.819
23	1.714	2.069	2.807
24	1.711	2.064	2.797
25	1.708	2.060	2.787
26	1.706	2.056	2.779
27	1.703	2.052	2.771
28	1.701	2.048	2.763
29	1.699	2.045	2.756
30	1.697	2.042	2.750
infinity	1.64485	1.95996	2.57582

Source: Table E is taken from Table IV of Fisher, *Statistical Methods for Research Workers*, published by Oliver & Boyd Ltd., Edinburgh, and by permission of the author and publishers.

Table F

CRITICAL VALUES OF χ_a^2 FOR SPECIFIED DEGREES OF FREEDOM

Degrees of Freedom	$\chi^2_{.10}$	$\chi^2_{.05}$	$\chi^2_{.025}$	$\chi^2_{.01}$
1	2.706	3.841	5.024	6.635
2	4.605	5.991	7.378	9.210
3	6.251	7.815	9.348	11.345
4	7.779	9.488	11.143	13.277
5	9.236	11.071	12.832	15.086
6	10.645	12.592	14.449	16.812
7	12.017	14.067	16.013	18.475
8	13.362	15.507	17.535	20.090
9	14.684	16.919	19.023	21.666
10	15.987	18.307	20.483	23.209
11	17.275	19.675	21.920	24.725
12	18.549	21.026	23.337	26.217
13	19.812	22.362	24.736	27.688
14	21.064	23.685	26.119	29.141
15	22.307	24.996	27.488	30.578
16	23.542	26.296	28.845	32.000
17	24.769	27.587	30.191	33.409
18	25.989	28.869	31.526	34.805
19	27.204	30.144	32.852	36.191
20	28.412	31.410	34.170	37.566
21	29.615	32.671	35.479	38.932
22	30.813	33.924	36.781	40.289
23	32.007	35.172	38.076	41.638
24	33.196	36.415	39.364	42.980
25	34.382	37.652	40.646	44.314

Source: From D. B. Owen, *Handbook of Statistical Tables*, 1962. Courtesy of United States Atomic Energy Commission and Addison-Wesley Publishing Company, Inc., Reading, Mass.

Table G

FOUR-PLACE LOGARITHMS

N	0	1	2	3	4	5	6	7	8	9
10	0000	0043	0086	0128	0170	0212	0253	0294	0334	0374
11	0414	0453	0492	0531	0569	0607	0645	0682	0719	0755
12	0792	0828	0864	0899	0934	0969	1004	1038	1072	1106
13	1139	1173	1206	1239	1271	1303	1335	1367	1399	1430
14	1461	1492	1523	1553	1584	1614	1644	1673	1703	1732
15	1761	1790	1818	1847	1875	1903	1931	1959	1987	2014
16	2041	2068	2095	2122	2148	2175	2201	2227	2253	2279
17	2304	2330	2355	2380	2405	2430	2455	2480	2504	2529
18	2553	2577	2601	2625	2648	2672	2695	2718	2742	2765
19	2788	2810	2833	2856	2878	2900	2923	2945	2967	2989
20	3010	3032	3054	3075	3096	3118	3139	3160	3181	3201
21	3222	3243	3263	3284	3304	3324	3345	3365	3385	3404
22	3424	3444	3464	3483	3502	3522	3541	3560	3579	3598
23	3617	3636	3655	3674	3692	3711	3729	3747	3766	3784
24	3802	3820	3838	3856	3874	3892	3909	3927	3945	3962
25	3979	3997	4014	4031	4048	4065	4082	4099	4116	4133
26	4150	4166	4183	4200	4216	4232	4249	4265	4281	4298
27	4314	4330	4346	4362	4378	4393	4409	4425	4440	4456
28	4472	4487	4502	4518	4533	4548	4564	4579	4594	4609
29	4624	4639	4654	4669	4683	4698	4713	4728	4742	4757
30	4771	4786	4800	4814	4829	4843	4857	4871	4886	4900
31	4914	4928	4942	4955	4969	4983	4997	5011	5024	5038
32	5051	5065	5079	5092	5105	5119	5132	5145	5159	5172
33	5185	5198	5211	5224	5237	5250	5263	5276	5289	5302
34	5315	5328	5340	5353	5366	5378	5391	5403	5416	5428
35	5441	5453	5465	5478	5490	5502	5514	5527	5539	5551
36	5563	5575	5587	5599	5611	5623	5635	5647	5658	5670
37	5682	5694	5705	5717	5729	5740	5752	5763	5775	5786
38	5798	5809	5821	5832	5843	5855	5866	5877	5888	5899
39	5911	5922	5933	5944	5955	5966	5977	5988	5999	6010
40	6021	6031	6042	6053	6064	6075	6085	6096	6107	6117
41	6128	6138	6149	6160	6170	6180	6191	6201	6212	6222
42	6232	6243	6253	6263	6274	6284	6294	6304	6314	6325
43	6335	6345	6355	6365	6375	6385	6395	6405	6415	6425
44	6435	6444	6454	6464	6474	6484	6493	6503	6513	6522
45	6532	6542	6551	6561	6571	6580	6590	6599	6609	6618
46	6628	6637	6646	6656	6665	6675	6684	6693	6702	6712
47	6721	6730	6739	6749	6758	6767	6776	6785	6794	6803
48	6812	6821	6830	6839	6848	6857	6866	6875	6884	6893
49	6902	6911	6920	6928	6937	6946	6955	6964	6972	6981
50	6990	6998	7007	7016	7024	7033	7042	7050	7059	7067
51	7076	7084	7093	7101	7110	7118	7126	7135	7143	7152
52	7160	7168	7177	7185	7193	7202	7210	7218	7226	7235
53	7243	7251	7259	7267	7275	7284	7292	7300	7308	7316
54	7324	7332	7340	7348	7356	7364	7372	7380	7388	7396

Table G (*Continued*)

N	0	1	2	3	4	5	6	7	8	9
55	7404	7412	7419	7427	7435	7443	7451	7459	7466	7474
56	7482	7490	7497	7505	7513	7520	7528	7536	7543	7551
57	7559	7566	7574	7582	7589	7597	7604	7612	7619	7627
58	7634	7642	7649	7657	7664	7672	7679	7686	7694	7701
59	7709	7716	7723	7731	7738	7745	7752	7760	7767	7774
60	7782	7789	7796	7803	7810	7818	7825	7832	7839	7846
61	7853	7860	7868	7875	7882	7889	7896	7903	7910	7917
62	7924	7931	7938	7945	7952	7959	7966	7973	7980	7987
63	7993	8000	8007	8014	8021	8028	8035	8041	8048	8055
64	8062	8069	8075	8082	8089	8096	8102	8109	8116	8122
65	8129	8136	8142	8149	8156	8162	8169	8176	8182	8189
66	8195	8202	8209	8215	8222	8228	8235	8241	8248	8254
67	8261	8267	8274	8280	8287	8293	8299	8306	8312	8319
68	8325	8331	8338	8344	8351	8357	8363	8370	8376	8382
69	8388	8395	8401	8407	8414	8420	8426	8432	8439	8445
70	8451	8457	8463	8470	8476	8482	8488	8494	8500	8506
71	8513	8519	8525	8531	8537	8543	8549	8555	8561	8567
72	8573	8579	8585	8591	8597	8603	8609	8615	8621	8627
73	8633	8639	8645	8651	8657	8663	8669	8675	8681	8686
74	8692	8698	8704	8710	8716	8722	8727	8733	8739	8745
75	8751	8756	8762	8768	8774	8779	8785	8791	8797	8802
76	8808	8814	8820	8825	8831	8837	8842	8848	8854	8859
77	8865	8871	8876	8882	8887	8893	8899	8904	8910	8915
78	8921	8927	8932	8938	8943	8949	8954	8960	8965	8971
79	8976	8982	8987	8993	8998	9004	9009	9015	9020	9025
80	9031	9036	9042	9047	9053	9058	9063	9069	9074	9079
81	9085	9090	9096	9101	9106	9112	9117	9122	9128	9133
82	9138	9143	9149	9154	9159	9165	9170	9175	9180	9186
83	9191	9196	9201	9206	9212	9217	9222	9227	9232	9238
84	9243	9248	9253	9258	9263	9269	9274	9279	9284	9289
85	9294	9299	9304	9309	9315	9320	9325	9330	9335	9340
86	9345	9350	9355	9360	9365	9370	9375	9380	9385	9390
87	9395	9400	9405	9410	9415	9420	9425	9430	9435	9440
88	9445	9450	9455	9460	9465	9469	9474	9479	9484	9489
89	9494	9499	9504	9509	9513	9518	9523	9528	9533	9538
90	9542	9547	9552	9557	9562	9566	9571	9576	9581	9586
91	9590	9595	9600	9605	9609	9614	9619	9624	9628	9633
92	9638	9643	9647	9652	9657	9661	9666	9671	9675	9680
93	9685	9689	9694	9699	9703	9708	9713	9717	9722	9727
94	9731	9736	9741	9745	9750	9754	9759	9763	9768	9773
95	9777	9782	9786	9791	9795	9800	9805	9809	9814	9818
96	9823	9827	9832	9836	9841	9845	9850	9854	9859	9863
97	9868	9872	9877	9881	9886	9890	9894	9899	9903	9908
98	9912	9917	9921	9926	9930	9934	9939	9943	9948	9952
99	9956	9961	9965	9969	9974	9978	9983	9987	9991	9996

Table H

LOGARITHMS OF FACTORIALS

	0	1	2	3	4	5	6	7	8	9
00	0.0000	0.0060	0.3010	0.7782	1.3802	2.0792	2.8573	3.7024	4.6055	5.5598
10	6.5598	7.6012	8.6803	9.7943	10.9404	12.1165	13.3206	14.5511	15.8063	17.0851
20	18.3861	19.7083	21.0508	22.4125	23.7927	25.1906	26.6056	28.0370	29.4841	30.9465
30	32.4237	33.9150	35.4202	36.9387	38.4702	40.0142	41.5705	43.1387	44.7185	46.3096
40	47.9116	49.5244	51.1477	52.7811	54.4246	56.0778	57.7406	59.4127	61.0939	62.7841
50	64.4831	66.1906	67.9066	69.6309	71.3633	73.1037	74.8519	76.6077	78.3712	80.1420
60	81.9202	83.7055	85.4979	87.2972	89.1034	90.9163	92.7359	94.5619	96.3945	98.2333
70	100.0784	101.9297	103.7870	105.6503	107.5196	109.3946	111.2754	113.1619	115.0540	116.9516
80	118.8547	120.7632	122.6770	124.5961	126.5204	128.4498	130.3843	132.3238	134.2683	136.2177
90	138.1719	140.1310	142.0948	144.0632	146.0364	148.0141	149.9964	151.9831	153.9744	155.9700
100	157.9700	159.9743	161.9829	163.9958	166.0128	168.0340	170.0593	172.0887	174.1221	176.1595

Index

This book has been set in 10 and 9 point Janson, leaded 2 points. Chapter numbers are 14 point Helvetica Bold italic; chapter titles are 18 point Helvetica Bold. The size of the type page is 27 by 45 ½ picas.